The Chemical
Basis of
Physiological
Regulation

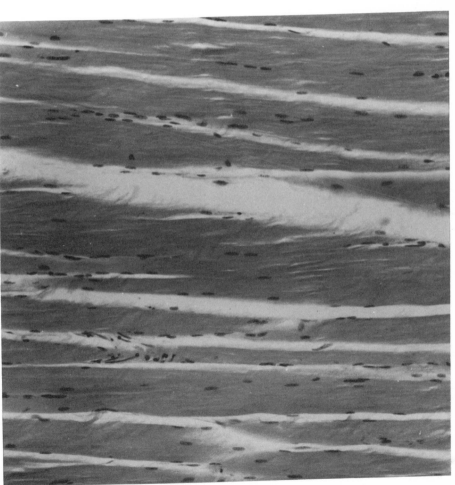

Photomicrograph by Dr. Willis Webb, Mead Johnson Research Center.

SCOTT, FORESMAN SERIES IN UNDERGRADUATE BIOLOGY

Samuel Matthews, *Williams College*, GENERAL EDITOR

The Chemical Basis of Physiological Regulation

E. J. W. Barrington F.R.S.

University of Nottingham

SCOTT, FORESMAN AND COMPANY

FOREWORD

In recent years interest in Biology has focused with increasing sharpness on two contrasting areas — the molecular basis of activities of cells and organisms and behavior and population studies. New concepts along with new and more precise methods of laboratory research have resulted in an explosive growth of information. This rapid increase of knowledge, which is doubling every two years, is the concern of all biologists. How may the changing emphasis in biology and the accompanying mass of new information be presented to the beginning student? How can he be adequately informed about areas necessary for further exploration, such as taxonomy, structure, and function, and at the same time be made aware of the new, conceptual dimensions of these areas? Such questions have caused considerable discussion, and suggestions for modification of the introductory course have ranged from abolishing it completely to making it entirely a problems course, with all the logistic and administrative difficulties such an approach would encounter.

One point seems clear. Early in his scientific studies the student must appreciate that science is a continually changing body of knowledge, not a fixed mass of information, and he must gain some concept of how growth in scientific understanding occurs. No clear method exists for achieving these objectives. Actual laboratory experience with someone actively engaged in research would be the most effective means, but opportunities of this kind can be provided for only a few students. Another approach, and one more readily available, would be to have each student read about such experiments, preferably in the words of the investigators themselves. In this way the student might look over the shoulders of those who are performing the experiments and gain some insight into how growth in understanding of the science is brought about.

There are two principal difficulties with the second suggested approach. First, adequate access to scientific journals would be difficult to provide. The cost of subscribing to and storing anything close to complete coverage of biological journals is prohibitive for most colleges, and the single copies of those journals available are woefully inadequate reading sources for large classes. Second, the language of scientific papers might confuse the beginning student. Careful selection and considerable annotation of material would clearly be necessary, and this alone would probably be inadequate. In order to appreciate the significance of newer studies in a particular area, the student would need a firm understanding of that area. Any treatment that would provide the background for such understanding for all the major segments into which biology has traditionally been divided (embryology, physiology, genetics, etc.) and which also would include a discussion of the newer concepts in these fields would need to be of formidable size. But could this be done for a few topics which are of fundamental significance to understanding present-day biology? And could these topics be presented in a form readily available to the student?

To test the possibility of this approach, a brief outline of the idea was sent to a number of biologists to invite their opinions. As a result of the interest shown, several agreed to undertake discussions of topics within their own areas of interest. This group met and discussed the objectives and nature of the series of volumes that would be prepared. The present series is the result of these efforts.

The topics chosen for discussion were selected in the belief that they exemplify the changing emphasis of modern biology. For each of these topics an attempt is made to establish fundamental principles and to indicate how the area is advancing by experimental work. There is a certain logic in the order of the volumes, proceeding as they do from ultrastructure, macromolecules, and the principles of biochemistry to physiological regulation and the biology of populations and evolution. Each volume, however, is complete in itself and may be used alone or in combination with some or all of the others, as the nature of the particular course and the objectives of a particular instructor dictate. In any case to provide either the terminal student with a sound grasp of the field or the biology major with an adequate background for further exploration, the topical approach utilized in this series would need to be supplemented by lectures on those areas of biology not covered in the volumes.

The Scott, Foresman Series in Undergraduate Biology is designed for use as basic texts for introductory biology courses, as useful supplementary material for lectures and laboratory work in other biology courses, and as review or supplementary sources for specialized, intermediate courses. It is hoped that these volumes may afford the student some idea of the recent and significant change in focus of biology and some concept of the excitement and challenge of this rapidly moving science.

Samuel A. Matthews, *Williams College*

CONTENTS

CHAPTER 1 The Uptake of Oxygen

■ LIFE AS AN OPEN SYSTEM

When a man shows great vigor and drive, he is sometimes said to have fire in his belly. It is a compliment that is not taken literally, although there was a time when it might have been. In classical Rome, for example, Cicero held it to be "a law of Nature that all things capable of nurture and growth contain within them a supply of heat without which their nurture and growth would not be possible." From this he inferred "that this element of heat possesses in itself a vital force that pervades the whole world."

Cicero was describing, in a way that now seems strange, a feature that characterizes living organisms and differentiates them from the non-living material which surrounds them. The material of the universe always tends toward a state of increasing inertness. If it is hot, it cools. If it is moving, it will ultimately stop. If it is capable of chemical change, it undergoes reactions that result in a reduction in the amount of what is called its free energy, which is that part of its energy available for chemical work. This property of matter is closely connected with the concept of entropy, which relates the free energy of materials to their degree of organization. According to this concept, a decrease in the free energy of a material system means an increase in its disorganization, and, because of this, a reduction in the possibility of further change within that system. This increase in disorganization is called an increase in entropy, for entropy is essentially a measure of the amount of disorder within a system.

The trend toward the increasing inertness of matter is embodied in the second law of thermodynamics, which states that changes in the material of the universe are unidirectional and irreversible, and result in a progressive increase of entropy. The universe, in short, is slowly "running down." It is apparent, however, that if these considerations applied without modification to living material, maintenance of life upon this earth would be impossible. In the long run all men are dead. But before man reaches this end, he has maintained a high level of activity in a body that preserves for many years a recognizably uniform appearance. Moreover, living organisms perpetuate themselves either by the transmission of germ cells or by a variety of nonsexual methods. Within living matter there is a potential immortality, however difficult the environmental hazards. However, this does not mean that living matter is an exception to the second law of thermodynamics.

Maintenance of life depends upon chemical reactions which replenish the energy lost by the activities of living systems. This process is possible, because two types of chemical reactions occur, namely exergonic and endergonic. While the first results in a reduction of free energy, the second effects an increase in free energy and sustains living systems by enabling them to take energy from an outside source, the sun. Photosynthetic organisms as well as important groups of photosynthetic bacteria and unicellular organisms initially capture the sun's energy and build it up by endergonic reactions to form energy-rich compounds of complex molecular constitution. Such compounds constitute the food that is the energy supply of animals.

Thus life maintains itself by functioning as an open system replenished by an external source of energy. Materials flow through this system to undergo chemical reactions called metabolism. The flow, moreover, is not passive and automatic. It is an active process that can be controlled and regulated by the organisms that it nourishes, so that these organisms maintain what is called a steady state in a constantly fluctuating environment. Although organisms adapt to their environment, that is, react to it in a manner calculated to promote their survival, the materials of which organisms are composed cannot escape from the consequences of the second law of thermodynamics. There is an inevitable cycle of death and decay, in which the bodies of plants and animals are broken down into inorganic materials with an increase of entropy. To this material is added the continuous discharge of waste resulting from the activities of living organisms. As long as solar energy is available, however, organization can be transmitted to new generations. Individual organisms will die, but the living systems of this earth will continue to survive; this is the potential immortality mentioned earlier.

The energy stored in living systems by endergonic reactions is released by oxidation, and it is because of this that a supply of oxygen is needed by all organisms, except the small number adapted for anaerobic life. Oxidative metabolism results in the production of carbon dioxide, so that there is a gaseous exchange between the organism and its environment. Such an exchange, involving an input of oxygen and an output of carbon dioxide, forms part of the process of respiration which may be referred to as external respiration. In man, as in terrestrial vertebrates in general (at least from reptiles upward), the exchange takes place in the lungs. The gases are transmitted between the lungs and the rest of the body by the blood stream — oxygen in loose combination with hemoglobin, and carbon dioxide mainly in solution as bicarbonate. This transport, together with the oxidative reactions taking place in the tissues, constitute internal aspects of respiration. The following section examines, as an example of adaptive organization, the ways in which some animals maintain continuity in their external gaseous exchanges and modify these exchanges in relation to alterations in the environment and in their own levels of activity.

■ NERVOUS CONTROL OF EXTERNAL RESPIRATION IN MAN

The general course of external respiration in man is familiar. During the process called inspiration, air is drawn into the lungs by suction. This intake of air is the result of increased negative pressure in the chest caused by expansion of the thoracic cavity. Expansion is effected by contraction of the diaphragm and the muscles which move the ribs; while discharge of the respired air (expiration) is brought about largely by elastic recoil of the lungs, as the diaphragm and intercostal muscles relax, and the ribs return to their resting position. These movements, termed the ventilation movements, result in a flow of air (the tidal flow) into and out of the bronchial passages and cavities of the lungs. Since it is impossible to expel all air from the lungs, as some degree of negative pressure always remains within the thoracic cavity, air remains which is termed residual. Part of this, the alveolar air, is contained within the alveoli, the ultimate cavities of the lung tissue where the gaseous exchange takes place between the air and the blood stream. As may be seen from the accompanying data (Table 1-1), the alveolar air, which thus stands intermediate between the atmosphere and the blood, differs in composition from both the inspired and expired air.

TABLE 1-1

Composition of Respiratory Air in Man
(in Volumes Per Cent)[a]

	Inspired Air	Expired Air	Alveolar Air
Oxygen	20.71	14.6	13.2
Carbon dioxide	0.04	3.8	5.0
Nitrogen	78.00	75.4	75.6
Water vapor	1.25	6.2	6.2

[a] Data from Frank R. Winton and Leonard E. Bayliss, *Human Physiology*, 2nd ed. (Philadelphia: Blakiston Co., 1937).

The extent to which animals can survive a temporary loss of their oxygen supply varies a great deal, depending partly on the level of complexity of their organization, and partly on the degree to which their respiration may be adapted in specific ways to peculiarities of their normal environment. In man the supply must be maintained virtually without interruption, although not all tissues stand in equal need. The arm or leg can be isolated from respiratory exchange for at least an hour, but the heart, and to a greater extent the nervous system, are immensely more sensitive. If the brain is cut off from its oxygen supply in the blood stream for as little as five minutes, it will normally be damaged beyond possibility of repair, although this need not be so if the body is artificially cooled (Chap. 6). Not only must the ventilation movements be continued without a break when the body is at its normal temperature, they must also be modifiable in relation to changing demands, if the steady state is to be maintained. These requirements are met by a complex of interrelated physiological devices which show some of the fundamental characteristics of adaptive organization.

It is theoretically conceivable that external respiration might be maintained by a reflex mechanism. For example, a reduction in the oxygen circulating in the blood stream might stimulate specialized sensory receptors somewhere in the body. Nerve impulses from these structures could then be propagated through predetermined pathways in the peripheral nerves and central nervous system to bring about contraction of appropriate respiratory muscles. It will be seen later in this chapter that reflex pathways are important in the control of respiration in the flea *Xenopsylla*. They also have a part to play in man's respiration, but they are not the primary source of the respiratory ventilation movements. These are evoked not by reflex action but by the more or less regular discharge of volleys of nerve impulses through certain spinal nerves, i.e., the phrenic nerves, running to the diaphragm, and the intercostal nerves, running to the muscles of the ribs (*Fig. 1-1*). The impulses arise in the medulla of the brain in a localized region called the respiratory center. The rhythmicity of the respiratory movements is in large measure a direct consequence of spontaneous rhythmic activity in that center. Within certain limits, therefore, the supply of air to the lungs is ensured by an essentially automatic process that does not arise from any special sensitivity to oxygen lack.

A medullary respiratory center occurs not only in mammals but also in fish. Indeed, the fact that rhythmic respiratory activity can be autonomous and independent of stimulation from peripheral sensory receptors was first demonstrated clearly in a pioneer study of the goldfish brain by E. D. Adrian and F. J. J. Buytendijk.

Since the original observations of Caton various workers have recorded changes of electrical potential in the brain. It has been established that active parts become negative to inactive, but it is difficult to say what elements of the central nervous system are responsible for the effect. The action potentials of the nerve fibres will presumably contribute something, though Bablioni's experiments with strychnine favoured the nerve cells as the most important factor. The structures involved are so complex, however, that in recent years very little has been added to our knowledge of the central nervous system by the investigation of its potential changes.

The present experiments fall into line with earlier work in showing changes which can be localized and related to the normal activity of the brain, and the same difficulty arises when we attempt a further analysis. But a tentative analysis is possible and its results are of some interest. They suggest a type of electrical activity which differs from that of the nerve fibre in its much more gradual rise and decline, and this agrees with what we might expect from entirely different lines of work on the central nervous system.

METHOD

The preparation employed was the isolated brain stem of the goldfish removed from the skull and placed on a glass slide. Complete isolation may seem an unnecessary precaution, and the damage occurring through manipulation and from loss of the circulation must have accounted for many failures to observe any sort of activity. But in making a preliminary survey we were anxious to avoid all extraneous electric changes such as those due to the heart and the skeletal muscles. With a sensitive amplifying system, electrodes placed on the brain surface may record changes developed in almost any part of the body, and it seemed best to begin with a preparation in which this source of confusion could be definitely excluded.

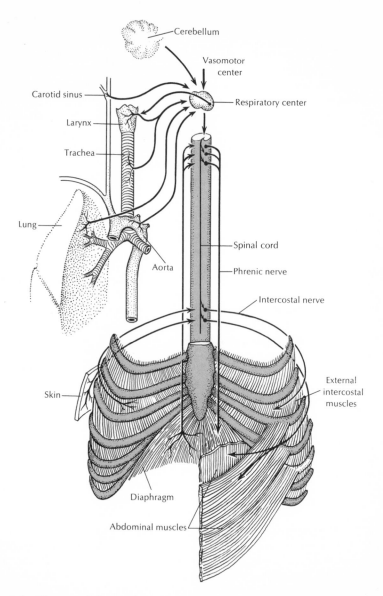

Fig. 1-1. Diagram of the respiratory muscles and the influences acting upon them. (Partly after Best and Taylor, from J. Z. Young, *The Life of Mammals*, Oxford: The Clarendon Press, 1957, p. 304.)

The goldfish was chosen because of the large size of its brain stem compared with that of the frog, but there is also the outstanding advantage that the respiratory centres are far more active. The importance of this will appear presently.

A diagram of the brain is shown in *Fig.* [*1-2*]. In making the brain stem preparation the fish was decapitated and the cerebrum destroyed by crushing. The brain stem was then carefully exposed, and after the roots of the cranial nerves had been cut, it was lifted or rolled out of its bed on to a glass microscope slide moistened with Ringer's fluid (containing 0.6 p.c. NaCl). In some preparations the base of the skull was removed with the brain stem. The preparation includes the medulla with the large vagal lobes on either side, the cerebellum which forms a rounded protrusion in the mid-line in front of the vagal lobes, and the mid-brain with its paired optic lobes (equivalent to the corpora quadrigemina in mammals). The primitive cerebrum is so placed that it can be destroyed by crushing the skull without much risk of damage to the lower part of the mid-brain.

The brain stem on its glass slide was placed on a stand carrying two non-polarizable electrodes (Ag, AgCl) ending in moist threads. The recording system was a valve amplifier leading to a Matthews oscillograph and a loud-speaker. The particular arrangement in use has been described recently, but as the experiments advanced, the coupling arrangements in the amplifier were progressively modified to give faithful records of slower and slower changes. The only other addition has been the provision of an alternative loud-speaker which gives prominence to sound waves of low frequency. This was installed for work on impulses of the slow type (*e.g.*, in sympathetic fibres), and it has been of great use in the present research where it is important to be able to detect potential fluctuations over the widest possible range of wave-lengths.

RESULTS

(1) RESPIRATORY WAVES: Unless the brain stem has suffered gross injury in the process of removal, it is nearly always possible to detect small and rapid potential oscillations which vary with the position of the electrodes and cease after an hour or more. As a rule they do not exceed about 0.005 millivolt. In many preparations, however, a much more striking effect appears, for the oscillograph records a succession of large, slow waves, occurring fairly regularly at intervals of 1 to 3 seconds. . . .

[These] potential changes have varied from 0.02 to 0.15 millivolt. If they occur at all they can usually be detected with any arrangement of the electrodes, provided that they are not placed symmetrically on either side of the brain stem. The waves may be evident as soon as the preparation is set up, or there may be a delay of some minutes before they begin: in some preparations they have only appeared for a few minutes, and in many they have never appeared at all. There is

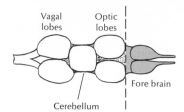

Vagal lobes   Optic lobes

Cerebellum   Fore brain

Fig. 1-2. Diagram of brain of goldfish *(Carassius auratus).* The preparation consists of the brain stem, the cerebral [forebrain] hemispheres (shaded) being destroyed. (From E. D. Adrian and F. J. J. Buytendijk, *Journal of Physiology,* 71 (1930), 122.)

usually some irregularity of the rhythm at the start, and a progressive slowing before the waves disappear.

These changes must indicate some kind of rhythmic activity, and the frequency at which they recur makes it almost certain that the activity is connected with respiration, for the respiratory movements in the goldfish occur at intervals of from 1 to 3 seconds and the motor nerves concerned take origin in the brain stem. The resemblance between the two rhythms is illustrated in *Fig. [1-3]*. The upper record is made from [an isolated brain], and the lower was made from an intact goldfish, breathing quietly in a tank of water, by throwing a shadow of the gills on to the slit of the recording camera.

The absence of rhythmic waves in many preparations is not surprising. Accidental damage to the brain stem must often be responsible, but in many fish the respiratory movements become irregular or cease when the fish is at rest in well-aerated water; and these fish are the least likely to furnish brain stem preparations with regular potential waves. The best preparations have been made from fish which breathe vigorously, and it is usually a favourable sign if rhythmic gill movements continue after decapitation and the destruction of the fore brain. . . .

LOCALIZATION: The waves are due to changes in the potential of the vagal lobes relative to the rest of the brain stem. If one electrode is on the mid-brain and the other on the caudal end of the medulla, either electrode may show negativity to the other. But if one is on the cephalic end of one of the vagal lobes, the deflection indicates negativity at this electrode wherever the other may be. . . . In agreement with this it is found that the maximum deflection occurs where one electrode is on the vagal lobe and the other at some distance either in front or behind, and also that the mid-brain can be extensively damaged without stopping the waves.[1]

Adrian and Buytendijk thought it likely that these slow potential waves were not due to nerve fiber discharges but were brought about by slow and continuous potential changes in a group of nerve cells in the brain stem. Moreover, they emphasized that these observations, regardless of the underlying cause, were a clear example of rhythmic activity in the absence of afferent impulses. Given an appropriate medium, the nervous tissue could beat as spontaneously as heart muscle.

The importance of the respiratory center of mammals can be demonstrated by cutting through the brain of experimental animals at carefully predetermined levels. A useful landmark is the pons Varolii on the underside of the cerebellum. If the cut is made at a level anterior to the pons (a process called decerebration), the normal respiratory movements continue. If, however, the cut is made at the hind end of the medulla, respiratory movements cease, for impulses from the center can no longer reach the spinal roots of the phrenic and intercostal nerves. The animal can now be kept alive only by some form of artificial respiration. The respiratory center is thus shown to be the power house of the ventilation movements, but to say this is to state only a small part of the story.

The functioning of the mammalian center has been explored further by applying electric stimulation to its different parts. This has shown that the center is differentiated into two regions (*Fig. 1-4*), one of which, lying ventrally, is an inspiratory center. Electric stimulation of this region in an experimental mammal brings about inspiratory movements. The more dorsal and lateral region of the respiratory center constitutes an expiratory center; stimulation of this results in an interruption of the movements of inspiration. In addition, there are cells in the pons which are functionally related to both the inspiratory and expiratory centers and which constitute a distinct center of their own, the pontine or neurotaxic center.

The interrelationship between these centers is complex, and it is here that reflex mechanisms have a part to play (*Fig. 1-4*). In the walls of the lungs are receptors that are sensitive to stretch. It has been shown by records of electrical activity in the vagus nerves that these receptors discharge nerve impulses along the sensory fibers of vagus nerves into the expiratory center. The lungs become expanded during inspiration; this stimulates the stretch receptors to increase their rate of discharge of nerve impulses. Consequently, such an increase is thought to stimulate the expiratory center which then discharges

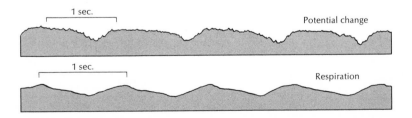

Fig. 1-3. Upper record: potential wave rhythm from the isolated brain of a goldfish. Lower record: rhythm of respiratory movements of intact fish. (From E. D. Adrian and F. J. J. Buytendijk, *Journal of Physiology*, 71 (1930), 125.)

impulses that arrest the activity of the inspiratory center. With the resulting advent of expiration, there is an accompanying reduction in tension of the lung walls leading to a decline in the discharge of nerve impulses from the stretch receptors. Thus at a certain stage expansion of the lungs effects a reflex inhibition of the inspiratory movements.

The significance of this reflex (the Hering-Breuer reflex) was not understood fully when it was first discovered. It seemed possible that it might be the primary factor in promoting the rhythmicity of the ventilation movements, but it is now known that this is not so. If both vagi of an experimental animal are cut, so that the impulses from the stretch receptors cannot reach the medulla, the animal will still continue to breathe, although the rhythm of the ventilation movements will be slower than normal. The Hering-Breuer reflex does not, therefore, initiate the rhythm, but it does exert some control over it. Although the significance of this reflex is obscure, one of its advantages may be that it can safeguard the lungs from overdistension.

While the respiratory rhythm continues in the absence of vagal inhibition, it ceases if the brain is cut immediately anterior to the medullary respiratory centers, separating the respiratory centers from the pontine center which is essential for the maintenance of their rhythmic activity. It is suggested that the inspiratory center, in addition to evoking the respiratory movements, acts also on both the expiratory and pontine centers. When these two areas are stimulated adequately by the respiratory center, they discharge inhibitory impulses into the inspiratory center and thus bring inspiration to an end. All the centers thus interact as a functional unit. Such, at least, are the lines along which the nervous control of respiration in man has traditionally been explained, although full understanding of how the respiratory rhythm is generated cannot be claimed.

■ CHEMICAL CONTROL OF EXTERNAL RESPIRATION IN MAN

So far mammalian ventilation movements have been described as dependent primarily upon an inherent neural rhythm, with some contribution also from reflex pathways. There is the further possibility of voluntary and conscious control from man's higher nervous centers. Human beings can control by their own volition both the depth of respiration (i.e., the volume of the tidal flow) and also the rate of ventilation. There are, however, strict limits to this control. A continuation of forced deep breathing, which amounts to over-ventilation of the lungs, soon results in a temporary cessation of breathing (apnoea). Conversely, breath can be held for only a limited time; the body soon takes control and restores normality by undergoing a period of increased ventilation (hyperpnoea). These lim-

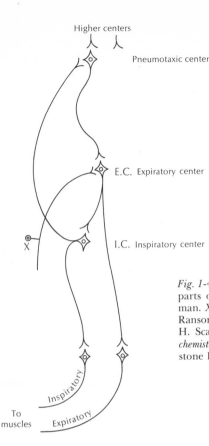

Higher centers

Pneumotaxic center

E.C. Expiratory center

I.C. Inspiratory center

X

To muscles

Inspiratory

Expiratory

Fig. 1-4. A simplified scheme of the various parts of the central respiratory connections in man. *X,* vagus nerve. (After Pitts, Magoun, and Ransom, from G. H. Bell, J. N. Davidson, and H. Scarborough, *Textbook of Physiology and Biochemistry,* 5th edition, Edinburgh: E. & S. Livingstone Ltd., 1963, p. 558.)

itations are expressions of reactions that safeguard man's supply of oxygen. They might be expected, therefore, to be direct responses to the availability of oxygen, but the situation is, in fact, more complicated than this. Both oxygen and carbon dioxide play a part in the regulation of respiratory exchanges, but they too can work only within limits that are ultimately determined by inescapable physical considerations.

Consider, as an illustration of these physical limitations, the experience of three French scientists, J. E. Crocé-Spinelli, T. Sivel, and G. Tissandier, who in 1875 made an ascent in the balloon *Zenith.* It was well known at the time of this famous enterprise that rarefied air at great heights presented a hazard that could be counteracted by breathing oxygen. The balloon, therefore, was provided with bags of this gas. However, because the bags were small, the balloonists decided not to use them until they felt the need. It was a disastrous decision. At 24,600 feet, with a barometric pressure of 300 mm (cf.

Fig. 1-6, p. 22), they unconcernedly released ballast to send themselves still higher. Meanwhile Tissandier recorded in his notebook, in scarcely legible writing, "Sivel throws ballast, Sivel throws ballast." He then tried to seize the mouthpiece of his oxygen tube, but he was too late, for his arms as well as his voice were already paralyzed. Shortly afterward he lost consciousness.

The meaningless repetition of phrase in Tissandier's notebook is now recognized as a characteristic symptom of oxygen deprivation. Yet he later recalled that he had felt no sense of danger at the time; on the contrary, he was happy that the balloon was continuing to rise. Later it began to descend, and both he and Crocé-Spinelli temporarily recovered consciousness. They did not, however, continue the descent; instead, they increased their difficulties by releasing more ballast and also the aspirator. Once again both men immediately became unconscious. Later the balloon began its final descent, and Tissandier recovered consciousness. After landing the *Zenith* with some difficulty, he found that both his companions were dead.

This tragedy was a consequence of the fact that the amount of oxygen taken up by the hemoglobin of blood (expressed as a percentage of the amount that it absorbs when fully saturated) depends upon the partial pressure of the oxygen in the air that enters the lungs. The relationship is shown graphically in *Fig. 1-5*, in which the percentage saturation of whole mammalian blood is plotted against partial pressure of oxygen, the values being obtained after a sample of blood has been equilibrated with a gas mixture in a suitable vessel. The curve so derived, called the oxygen dissociation curve, has a characteristic sigmoid shape, which is itself an expression of adaptive organization in the properties of whole blood. The figure shows that the blood will be almost completely saturated with oxygen at the partial pressure occurring in the lungs (about 95 mm Hg), while substantial unloading of oxygen will take place in the veins, where the oxygen tension is at about 40 mm.* It is important that this should be so. The oxygen tension in resting muscle is of the order of 20 mm, and it is essential that the tension in the veins be substantially higher than this, so that the gradient between blood and tissues is sufficiently steep to ensure adequate diffusion of oxygen to the cells.

Efficient oxygenation of the tissues is further aided by another biochemical adaptation. The form of the oxygen dissociation curve of mammalian blood is influenced by pH in such a way that an increase in acidity decreases the percentage saturation at any given partial pressure, causing the curve to be shifted toward the right. Thus the accumulation of carbon dioxide, which occurs at periods of activity, promotes a more rapid release of oxygen because it increases the

---

* The tension of a gas in solution is equivalent to the partial pressure of an overlying gas with which it would be in equilibrium.

acidity of the tissue fluids (p. 18). This effect, called the Bohr effect, after the Danish investigator who first discovered it, thus makes oxygen more readily available at precisely the times and places where it is needed.

It follows from the above considerations that a dissociation curve of the rectangular hyperbolic type shown on the left in *Fig. 1-5* is ill adapted for oxygen transport in the blood. This type of curve, however, is shown by myoglobin, a variant of hemoglobin that is found in muscle fibers, and it is often shown also by the hemoglobins that occur in solution in the body fluids of certain invertebrates. It is apparent from the shape of the curve that unloading of oxygen occurs only at very low partial pressures of oxygen, but this, too, has its adaptive value. Such hemoglobins often act as stores of oxygen, releasing it at times when there is a shortage. It is probable that they also take up oxygen from the circulatory system and pass it on to the tissues, where the intracellular cytochrome oxidase system func-

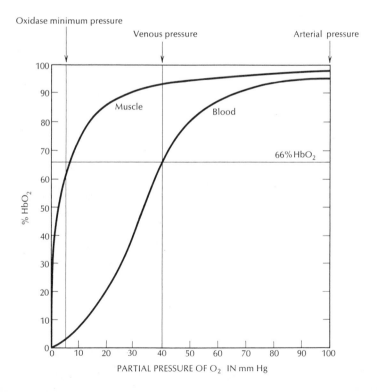

Fig. 1-5. The oxygen dissociation curves of mammalian hemoglobin and blood hemoglobin, and their relationships to the minimum oxygen pressure required by the tissues. (From R. Hill, *Proceedings of the Royal Society of London, Series B*, 120 (1936), 482.)

tions at low oxygen tensions to which the unloading value of the blood hemoglobin is closely adapted. Both functions are satisfied by the hyperbolic type of curve.

It is evident, then, that there is no one particular compound that can be called hemoglobin. The term is given to a type of molecule in which a protein called globin is associated with an iron porphyrin complex called heme. The globin component shows much interspecific variation, while there is also variation in the number of heme complexes included in the molecule. For example, vertebrate myoglobin contains only one of these complexes in its molecule, while the hemoglobins of the blood of most vertebrates contain four. Porphyrins are widespread throughout living organisms, being found, for example, in the cytochromes that play an essential part in intracellular energy transformations within the cell. It is this wide distribution of the porphyrins that has made it possible for hemoglobins to be evolved quite independently, and often quite sporadically, in many groups of animals in addition to vertebrates. Earthworms are familiar examples. Always, however, these various hemoglobins each have characteristic properties, closely related to the requirements of the animals possessing them. Such properties, undoubtedly, have become established as a result of natural selection acting upon the abundant variation of structure possible in complex molecules, and as a result of individual molecular capacity for uniting into larger complexes.

The bearing of this discussion upon the tragedy of the French balloonists arises from the way in which atmospheric pressure falls with increasing height, with the partial pressure of oxygen falling with it. Thus, as the balloonists ascended higher, their hemoglobin was saturated less, and, in consequence, the amount of oxygen circulating in their blood streams was smaller. Such reduced availability of oxygen, technically known as hypoxia, has devastating consequences apparent in this episode and documented by J. B. S. Haldane in an account of experiments in which he was subjected to reduced pressure within a sealed pressure chamber.

> We go in, the door is bolted behind us, and the pump starts working. As the pressure falls it becomes cold and foggy. The reason is obvious. The air which leaves the chamber is not really pulled out by the pump, but pushed out by the air which remains behind. So this air is doing work, and the only available source of energy is its heat.
>
> We stop at a pressure of half an atmosphere, corresponding to 18,000 feet. For a minute or two we breathe a little faster than usual, but this soon passes off. I feel grand, and tell you so. But I notice that you are not too steady on your feet, and making silly jokes. Curiously enough you have just the same experience about me. The symptoms of oxygen want are very like those of alcohol poisoning. If

we stayed for several hours at this pressure we should get bad head-
aches and vomit. At lower pressure still one becomes unconscious,
and unacclimatized people die at heights well below that of Mount
Everest. None of these things happens if one breathes oxygen, so
they are clearly effects of oxygen want, and not of low pressures.

The danger for an airman is obvious. Even at 12,000 feet his judge-
ment and skill may be a little below normal, like those of a motorist
who, though not drunk, has "had one or two." Higher up the danger
is far greater. . . . So the airman must have a supply of oxygen, and
must obey orders as to breathing it, even when he is sure they are
quite unnecessary.[2]

Since the time Haldane wrote, the lesson has been well learned.
Winston Churchill remarks in *The Second World War* that when he
was flying to Moscow on the night of August 10, 1942, and had in-
structed the pilot to cross the mountains of Kurdistan at 12,000 feet,
his party began sucking their oxygen tubes. Today pressurized cabins
are used. In piston and turboprop machines the pressure is adjusted
to correspond to a height of 5000–6000 feet, in jet aircraft to perhaps
8000 feet. The percentage saturation of the blood at these height-
equivalents is lower than at sea level but not enough lower to cause
discomfort. Passengers are amply safeguarded by twentieth-century
technology based upon fundamental principles of respiratory
physiology. The care that must be exerted in this matter, and the
experience of the nineteenth-century balloonists, leads to a sharp
realization of the limit beyond which our respiratory mechanisms
cannot maintain life.

These limitations, however, do not mean that the respiratory mechanism is lacking in powers of response to environmental stress. On
the contrary, it can react in highly adaptive ways to two distinct signals. One of these is an increase in the carbon dioxide tension in the
blood; to this the respiratory mechanism reacts with exquisite sensitivity. The second signal is a decrease in oxygen tension; to this
the respiratory mechanism is less sensitive, yet the signal can nevertheless evoke some vitally important responses.

It had been suggested in the nineteenth century that carbon dioxide might play a part in the regulation of respiratory movements;
and in the early years of the twentieth century, J. S. Haldane clearly
established this relationship. His son, J. B. S. Haldane, has described
how his father started working on the problem of the nature of bad
air and of the supposedly harmful substances that were thought to
be present in it.

He started work in Dundee. He collected samples of the very worst
air that he could find. He went, between 12:30 and 4:30 in the morn-

ing, to the worst slums, taking samples of air from rooms where as many as eight people were sleeping in one bed. He went down the sewers also. Many years later I was with him in Dundee, and to remember his way above ground, he had to imagine himself back in the sewers below the streets.[3]

The story is best continued in the words of J. S. Haldane himself.

Our interest in the regulation of breathing arose out of a series of experiments carried out by Haldane and Lorrain Smith with reference to the question whether, as had been asserted shortly before by Brown-Séquard and d'Arsonval in view of an apparently convincing series of experiments, a poisonous organic substance is given off in expired air. The experiments of Haldane and Lorrain Smith, on the contrary, yielded results which were entirely negative. In the experiments on man an air-tight respiration chamber of about 70 cubic feet capacity was used, the air in which was allowed to become more and more vitiated by respiration. They seemed to leave no doubt that the apparent positive results described by Brown-Séquard and d'Arsonval were due partly to undetected air leaks which led to the animals being asphyxiated, and partly to other experimental errors.

The effects on the breathing of air so vitiated attracted attention particularly. It was found that when the proportion of CO_2 in the air rose to about 3 per cent and the oxygen fell simultaneously to about 17 per cent (there being 20.03 per cent of oxygen and 0.03 per cent of CO_2 in fresh air) the breathing began to be noticeably increased. With further vitiation the increase in breathing became more and more marked, until with about 6 per cent of CO_2 and 13 per cent of oxygen the panting was very great and caused much subsequent exhaustion.

When the experiment was repeated, with the difference that the CO_2 was absorbed by means of soda lime, there was no noticeable increase in the breathing before the oxygen fell below about 14 per cent. When, finally, the CO_2 was left in the air, but oxygen was first added so that the proportion of this gas present remained abnormally high throughout, the panting was just the same as when ordinary air was used. In short experiments in which the same air was rebreathed from a large bag to the limit of endurance it was found that the experiment had to stop at about 10 per cent of CO_2 whether oxygen was added or not, and that the percentage of oxygen made no difference to the distress produced. In the experiments with air there was only about 8 to 9 per cent of oxygen in the rebreathed air at the end of the experiment; but even this low proportion made no appreciable difference to the breathing. When, on the other hand, a mixture containing a very much reduced percentage of oxygen, but without any addition of CO_2, was breathed, the respiration was increased distinctly, as shown by graphic records taken with a stethograph, when the oxygen fell to about 12 per cent. The breathing was still more greatly increased by yet lower percentages of oxygen. If the proportion of oxygen was extremely low, e.g. about 2 per cent, consciousness was lost quite suddenly after about 50 seconds, and before there was time to notice any increase in the breathing.

It was quite evident from these experiments that when the same air is rebreathed, or an insufficient proportion of fresh air is supplied, the increased breathing produced is due simply to excess of CO_2 until, at least, the oxygen percentage becomes extremely low. It appeared, therefore, that the variations in ordinary breathing in response to variations in the respiratory exchange must be due to the increased CO_2 produced, and not to the increased consumption of oxygen. This conclusion was the same as that of Miescher-Rusch, and supported his views as to the regulation of respiration.

When more than about 10 per cent of CO_2 was breathed the effect of the mixture was to produce stupefaction, which was very marked with higher percentages. This effect was already well known in animals, and CO_2 was one of the gases tried as an anaesthetic by Sir James Simpson before he adopted chloroform. The effect of excess of CO_2 in producing ataxia, stupefaction, and loss of consciousness is very familiar in connexion with experiments with mine-rescue apparatus and diving apparatus, and there can be no doubt that the statement of Brown-Séquard and d'Arsonval that they were able to breathe air containing 20 per cent of CO_2 for two hours without much distress must have been founded on some error. These effects are readily produced in the presence of a large excess of oxygen and are therefore quite independent of the effects of want of oxygen. The narcotic effect of a large excess of CO_2 quiets down the respiration, and this result in animals led many previous observers to overlook almost entirely the ordinary effects of CO_2 in stimulating the breathing.[4]

From the work of J. S. Haldane and others, it has been demonstrated convincingly that carbon dioxide acts as a chemical signal in the regulation of respiratory rhythm in man. It exerts its action upon the medullary respiratory center, where there are cells that are very sensitive to the concentration of carbonic acid brought to them in the blood stream. The sensitivity of this mechanism is extraordinarily high. A steady increase in the CO_2 content of the air inspired by a man (Table 1-2) has as its first effect an increase in the depth of ventilation (hyperpnoea). Later, when the concentration of CO_2 is 3–5 per cent, the rate of ventilation also increases. The effect of these responses is to sweep out the extra CO_2 from the lungs, so that the composition of the alveolar air departs as little as possible from normal. The control is so delicate and successful that during the early stages the change in the CO_2 content of the alveolar air is too small to be detected by the usual methods of gas analysis; a change in composition first becomes readily detectable when about 5 per cent of CO_2 is present in the inspired air.

TABLE 1-2

Influence of Atmospheric Carbon Dioxide upon Respiratory Movements and Composition of Alveolar Air in Man[a]

Per Cent CO_2 in Inspired Air	Depth of Respiration (Normal = 100)	Frequency of Respiration (Normal = 100)	Per Cent CO_2 in Alveolar Air
0.79	112	100	5.5
2.02	130	107	5.6
3.11	192	100	5.5
5.14	313	120	6.2
6.02	372	169	6.6

[a] Data from J. S. Haldane and J. G. Priestley, *Journal of Physiology*, 32 (1905), 225–260.

Carbon dioxide, a mere waste product of metabolism, is thus revealed as a chemical factor of fundamental significance in the control of external respiration. Exactly how it influences the respiratory center is uncertain, although it may well be that its action is mediated through its effect upon the pH of the circulating blood. That a waste substance should have such a singular regulatory capacity may also be related to the same factor. Because carbon dioxide dissolves in the blood to form carbonic acid, an increased intake of the gas, or an increased production of it within the body, leads to an increase of hydrogen ions:

$$CO_2 + H_2O \rightarrow H_2CO_3 \rightleftharpoons H^+ + HCO_3^-$$

Here there is a danger, for the cells of human bodies are highly sensitive to fluctuations in the acidity of the blood and tissue fluids and require to be surrounded by fluid with a pH of about 7.4.

The increased acidity is reduced to a minimum by the buffering action of proteins and phosphates which are in the blood and which tend to take up the additional hydrogen ions:

$$H_2CO_3 + Na \text{ proteinate} \rightarrow NaHCO_3 + H \text{ proteinate}$$

Even so, an increased entry of CO_2 into the blood must produce some increase in acidity, and it is imperative that this should be reduced as quickly as possible. The reduction is effected by increased ventilation which sweeps the CO_2 out of the lungs. Thus the respiratory mechanism is highly sensitive to changes in the level of CO_2 in the air within the lungs.

The respiratory mechanism is one example of an adaptation designed to maintain a constancy of conditions within the body fluids.

This constancy is called homeostasis, a term that was defined at the eighteenth symposium of the Society for Experimental Biology as including in its widest context

> the co-ordinated physiological processes which maintain most of the steady states in organisms. It . . . does not necessarily imply a lack of change, because the "steady states" to which the regulatory mechanisms are directed may shift with time. But throughout the change they remain under more or less close control.[5]

In later chapters other aspects of homeostasis are stressed; it is perhaps the most important single expression of the steady states that characterize living systems and is a dominant theme throughout this book.

So striking is the effect of carbon dioxide upon respiratory activity that at one time it was doubted whether shortage of oxygen had an influence at all upon the process. It is now clear, however, that the respiratory mechanism of mammals is indeed influenced by a lowering of oxygen tension in the blood. The effect is believed to be mediated through chemoreceptors situated in glandlike structures called the carotid and aortic bodies. A carotid body is found where the common carotid artery forks into the external and internal carotid arteries, while the aortic body lies on the aortic arch near the pulmonary artery. These structures, closely related as they are to the blood system, are richly supplied by arterial blood and contain receptors that are believed to be sensitive to changes in the composition of that blood. To some extent they are sensitive to increased carbon dioxide tension, but less so than is the respiratory center. More important is their sensitivity to lowered oxygen tension.

Sensitivity of these structures becomes apparent in man when the oxygen tension in the blood falls below about 70 mm Hg, a level equivalent to breathing air containing about 18 per cent oxygen, which again is equivalent to ascending to a height of about 4000 feet. At this point the hypoxia stimulates the carotid and aortic bodies, the result being a reflex increase in both the depth and the frequency of respiration, the same type of response as is produced in other circumstances when the respiratory center responds to an increased carbon dioxide tension. As previously noted, the latter response removes excess carbon dioxide from the pulmonary alveoli. Increased pulmonary ventilation produced by hypoxia also removes carbon dioxide, with the result that its partial pressure in the alveoli falls below what would be normal at sea level. This fall, for reasons explained earlier, is reflected in an increased alkalinity of the blood which opposes the action of the hypoxia, in that it tends to exert an inhibitory action upon the respiratory center. The situation is soon rectified by the excretory activity of the kidney, which removes bicarbonate and restores the blood to its normal pH value.

The effect of hypoxia upon carbon dioxide tension is incidental to the adaptively significant effect of the increased respiratory activity, which brings about improved ventilation of the lungs. The increased movement of air through the lungs results in the alveolar oxygen tension being brought closer to the atmospheric oxygen tension than it would be at sea level. Although the alveolar tension is lower than normal, the extent of the fall is less than it would have been had the ventilation not been improved; thus the degree of saturation of the blood is not as low as it would otherwise have been.

The body is also capable of additional adaptive responses to oxygen deprivation. Other resources become significant when there is continued exposure to hypoxia, for example, when human beings live at great heights. In these circumstances the body shows a capacity to develop physiological compensations that improve activity and prospects of survival. Such compensatory responses to changed climatic and physical conditions constitute the phenomenon of acclimatization, a type of adaptive response that is by no means confined to respiratory activity (see Chapter 5). Acclimatization is well shown in mountainous country, where the visitor may suffer at first from some degree of mountain sickness but, after a short residence, secures rapid relief. Such an experience is described in A. C. Redfield's account of arrival in the Andes:

> Making the ascent by train, one lightly touched by "seroche" [mountain sickness] experiences his first symptoms at an altitude of 10,000 feet or more. Subjectively lassitude, then headache, usually frontal, growing in severity, and perhaps nausea are felt. One feels cold, particularly in the extremities, the pulse quickens, respiration becomes deeper and more frequent, the face is pallid, lips and nails are cyanotic. On descending from the summit to Oroya at 12,000 feet, though a marked improvement is felt one finds himself reduced to a helpless condition of weakness which renders the least muscular effort irksome and productive of shortness of breath, dizziness, and palpitation. The night's sleep is restless and on waking one feels much as he does on venturing on to his feet after recovering from an acute infection. In two or three days, one's strength returns, the colour improves somewhat and all but the more severe forms of exertion may be undertaken without distress. The majority are less fortunate than this. During the ascent the symptoms are qualitatively the same, but frequently more severe, and nausea gives way to vomiting. The night's sleep fails to bring relief; severe headache, gastro-intestinal instability, and weakness continue for several days; the body temperature may be supranormal (102°F. by rectum), and at times one is aware of palpitation. Cyanosis is marked. After three or four days in bed, relief comes and in a week normal activity may be resumed.[6]

A number of changes contribute to the improvement brought about by acclimatization. One is regulation of the pH of the blood. Another is an increased content of red corpuscles and hemoglobin in the blood, which increases the blood's oxygen-carrying capacity. This facilitates the oxygenation of the tissues, for it means that oxygen can be yielded up to them by the blood without unduly lowering the gradient of oxygen tension between the blood and the tissue fluids. Part of this response is effected by the release of a reserve of blood corpuscles from the spleen. This provides a rapid reaction to hypoxia, but its effect can be only short-lived, since mammalian red blood corpuscles have a life of only some 120 days and must constantly be replaced. The blood of a man is estimated to contain about 32 trillion (32×10^{12}) of these cells, and they are destroyed at the rate of billions per day. Continuous acclimatization of human beings and other mammals living for long periods at high altitudes demands, therefore, increased production of corpuscles and hemoglobin. An increase certainly occurs, although the mechanism by which it is contrived is not clear. It is believed, however, that an element which circulates in the blood stream stimulates production of red corpuscles and acts directly upon the bone marrow to increase the rate at which the corpuscles are produced and released.

In the early years of the twentieth century, partly under the stimulus of the Anglo-American expedition to Pike's Peak in Colorado, much attention was given to establishing the degree of acclimatization achieved by individuals living and working at various heights in the Rocky Mountains. *Figure 1-6* illustrates some data obtained at that time. In acclimatized men the percentage of hemoglobin in the blood was increased by about 10 per cent for every 100 mm fall of atmospheric pressure; the values for women showed a similar increase, but were about 11 per cent lower throughout. In addition to this sex difference, there was also considerable variation in both the speed and the extent of the response. Individuals on Pike's Peak living at a height of 14,100 feet (equivalent to 453 mm Hg pressure), showed an increase in hemoglobin content of their blood varying from 13 to 53 per cent.

The effect of such acclimatization is undeniably spectacular. D. B. Dill, in his account of studies in South America, records the case of a Chilean sulfur miner, living in camp at a height of 17,500 feet and starting his day's work by climbing 1300 feet to the mine. His arterial blood was so viscous that the blood pressure could not drive it into the sampling syringe. Because of its relatively low saturation, the blood was dark like venous blood; yet, says Dill, the man climbed straight up to the mine through sand and powdered sulfur in preference to using the zigzag trail.

Clearly, the body has remarkable reserves upon which to base its

adaptive responses; but it also has limits which are, in part, physiological and, in part, a consequence of the physical laws that govern
its environment. Serious malfunctioning of the unaided human body
is said to set in at 20,000 feet, and consciousness is difficult to sustain
at heights above 26,000 feet. G. L. Mallory and A. C. Irvine, in their
assault upon Mount Everest in 1924, were climbing at around 29,000
feet without the assistance of additional oxygen. They never returned. E. Hillary and N. Tenzing, in the British assault of 1953,
reached the summit at 29,002 feet, at a partial pressure of oxygen of
about 47 mm Hg; but they depended upon the aid of oxygen masks.
At greater heights even this help would fail. At 40,000 feet the
delivery of pure oxygen at ambient atmospheric pressure would not

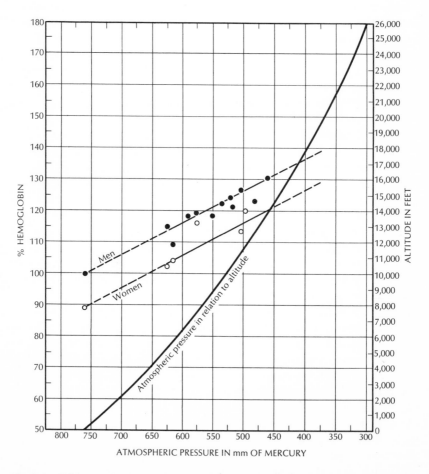

Fig. 1-6. Influence of atmospheric pressure on the hemoglobin content of the blood
of men and women acclimatized to living at the heights shown. (From M. P. Fitzgerald,
Philosophical Transactions of the Royal Society of London, Series B, 203 (1913), 482.)

achieve adequate saturation of the blood. At 70,000 feet the blood would be boiling. The only remaining resources are more sophisticated inventions of human technology—pressurized cabins, capsules, and space suits—products of the profoundly important and entirely novel phase of adaptive evolution that takes its origin from the human brain.

■ THE RESPIRATORY MECHANISMS OF SOME INVERTEBRATES

The means by which animals satisfy their need for oxygen vary greatly, for there are many different plans of organization within the animal kingdom, each lending itself to characteristic patterns of adaptive specialization. It is instructive to pay some attention to these not only because of their inherent beauty and interest, but also because an understanding of how different groups of animals have solved their problems enlarges man's understanding of the origin and mode of operation of his own adaptations.

The underlying similarity in molecular and biochemical organization found throughout the animal kingdom has led to discovery of similar adaptations arising independently in groups that have no close phylogenetic relationships. An illustration of this is the occurrence of hemoglobin in various invertebrates (discussed earlier). The crustacean water flea, *Daphnia pulex*, is a good example. This pond-living individual is often colored pink or red by hemoglobin dissolved in its blood. Jan Swammerdam, who knew of this phenomenon in 1758, tells of his initial shock when he first observed the water flea; his momentary impression was that the water had been turned into blood. The color is not found in individuals living in well-aerated lake water, which suggests that the hemoglobin may be serving some respiratory function in the less well-oxygenated water of ponds. That this is indeed so was shown by H. Munro Fox, who found that the amount of hemoglobin in the blood of *Daphnia* increased in conditions of oxygen deficiency, just as it does in man and other mammals. This increase has been observed also in both the parthenogenetic eggs of *Daphnia*, which take up hemoglobin in the ovary, and the blood of certain other entomostracan crustaceans, including *Leptestheria*, *Artemia*, and *Branchipus*. The situation in *Daphnia* is illustrated in *Fig. 1-7*. Comparison with *Fig. 1-6* (p. 22) shows how strikingly similar in its effect is the response of men in the Rocky Mountains and water fleas in little ponds, an impressive example of a similar principle of adaptation being deployed in two widely separated groups of animals.

Fox and his colleagues were able to show convincingly that the increase in hemoglobin content of *Daphnia* in response to hypoxia was not a chance phenomenon but undoubtedly an adaptive response, lengthening the survival time of animals kept in oxygen-deficient

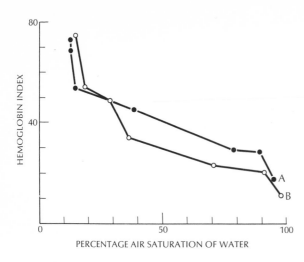

Fig. 1-7. Relation of hemoglobin concentration in the blood of *Daphnia pulex* to oxygen content of water (expressed as percentage of the air-saturation value) in two series of seven cultures each, which lasted: *A*, 7 days, and *B*, 9 days at 22-23° C. Each point gives the hemoglobin index for one culture at the end of the period. Initial hemoglobin index: 36. Note that some cultures lost, and others gained hemoglobin. (From H. Munro Fox, B. M. Gilchrist, and E. A. Phear, *Proceedings of the Royal Society of London, Series B*, 138 (1951), 517.)

water. The increase in hemoglobin aids them in their muscular work and thus enables them to gather more food. Finally, it results in more parthenogenetic eggs being produced than would otherwise be the case, while its presence in the eggs accelerates their development. When these pink and red water fleas are transferred to well-aerated water, the extra hemoglobin disappears; but how it does so, or what becomes of it, is no more clear than how the initial increase is effected.

Arthropods, like vertebrates, evolved from an aquatic ancestry, and crustaceans like *Daphnia* show us how well the arthropod plan of structure is suited for life in water. But again, like the vertebrates, the arthropods have exploited life on land with great success and have done so along more than one line of evolution. The following discussion refers to only one of those lines, represented by the insects, which in so many features of their organization present an instructive comparison with mammals.

In arthropods, as in mammals, the conditions of terrestrial life have compelled the development of an internal respiratory system with a large surface area protected from the danger of desiccation. Arthropods, however, have met the need for such a system in a manner very different from mammals. Like certain other arthropod groups, insects effect their gaseous exchange through a system of tubes, the tracheae. These open to the outside by openings called stigmata, or spiracles, of which there are typically two pairs on the thorax and eight pairs on the abdomen. Internally, the tracheae end by branching into delicate tubules, the tracheoles, which surround and often penetrate the tissue cells.

The movements of the stigmata of the small flea *Xenopsylla* are controlled by segmental nerves running out from the segmental ganglia of the central nervous system. It is supposed that these ganglia contain respiratory centers that are sensitive to changes in acidity within the body. In principle this resembles the situation in the respiratory center of the mammal, with the difference that the flea lacks the inherent automatic and spontaneous rhythm of the latter.

One would suppose that in mammals great adaptive value is attached to the possession of an automatic drive to respiratory ventilation; yet such is not always the case in insects, if one may judge from conditions in *Xenopsylla*, as analyzed by V. B. Wigglesworth (*Fig. 1-8*). There are no ventilation movements in this insect, presumably because it is sufficiently small for oxygen to pass along the tracheae by diffusion. Some of the carbon dioxide doubtlessly passes out in the same way; however, since it diffuses through the tissues much more quickly than oxygen, much is probably lost through the body surface. As previously implied, tracheae are protected from losing water to the atmosphere. This protection, however, is only partial and depends upon the animal being able to close its stigmata, except when communication with the air is necessary. Without these closing mechanisms, which take different forms in different insects, the animals would rapidly die through loss of water by evaporation.

When the flea is resting, it breathes through the first and eighth pair of abdominal spiracles, the others being closed. Moreover, the

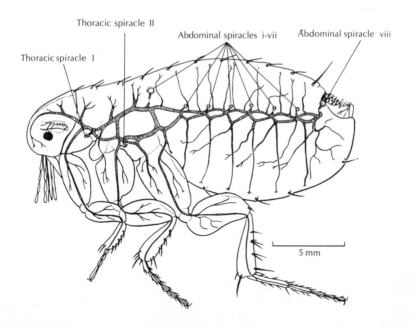

Fig. 1-8. Tracheal system of *Xenopsylla cheopsis*. (From V. B. Wigglesworth, *The Principles of Insect Physiology*, 3rd edition, London: Methuen & Co. Ltd., 1947, p. 190.)

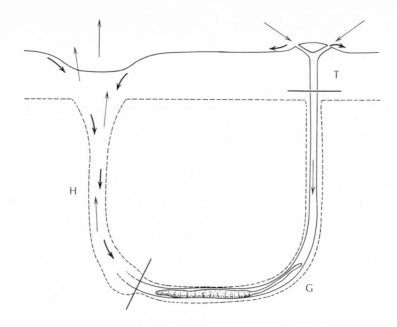

Fig. 1-9. Generalized diagram of a lugworm burrow with the worm lying quietly in the gallery. The cross lines are drawn at the boundaries between the head shaft (*H*), gallery (*G*), and tail shaft (*T*). The dotted line is the boundary between yellow and black sand. The long, thin arrows show the movement of water, and the short, thick ones that of sand. (From G. P. Wells, *Symposia of the Society for Experimental Biology*, 4 (1950), 128.)

two functioning pairs show a rhythmical opening and closing, with a regularity of some five to ten seconds. When the flea is respiring more actively, these two pairs remain permanently open, and the two thoracic pairs and the remaining abdominal pairs come into action; they, too, may now show a rhythmic opening and closing, or they may remain permanently open.

The respiratory reactions in the flea depend in no way upon an inherent neural rhythm. On the contrary, each act of opening or closing is a direct response to a reduction of oxygen in the tracheae and to an accumulation of carbon dioxide within the body. In both cases the operative stimulus is probably an increase in acidity, which results, in part, from an accumulation of carbon dioxide and, in part, from the production of lactic acid caused by oxygen deprivation. Determination of the periodicity of the rhythm is somewhat complicated. The duration of closure of the spiracles is proportional to the amount of oxygen in the air; if this falls below about 1 per cent, they close for only brief periods and remain open for most of the time. How long they remain open, however, is determined by the amount of carbon dioxide that has accumulated during their closure. In this way the system is elegantly adapted to provide adequate time for the carbon dioxide to diffuse out.

Not all insects can rely solely upon diffusion for the movement of oxygen. In larger individuals this would prove too slow, and it must, therefore, be aided by ventilation movements brought about by various types of movement of the body wall. An example is provided by the cockroach *Periplaneta*. At low concentrations of carbon dioxide, it resembles the flea. In both animals the spiracles remain permanently open if the carbon dioxide concentration in the air rises to only 2 per cent. At a concentration of 10 per cent, however, the cockroach begins a pumping movement. The pulsation rate at this stage is eight to ten per minute; but the rate increases as the carbon dioxide concentration rises, until at a concentration of 20 per cent the rate may be as high as 180 per minute. A subtle feature of this adaptive response is that when pulsation begins, certain of the spiracles may also pulsate, as they do in the flea. The advantage of this is that closure of the spiracles at one point of the body and opening of them at another will, if properly correlated with the pulsation of the body, facilitate respiratory exchange by encouraging a flow of air through the tracheal system. Here, as in the flea, the nervous system is highly organized so as to coordinate the separate parts of the respiratory system into a single functional unit. Again, as in the earlier discussion of mammalian respiration, one sees how adaptive mechanisms, through their unifying action upon the component parts of the body, bring the animal into the most effective relationship with its environment.

Mammals provide an illustration of external respiration dependent primarily upon an inherent rhythm but continuously modified by chemical influences that are directly associated with the respiratory process. In insects one finds examples of chemical influences directing the whole process and establishing a rhythm that is suited to conditions occurring at any particular time. The following, third example differs from both of these and shows how an animal of a much simpler level of general organization can be remarkably well adapted to a mode of life that is distinctly unpromising, as far as respiratory mechanisms are concerned.

Arenicola, the lugworm, lives in U-shaped burrows in the sand of the tidal zone (*Fig. 1-9*). Its organization is only poorly adapted for movement over the surface; and, therefore, it spends the greater part of its life within the burrow. When the burrow is covered by the tide, the lugworm's respiration depends upon ventilation movements that irrigate the burrow by inward and outward movement of water. When the tide is out and the burrow is uncovered, the problem of respiration is complicated by there being little, if any, opportunity for renewing the water. It is a measure of the economy and elegance

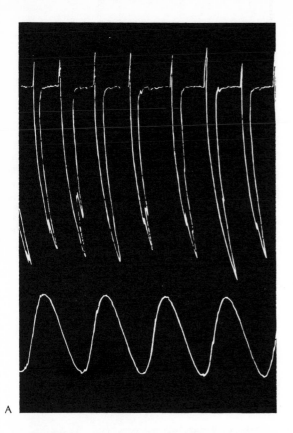

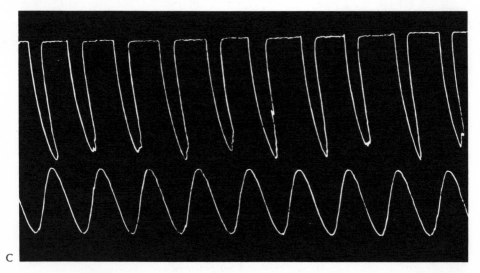

Fig. 1-10. Records of the water circulation produced by lugworms in glass U-tubes. Read from left to right. Downstroke of lever means a headward propulsion of water; time trace (below) at one cycle per hour. (From G. P. Wells, *Symposia of the Society for Experimental Biology,* 4 (1950), 134.)

of animal adaptation that respiration in both conditions is mediated by one and the same pattern of activity. The solution of the problem is described by G. P. Wells, who reports the results of observing the animals living in the laboratory in glass tubes, under conditions in which it is possible to obtain continuous records of their activities.

In glass tubes, lugworms (once they have settled down) propel the water headwards through the tube in a series of very regular outbursts. This irrigation cycle has a period which — although somewhat variable from worm to worm, and from day to day — is much longer than that of the feeding cycle [see p. 43]; it is commonly about 40 min. Closer investigation shows that the headward irrigation is the second, and most prominent, phase of a three-phase outburst; the first is tailward creeping and the third is tailward irrigation.

The three extracts of *Fig. [1-10]* illustrate the point. They were obtained by putting the worm in a U-tube of sea water *Fig. [1-11]*, whose diameter approximated to that of the burrow; the upper ends of the limbs of the U opened into wide cylinders, one of which contained an aeration jet and the other a float connected with a writing lever; the cylinders were also connected by a fairly wide capillary. The pumping movements of the worm circulated the water in the whole system, and owing to the slight resistance of the capillary, caused fluctuations of level of the float which appear, much magnified, on the tracing. In each case, the worm's head was towards the float, so that a headward movement of water causes a downward movement of the writing point.

The three phases of the cycle can be seen to vary in relative prominence. The worm of extract A rested between outbursts at the bottom of the U; as each outburst began, it crept vigorously tail-

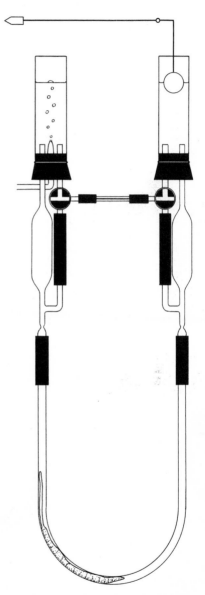

Fig. 1-11. Apparatus for recording the irrigation cycles of the lugworm. (From G. P. Wells, *Journal of the Marine Biological Association, U.K.*, Council of the Marine Biological Association of the U.K., 28 (1949), 448.)

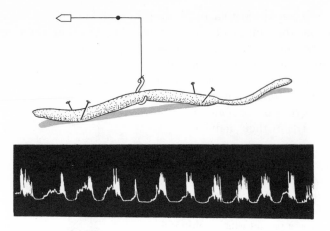

Fig. 1-12. Above: lugworm pinned to a cork sheet on the bottom of a flat dish. *Below:* record traced by the worm. Duration of the printed extract of the record, 7 hr. (From G. P. Wells, *Journal of the Marine Biological Association, U.K.*, Council of the Marine Biological Association of the U.K., 28 (1949), 453.)

wards into one of the vertical limbs (upstroke of the lever); this then passed into headward irrigation (downstroke) during which it crept gently (synkinetically) back to the starting point; the third phase was vestigial. The worm of extract B gave only slight tailward creeps, but very well-marked third phases (tailward irrigation) except in one of the outbursts. The same worm, on another occasion, traced extract C; here the first and third phases are both vestigial, though they could just be seen when the worm was watched. Whatever the particular form of the outbursts at the time, they often continue, with almost clock-like regularity, for many hours on end.

The onset of an outburst involves a change in the whole attitude of the worm. During the pauses, its body is shortened and generally presses on all sides against the tube. During the outbursts, the body is lengthened and narrowed. The appearances rather suggest, as one watches, a periodic awakening of the worm.

One might assume that the basis of intermittent irrigation is reflex; the appearance of an outburst being stimulated by oxygen lack or carbon dioxide accumulation in the tube. In this case, the outbursts would become more frequent and prolonged if for any reason the pumping movements failed to bring aerated water. In fact, however, if the recording U-tube system is modified so that the worm can circulate a small amount of water (about 35 c.c.) without thereby getting access to an air supply, the bursts appear at about the same intervals as before, but considerably less water is now pumped at each burst. On admitting aerated water again, after a few hours under "no-air" conditions, the worm responds by pumping vigorously and continuously for a long period (e.g. 40 min.), and thereafter the outbursts are temporarily accelerated. These results show that the intermittence is due to an internal pacemaker whose action can be modified, much as the heart beat can, according to circumstances.

The existence of a pacemaker of suitable frequency can be demonstrated by two other methods.

(i) An intact worm is pinned to a cork sheet with two pairs of pins, one anteriorly and one at the base of the tail; the whole is immersed in a dish of aerated and stirred sea-water; the worm's movements are simply recorded by means of a glass hook passing under the middle of the body and connected to a light lever. Worms so treated often trace bursts of activity, following each other with great regularity for hours, and corresponding in timing with the irrigation cycles [*Fig. 1-12*].

(ii) Longitudinal body-wall strips containing the ventral nerve cord, suspended in sea water, trace a complicated pattern in which conspicuously vigorous outbursts, of about the same timing as the irrigation cycles, can often be seen. The presence of the brain is unnecessary. As body-wall strips are motionless in the absence of the ventral cord, the pacemaker may tentatively be placed in the cord.

De-afferentation of the cord is unfortunately impossible; it may be that a steady feed-in from peripheral sense organs is necessary to keep the cord active; but it seems clear, from the length of the intervals between outbursts, that the form of the cycle must depend on a spontaneously cyclic pacemaker.[7]

Wells' account demonstrates that there is something in common between man's respiratory organization and that of a lugworm, for both depend upon a spontaneously active region in the central nervous system. The difference is that in the worm the ventilation is uninfluenced by reflex pathways, by the concentration of available oxygen, or by the rate of production of carbon dioxide. No doubt the general organization of a lugworm may justly be regarded as altogether simpler than that of man, but it would show a lack of biological understanding to dismiss the worm as an imperfectly constructed organism, or its activities as those of a poor relation. The studies of Wells have shown that it is admirably fitted to live successfully in a difficult environment.

■ THE APPROACH TO THE INTERPRETATION OF ADAPTIVE ORGANIZATION

In looking back over this brief and highly selective survey of respiratory adaptation, some principles of general significance begin to emerge. First, one sees that it is possible to analyze adaptive behavior, for descriptive purposes, in comparatively simple units: the movements of ribs and diaphragm in mammals; the ventilation movements and closing of stigmata in insects. These units, however, are abstractions from a much more complex, integrated system which allows the animal to behave as a whole organism. It should be remembered that the movements of external respiration, on which this chapter concentrates, are themselves closely linked with other adaptive features. For example, the transport of oxygen by hemoglobin and its release to the tissues is subtly influenced both by the local concentration of carbon dioxide and by the type of atmosphere in which the animal is breathing. This integration and unification are characteristic of living systems and make possible both maintenance of the steady state and regulation of the animal's life, so that it preserves its integrity in a hostile environment that is always tending to destroy and absorb it.

Biologists, conscious of the unity and regulatory capacity that characterize living organisms, and confronted with the difficulty of interpreting these properties in terms of nonliving matter, have sometimes been led to adopt the mode of thought called vitalism. The essential feature of this is the supposition that the material body is controlled by a nonmaterial influence which Aristotle termed entelechy. Understandably, this kind of interpretation is outmoded now, for to adopt it is to accept the view that explanations or understanding of the most absorbing and interesting problems of animal organization are forever beyond the reach of experimental investigation. Human experience does not justify this defeatism. Had such an attitude been generally accepted, the concepts discussed in this chapter and, consequently, air travel and space exploration might never have developed.

Contrasted with vitalist interpretations of life are materialist explanations. These suppose that living processes depend upon causal relationships between the component parts of the body, relationships governed by principles identical to those determining the behavior of nonliving matter and susceptible to investigation in the laboratory by methods no different in principle from those of physics and chemistry. To adopt this approach is not necessarily to be committed to the view that the whole of the universe, and the position of life within it, are explicable in terms of physics and chemistry. A biologist may feel intuitively that his picture of the universe must be only partial; indeed, as a good biologist he can hardly deny the limitations of his sense organs and of the equipment with which he supplements them. What he is adopting is a method of scientific enquiry which has justified itself by the results that it has secured.

The materialist viewpoint of today derives particularly from the dualistic philosophy of Descartes. He drew a distinction between the mind or spirit of man (the thinking substance, which he believed to be located in the pineal gland) and the material or extended substance of the body. Other animals, lacking the spirit, consisted only of extended substance. The material body, he believed, could be regarded as a machine or automaton, whose functions result from the arrangement of its organs, just as the functioning of a clock results from the pattern of its weights and wheels. From this concept, more than from anything else, mechanical models have developed with which successive generations of biologists have sought to explain the workings of the animal body.

Models of varying degrees of complexity are still used by biologists; but if they are to be useful, they must be truly functioning models which accurately represent the essential features of the living system they are illustrating. Herein lies the fundamental difficulty inherent in models. Mechanical interpretation of the living body remains grossly incomplete if it fails to represent the processes that unify the constituent parts into an organized and self-regulating whole. The difficulty is well recognized, and some have sought to overcome it by a combination of mechanist and vitalist modes. Using this combined approach, the animal is interpreted in mechanistic terms as far as may be possible, but the ultimate coordination and integration is regarded as something that is inherent in the living system.

To many contemporary biologists this combined approach is little more than pure verbal evasion of the difficulty. Fortunately, in recent years a more promising approach has become possible with the development of computers and other types of electronic machinery; these devices contain built-in powers of self-regulation dependent upon control exercised through the operation of complex circuitry. Of course, these regulatory powers are inserted into the machine by its human designers. But the fact that a machine can be programmed in this way suggests the inviting possibility that living organisms may be programmed according to similar principles. It is now conceivable that organisms inherit in their chromosomes a code of instructions—established under the influence of natural selection during the earlier history of the group—that programs the responses the organism must make to its environment to preserve its steady state.

This new and potentially fertile development in the mechanist approach suggests a closer parallel than has previously been envisaged between living organisms and inanimate machinery. It is comprised in the general field of cybernetics, a term that was introduced in 1947 to designate the science of control and communication in its application both to engineering and to biological problems. The recognition of common principles in these fields makes possible the design of new types of models and, in consequence, the devising of new and helpful ways of describing problems of biological organization. Such description is an essential first step toward the investigation of problems at the laboratory bench.

An illustration of the value of programmed machinery is the concept of negative feed-back, a central feature of cybernetic theory and a concept familiar in the design of electronic machinery. Negative feed-back refers to that portion of the output of a particular activity that is fed back into the machine to correct errors in performance. For example, a signal of excessive output can be fed back to the source and cause a compensating reduction of output. In this way the machine can be programmed, so that divergences from the required behavior are rapidly compensated.

The principle of negative feed-back is illustrated in *Fig. 1-13*. Note that the circuit contains a small rectangle. This represents what is called, in a current colloquialism, a black box, which is the complex of electronic "hardware" that detects the feed-back signal, compares it with a predetermined reference, and signals the result to the output circuit. There are good reasons for believing that negative feed-back plays a fundamentally important part in securing regulation within the animal body. In formulating such systems, however, it is important for the biologist to remember that animals, too, have their black boxes. To forget these is to generate unjustified euphoria when contemplating electronic models. Virtually nothing is known of what lies within these biological black boxes, so that models at this stage often can express little more than paths of input and output. Nevertheless, they provide a descriptive basis that can make a substantial contribution toward understanding the mechanism of adaptive regulation and can help scientists devise experimental procedures for further analysis.

One example of the negative feed-back device has been encountered already in the foregoing survey of mammalian respiration. This is the Hering-Breuer reflex, which can be formulated along the lines illustrated in *Fig. 1-14*. In this instance the black box is the respiratory center, the output of which brings about inspiratory movements by activating certain muscle effectors. Information from pulmonary receptors is fed back into the center, which can be imagined to act as a computer, comparing the degree of expansion of the lungs with a standard of reference that has been established by genetic coding. Correction is introduced when the departure from

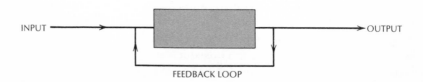

INPUT   OUTPUT

FEEDBACK LOOP

Fig. 1-13.   Simplified diagram of a feedback circuit.

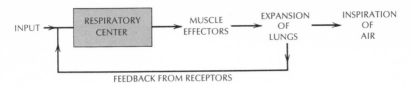

Fig. 1-14. Simplified diagram of the Hering-Breuer reflex interpreted as a feedback circuit.

the standard has reached the predetermined level; the pattern of output is modified and inspiration replaced by expiration. It should be noted that in this instance the source of the input (i.e., the origin of the rhythmicity of the respiratory center) is not properly understood. Conceivably, the activity may arise within the respiratory center itself. It is just such difficulties that are only too easily obscured by simplified feed-back diagrams.

The Hering-Breuer reflex is only one element in the regulation of respiratory movements. In addition, changes in the inspired air, or in the metabolic rate, will disturb the chemical composition of the blood; this composition is monitored by chemoreceptors which feed back information leading to compensating modifications of the ventilation rate. A model of this element of control is suggested in *Fig. 1-15*.

If these various control mechanisms are combined, the complex model shown in *Fig. 1-16* appears. Here the central control is interpreted as consisting, in part, of a computer and, in part, of a servo-mechanism. The computer receives stimuli from the higher nervous centers, from the tissues, and from the blood stream; its output establishes the required ventilation rate. Information regarding departures from the required ventilation rate is fed back to the computer. In this model, however, ventilation is further influenced by a servo-mechanism. This term is applied to an independently-powered slave (servo-) system controlled by a primary or master mechanism in such a way that it either follows the latter precisely or magnifies its power. Justification for postulating such a mechanism in the design of the respiratory control system of mammals lies in the existence of muscle spindles in the respiratory muscles; the spindles monitor the changes in length of the muscles. Should these muscles meet increased resistance, as may very well happen in clinical conditions in man, information provided by the spindles leads to increase in the force applied to the respiratory muscles. Thus tidal volume can be maintained despite increase in mechanical load.

A common result of setting up biological models is to find that one particular pattern is applicable to more than one type of animal, whether or not the animals belong to groups that have a close evolutionary relationship. A similar experience is familiar to students of comparative anatomy. It is an important duty of the zoologist to bring to contemporary discussions of functional organization a clear and precise analysis of the significance of these resemblances. In approaching this analysis at the anatomical level, it has long been customary to make use of the concepts of homology and analogy. These terms were introduced gradually into biological thinking, but they received their first formal definition in 1848 from Richard Owen. He defined a homologue as the same organ in different animals under every variety of form and function. An analogue was defined as a part or organ in one animal which has the same function as another part or organ in a different animal.

To comprehend the above definitions, one necessarily must ask what exactly is meant by the "same" organ. The answer was clear, however, in the context in which Owen was writing. He was thinking in terms of the principle of unity of type, which expresses the observed fact that within any one group of animals the variant forms can all be related to a common ground plan. From this arose the concept of the idealized archetype—a hypothetical organism that possesses in fully developed form all the organs that are characteristic of any particular group. Thus one can conceive of a vertebrate archetype that is wholly different from an arthropod archetype. In this context organs in a particular group were the same when they corresponded to one and the same organ in the archetype of that group. The concept of archetypes was a product of idealist philosophy. Subsequent to the publication of the *Origin of Species*, however, the concepts of homology and analogy acquired an evolutionary connotation and a more realistic basis. Organs in a particular group that had been assessed as homologous were now believed to be so because they descended from one and the same organ in the common ancestral group. Analogy, by contrast, was similarity resulting solely from community of function and was independent of any common evolutionary ancestry.

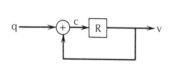

Fig. 1-15. Simplified diagram suggesting the pathways by which respiratory ventilation is kept proportional to metabolic rate, with consequent stabilization of the chemical composition of the blood. R, the whole respiratory system; c, chemical stimulus; q, metabolic rate; v, ventilation. (From A. C. Dornhorst, *British Medical Bulletin*, 19 (1963), 4.)

Advances in man's understanding of the evolutionary process and of the programming of information within the chromosomes have made these concepts more difficult to apply, although their validity has not been destroyed. It is now recognized that the possession of

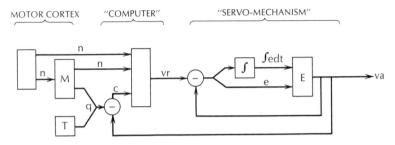

MOTOR CORTEX   "COMPUTER"   "SERVO-MECHANISM"

Fig. 1-16. Diagram of respiratory regulation in mammals, using control-system theory and suggesting possible interrelations of the various factors involved. *M,* muscles; *T,* other tissues; *E,* effector, i.e., respiratory motor nerves and muscles; *c,* chemical stimuli; *e,* error (i.e., *vr − va*); *n,* nervous stimuli; *q,* metabolic rate; *va,* achieved ventilation; *vr,* required ventilation. The error integration makes the right-hand side of the model a true servo-mechanism. (From A. C. Dornhorst, *British Medical Bulletin,* 19 (1963), 5.)

apparently homologous organs by related animals may not necessarily be due to the existence of a similar structure in a common ancestral group. It is possible that what that ancestral group possessed was not the organ itself, but the genetic potentiality to develop that organ, given the existence of conditions that would favor its encouragement by natural selection. Such an organ may arise independently in more than one line of descent from that ancestral group, yet the possession of that organ by the descendants may still be said to be an expression of homology. This type of homology is often referred to as latent or plastic homology.

Considerations based on the concepts of homology and analogy must be applied to an analysis of adaptive mechanisms. To take some examples from the respiratory mechanisms already considered, it is possible that the medullary respiratory center of fish is homologous with that of mammals. While this cannot be stated positively, of course, it is at least plausible to suppose that the imperative need to ensure a supply of oxygen led early in the history of vertebrates to the evolution of a device for spontaneous activation of the respiratory rhythm. On the other hand, the existence of a similar rhythmic center in *Arenicola* must be an example of analogy, for annelid worms and vertebrates occupy two widely separated evolutionary lines. The same is true of the sensitivity of insect and vertebrate respiratory systems to carbon dioxide; this must have been developed independently. These examples of analogy provide instructive example of how two groups of animals can proceed independently to the use of a metabolic product as a respiratory signal. Further discussion regarding the origins and uses of such chemical messengers in regulatory systems appears in Chapters 2, 3, and 4.

1. E. D. Adrian and F. J. J. Buytendijk, "Potential Changes in the Isolated Brain Stem of the Goldfish," *Journal of Physiology*, 71 (1931), 121–125, 126–127.
2. J. B. S. Haldane, *Keeping Cool* (London: Chatto and Windus, Ltd., 1940, pp. 83–84. Published in the United States as *The Adventures of A Biologist* by Harper & Row, Publishers, 1928. Reprinted by permission.
3. *Ibid.*, p. 87.
4. J. S. Haldane and J. G. Priestley, *Respiration* (London: The Clarendon Press, 1935), pp. 16–17. By permission of the Clarendon Press, Oxford.
5. *Symposia of the Society for Experimental Biology*, 18 (1964), p. vii.
6. J. Barcroft, *The Respiratory Function of the Blood* (London: Cambridge University Press, 1925), p. 13.
7. G. P. Wells, "Spontaneous Activity Cycles in Polychaete Worms," *Symposia of the Society for Experimental Biology*, 4 (1950), 133–136.

CHAPTER 2   ■   The Uptake
of Energy

■ SOME PRINCIPLES OF INGESTION AND DIGESTION

The entry of energy-rich compounds into the open system of the
animal body presents problems of organization and adaptation that
are no less demanding than those involved in the entry of oxygen.
In man, as in the great majority of animals, the process is divisible
into three phases: ingestion, digestion, and absorption. Ingestion
involves the seizing and manipulation of the food material and its
subsequent passage into the cavity of the alimentary tract. This cavity
is directly continuous with the external environment, so that ingestion is to some extent comparable to the taking of air into the lungs.
The second phase, however, has no parallel in the respiratory processes. It occurs, because energy-rich molecules, unlike oxygen, usually cannot be absorbed straight into the blood stream. They must
first be hydrolyzed into simpler molecules by the catalytic action of
digestive enzymes; this hydrolysis constitutes the process of digestion. The absorption of the digestive products suggests a comparison
with the absorption of oxygen, but the analogy is only superficial.
Whereas the passage of oxygen through the pulmonary epithelium
is a passive process of diffusion, the passage of the digestion products
involves active metabolic processes.

Ingestion in man, as in many other animals, differs from the intake
of oxygen, in that it is not directed by a continuous rhythmic drive
like that of the respiratory center. For several reasons feeding is
necessarily a discontinuous process. For example, the search for food
may expose animals in the wild to attack from predators, so that there
is an advantage in reducing the time spent upon this activity. More-

over, a carnivore must adjust its feeding habits to the times of its prey's appearance; these occasions may be restricted to particular hours of light or darkness. In the specialized habitat of the seashore, feeding habits must often be determined by the sequence of tidal movements. Thus the limpet, *Patella*, is free to move and graze only when it is covered by water.

Mention of the limpet raises the question of marine animals that live on the sea bottom below the tide marks. Many of these animals are filter feeders, drawing in and abstracting food material from a current of water. In theory they should be able to do this continuously, for their food supply is never interrupted; but it is not certain that they do, in fact, practice continuous ingestion. It is thought that the ciliary feeding currents of amphioxus (one of the lower members of the Phylum Chordata) are periodically interrupted, so that the animal's feeding is a discontinuous process like that of most of its vertebrate relatives.

It is not difficult to see why animals may be organized to feed discontinuously, even when food is available for them without interruption. So far only ecological considerations have been mentioned, but there is also an important physiological reason. Digestion takes a long time, particularly at the low temperatures that may often exist within the bodies of animals other than birds and mammals. Continuous passage of food through the alimentary tract, therefore, is likely to result in premature expulsion at the hind end of undigested or, at best, partially digested material. In these circumstances the digestive process proceeds inefficiently, and the energy expended in securing the food is not used to advantage. Periodicity of feeding may thus be physiologically advantageous or even essential.

Efficiency of digestion, however, is not merely a function of time; it demands also a high level of biochemical and physiological specialization. This aspect of digestion will be considered mainly as it occurs in the alimentary system of mammals, for it is in this group that digestive physiology has been most closely studied and the associated problems of adaptive regulation most clearly defined. As far as the breakdown of proteins is concerned, provision must be made for the programming of precise relationships between enzymes and food material. The complex molecules of proteins must undergo stepwise digestion, each step being catalyzed by a specific enzyme. This is true for all animals; but in the vertebrates, and more particularly in the mammals, the stepwise action of the enzymes is facilitated by their being separated from each other to some extent within the alimentary tract. As a result, the actions of the various enzymes can be separated in time—an arrangement that demands precise physiological regulation, if enzyme release is to occur in the correct sequence.

The stomach is the most obvious illustration of the stepwise action of enzymes, for it is in this organ that digestion of proteins is initiated by an acid gastric juice. Most vertebrates have this adaptation, exceptions being the lampreys and hagfish, survivors of the ancient jawless vertebrates which seem never to have developed a stomach, and a number of fish which have secondarily lost this organ. The wall of the stomach secretes hydrochloric acid and pepsinogen, the latter being an inactive substance which is activated autocatalytically in an acid medium (below pH 6) to form the enzyme pepsin. This enzyme, which is probably peculiar to the vertebrates, is an endopeptidase, so-called because it breaks peptide bonds in the interior of protein molecules (*Fig. 2-1*), as well as terminal bonds at the ends of the polypeptide chains. Functioning over a pH range of 1.0 to 5.0, it specifically hydrolyzes peptide bonds between an aromatic amino acid (tyrosine or phenylalanine) and a dicarboxylic acid (glutamic or aspartic acid), provided that the second carboxyl group of the latter is free, and that there is no free amino group near the bond concerned.

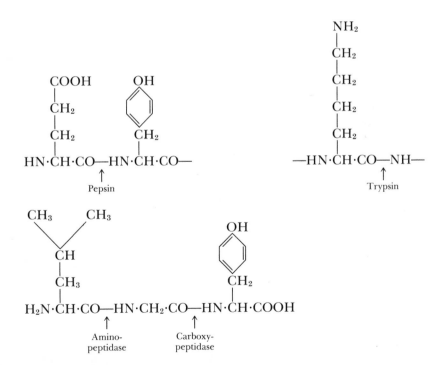

Fig. 2-1. Examples of the specific peptide linkages that are broken by pepsin, trypsin, aminopeptidase, and carboxypeptidase. The arrows show the points of attack (cf. *Fig. 3-14*).

Protein breakdown is continued in the near-neutral medium of the intestine, the acidity of the gastric juice having been neutralized by the secretions of the pancreas and liver. Another endopeptidase, trypsin, is secreted by the pancreas as the inactive trypsinogen. This is activated either autocatalytically or by the enzyme enterokinase, which is secreted by the intestine. Trypsin differs from pepsin not only in its pH range, which is commonly about 7.0 to 9.0, but also in its specificity; it breaks bonds that are adjacent to arginine or to lysine (*Fig. 2-1*).

The action of these two enzymes releases short peptide chains, whose digestion is completed by a series of exopeptidases, so-called because they act only on terminal bonds. Carboxypeptidase, secreted by the pancreas, removes terminal amino acids with a free carboxyl group. Aminopeptidase, secreted by the intestine, removes those with a free amino group (*Fig. 2-1*). Finally, dipeptides are broken by a series of dipeptidases, also secreted by the intestine. Some of these appear to act within the epithelial cells, after they have taken up the dipeptides.

Although simpler in detail, the digestion of carbohydrates is similar in principle to that of proteins. It may be illustrated by reference to the fate of starch. In man, as in many other mammals, the digestion of starch is initiated in the mouth by the enzyme amylase. This enzyme breaks down starch into the oligosaccharide, maltose, with some production of another oligosaccharide, dextrin, and the monosaccharide, glucose. The buccal amylase is secreted in the saliva, a fluid that is important even when it lacks the enzyme because of its action in moistening and lubricating food and cleansing the lining of the mouth. An amylase is also secreted by the pancreas. The sequential process is completed by oligosaccharases secreted by the intestine; their action results in the release of monosaccharides.

The digestion of fats does not show this sequential pattern, but it has its own peculiar complexity. Lipase, secreted by the pancreas, hydrolyzes fats into glycerol and fatty acids. This enzyme, however, must act in association with the bile salts secreted by the liver. The latter are needed by the lipase for full development of its own activity. They also facilitate lipase action by emulsifying fats and interacting with the products of fat digestion to facilitate fat absorption.

From the foregoing brief survey, one can appreciate the very high level of adaptive regulation that operates within the mammalian alimentary tract. The elaboration of a sequential pattern is a special peculiarity of this group. In lower vertebrates it seems to be less marked. For example, in fish we do not find the same division of enzyme production between pancreas and intestine; the pancreas in these animals takes the major part in secretory production. Among invertebrates the tendency is to mix the food at one and the same time with a range of digestive enzymes. One may suppose that the need for precise regulation is correspondingly high in all mammals. In this class the pH must be regulated to different values at different points, while the food not only must be mixed with the enzymes but also must be moved on so that it encounters the various secretions at times appropriate to their sequential action. The mode of regulation of these alimentary functions bears some resemblance to the regulation of respiration, insofar as both involve the interaction of nervous and chemical factors. However, as discussed later in this chapter, the chemical aspects introduce a new and fundamentally important principle.

■ ASPECTS OF NEURAL REGULATION OF DIGESTION

As discussed previously, the respiratory mechanism of *Arenicola* is activated by a spontaneous cyclic pacemaker in the central nervous system. The feeding mechanism of the animal provides another example of cyclic regulation. In a regular cycle of activity, the lugworm feeds by stirring and swallowing the sand at the head end of its burrow (*Fig. 1-9*, p. 26). This process is distinct from the respiratory cycle; but, like that cycle, it is evoked by a rhythmic pacemaker in its central nervous system. The situation is quite different in mammals, whose feeding activities obviously are not governed by a continuous rhythmic drive like that of the respiratory center. Yet animals in general are evidently adapted to take in sufficient food to satisfy their requirements for growth and maintenance; the need for the adaptation is self-evident, but scientists are far from understanding how it is achieved.

There is evidence that certain centers in the hypothalamus of the mammalian brain are involved in the regulation of food intake. The hypothalamus is formed by the ventral parts of the thick walls of the diencephalon—the hinder region of the fore-brain which lies immediately behind the cerebral hemispheres. Studies of the effects of localized injuries of the hypothalamus suggest that there is a "hunger center" or "feeding center" in the lateral hypothalamus and a "satiety center" in the ventro-medial region. Destruction of the feeding center in various mammals is followed by cessation of feeding, leading to starvation and death. On the other hand, if the intact center is stimulated electrically, the animal involved increases its food intake. It is from this center, therefore, that the drive to feed seems to originate. Conversely, if the satiety center is destroyed, the animal overeats and becomes fat, while stimulation of this center can abolish the feeding drive.

Even if one grants the importance of these centers, it is not clear how they are regulated to evoke the feeding characteristics of the species. It has been suggested that in normal circumstances the centers are influenced by the level of glucose in the blood stream regulated by a homeostatic feed-back mechanism. This suggestion is based on the assumption that there are glucose-sensitive receptors in the hypothalamus. It is supposed that a fall in blood-sugar level stimulates the hunger center and evokes feeding, while a rise in blood-sugar level stimulates the satiety center and brings about a reduced food intake. A model of such a mechanism is illustrated in *Fig. 2-2*. It is by no means agreed, however, that these two centers respond in this way to circulating glucose. In short, there is no clear understanding of how this fundamental requirement of mammalian open systems is actually regulated, although experience suggests that habit and routine are important factors in man's food drive, along with his normal 24-hour cycle of activity and rest.

Knowledge of the control of food movements within the alimentary tract is more complete. This control is primarily nervous; within the mouth it is entirely so. The salivary glands of mammals have developed out of secretory cells that are common in the buccal epithelium of lower vertebrates. In man there are three pairs of glands (the parotid, sublingual, and submaxillary), and in other mammals there may be additional ones. Within these glands two types of secretory cell are found. One type is the serous cell, which secretes a watery fluid containing salivary amylase; the other is the mucous cell, which secretes a lubricating mucus. Experiments on dogs have shown that

Fig. 2-2. Diagram to illustrate a possible homeostatic mechanism by which the hypothalamus might regulate the level of blood sugar. (From B. A. Cross, *Symposia of the Society for Experimental Biology*, 18 (1964), 172.)

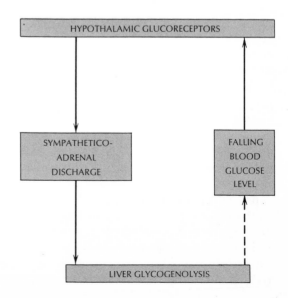

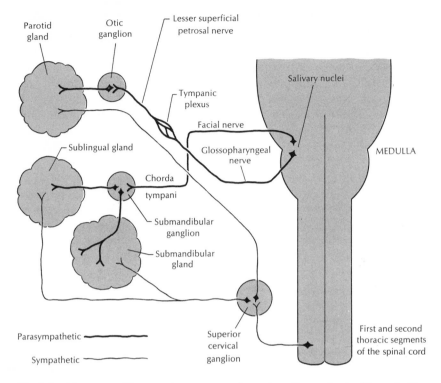

Parotid gland

Otic ganglion

Lesser superficial petrosal nerve

Salivary nuclei

Tympanic plexus

Facial nerve

Sublingual gland

Glossopharyngeal nerve

MEDULLA

Chorda tympani

Submandibular ganglion

Submandibular gland

Parasympathetic ———————

Sympathetic - - - - - - - -

Superior cervical ganglion

First and second thoracic segments of the spinal cord

Fig. 2-3. Diagram to illustrate the nerve supply to the salivary glands. (From G. H. Bell, J. N. Davidson, and H. Scarborough, *Textbook of Physiology and Biochemistry*, 5th edition, Edinburgh: E. & S. Livingstone Ltd., 1963, opp. p. 217.)

the composition of the secretion is adapted to the needs of the moment. Harmful or disagreeable substances evoke a thin, watery secretion that serves to wash the substances away. On the other hand, food material, in general, will be lubricated by the addition of mucus.

These glandular responses are nervous in origin, their diversity and adaptability depending partly on the varying proportions of the two cells in the different glands and partly on the way in which the glands are innervated. The salivary glands, like the rest of the alimentary tract, take their nerve supply from the autonomic nervous system. This part of the nervous system is concerned with responses that are usually involuntary (i.e., uncontrollable by human will) and that normally do not impinge upon man's consciousness. The autonomic system is divided into two sections (*Fig. 2-3*): the parasympathetic nervous system leaves the central nervous system in the head and sacral regions (cranio-sacral outflow); while the sympathetic nervous system leaves the central system in the area between the head and sacral regions (thoracico-lumbar outflow). Most internal organs in mammals are innervated by both systems, which commonly act antagonistically, i.e., they affect organs in opposite ways. Such antagonistic action is a principle of fundamental importance in physiological regulation, for it facilitates the achievement of a precise equilibrium in a fluctuating system.

That the salivary glands have a double innervation is readily shown by electrically stimulating their nerve supply. For example, stimulation of the chorda tympani nerve (*Fig. 2-3*), which carries parasympathetic fibers to the glands, results in the discharge of a watery saliva; stimulation of sympathetic fibers, which run to the glands from the anterior cervical sympathetic ganglion at the anterior end of the neck, produces a secretion rich in mucin. This double innervation is presumably an important factor in determining the content of the salivary secretion, but it must be aided by the sensory receptors in the lining of the buccal cavity. Nervous impulses from these receptors, evoked by different types of food material, are propagated along pathways determined during development through operation of the genetic code. The responses thus produced in the salivary glands and mediated by the autonomic nervous system, constitute the unconditioned reflexes that are part of the programming of the activities of the alimentary tract. Early in life, however, man develops the capacity to respond by salivation to the sight or smell of food, and such a response is far in advance of the direct stimulation of receptors by the entry of food into the mouth. These responses, too, are reflexes, in that the pathways are fixed; but they are not established at birth. They are conditioned reflexes, a consequence of the process of learning by experience, in which a new type of stimulus (sight or smell in this instance) becomes associated with an existing response and eventually displaces the original stimulus.

From the foregoing discussion, it is clear that purely nervous mechanisms are able to secure a high measure of adaptive response in the preliminary manipulation of food. They play a major part also in the subsequent movement of food by the musculature of the wall of the alimentary tract. Swallowing is a reflex response to the presence of material at the hind end of the pharynx. It is under voluntary control, insofar as man can deliberately transfer material to that point; but from there onward, its movements pass beyond human control. It is propelled down the esophagus by peristalsis—successive waves of contraction of the circular muscles which seize the food and drive it onward. Within the stomach the movements become more complex, for here they are adapted to break up the food and mix it with the gastric juice. Later, the mixture of secretion and food (chyme) passes on into the intestine, where it is subjected to peristalsis and other patterns of contraction. These mix the chyme with the later elements in the chains of enzyme action, while they also bring the material into close contact with the intestinal epithelium, thereby facilitating absorption. Finally, the indigestible residue reaches the large intestine; water is absorbed here, and the resultant feces are eventually voided through the anus.

The whole of the musculature responsible for these movements is under the control of the dual innervation of the autonomic nervous system. Broadly speaking, the parasympathetic system produces an excitatory effect upon the movements, whereas the sympathetic system inhibits them. These two alternatives make it possible for the movements of the alimentary tract to be regulated in accordance with the needs of the body as a whole. Once again, one should remember that this is a system that comes to full fruition in the higher vertebrates. In fish it is doubtful whether much of the alimentary tract has a dual innervation; and certainly the two autonomic components are not sharply differentiated from each other, nor do they act antagonistically (*Fig. 2-4*). The control of the digestive system in these animals must, therefore, be less precise. This is only one of many respects in which physiological adaptation is carried to a much higher level of specialization in the higher vertebrates.

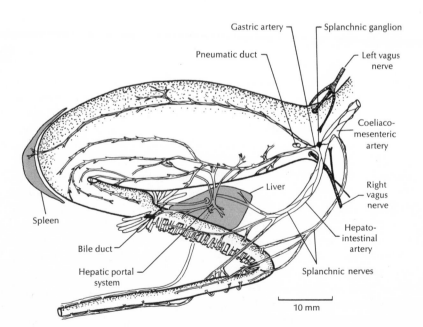

Fig. 2-4.   Innervation of the alimentary tract of the trout *(Salmo trutta)*. The vagus nerves run in the wall of the stomach but do not reach the intestine. Branches of the anterior splanchnic nerve follow all the major branches of the coeliaco-mesenteric artery and innervate both the stomach and the intestine. (From G. Burnstock, *Quarterly Journal of Microscopal Science*, 100 (1959), 206.)

The effect of the dual control of the alimentary tract is reflected in man's own experiences. The sight of food and the consequent pleasurable expectations that this arouses promote contractions of the alimentary tract through mediation of the parasympathetic system, thereby preparing the body in advance for the digestive processes. This in itself is good justification for the appetizer course. In contrast, and also well within man's experience, such powerful emotions as fear and rage inhibit the movements of the alimentary tract and, accordingly, inhibit the production of its secretions. Extreme fear may even cause defecation. The effect of such disturbances, and of milder forms of anxiety, may thus be to cause indigestion. This does not mean, however, that the inhibition of digestive activities is biologically meaningless or disadvantageous. On the contrary, as pointed out in Chapter 4, it is part of a wider range of responses that adapt the body at moments of crisis, when the expenditure of energy needs to be temporarily concentrated upon those reactions that are most likely to ensure survival. It is the prolongation of anxiety and other forms of mental disturbance beyond these limited periods that causes physiological disorder. This is part of the price paid for the benefits of a highly specialized nervous system and the highly organized social life into which it has led man.

■ THE APPROACH TO EXPERIMENTAL ANALYSIS OF FUNCTION IN THE ALIMENTARY TRACT

The major difficulty in studying the functioning of the digestive system in any animal is that the system is out of sight and cannot be exposed to view without setting up disturbances that grossly interfere with its normal behavior. A good deal can be learned about the movement of food by using X rays to reveal the passage of an opaque bismuth meal; but this is a technique of the present century. During much of the nineteenth century, the alimentary movements and secretory activity were little understood. Indeed, at the beginning of that century, even so fundamental an issue as the relative importance of mechanical and chemical breakdown of food was still undecided. It was only after much laborious investigation, associated particularly with the name of the great Russian physiologist, I. P. Pavlov, that the contributions of those two factors to mammalian digestion became more clear. From this enlarged understanding, the full complexity of the associated regulatory processes was exposed.

Pavlov's investigations, however, were preceded by the work of a remarkable pioneer, William Beaumont, a surgeon in the United States Army. By taking advantage of quite exceptional circumstances, Beaumont opened up a new field of digestive studies. On a morning in June, 1822, the village of Fort Mackinac presented an animated scene. The annual return tide to the trading post was in full course, and the beach was thronged with canoes and batteaus laden with pelts of the winter's hunt. Voyageurs and Indians, men, women and children, with here and there a few soldiers, made up a motley crowd. Suddenly from the company's store there is a loud report of a gun, and amid the confusion and excitement the rumor spreads of an accident, and there is a hurrying of messengers to the barracks for a doctor. In a few minutes . . . an alert-looking man in the uniform of a U.S. Army surgeon made his way through the crowd and was at the side of a young French Canadian who had been wounded by the discharge of a gun. The man and the opportunity had met. . . .[1]

Thanks to Beaumont's skill, the French Canadian, Alexis St. Martin, recovered from his wound but was left with a permanent opening, called a gastric fistula, extending from the stomach to the outside of his body (*Fig. 2-5*). Interested in this development, Beaumont persuaded St. Martin to take up service with him and, in consequence, was able for many years to make direct observations of the activities of the living stomach. Among many other things, he laid the foundation of man's understanding of the regulation of digestion, for he established that the acid gastric juice was detectable only when food or other suitable stimulants came in contact with the stomach lining.

On applying the tongue to the mucous coat of the stomach, in its empty, unirritated state, no acid taste can be perceived. When food, or other irritants, have been applied to the villous membrane, and the gastric papillae excited, the acid taste is immediately perceptible. These papillae, I am convinced, from observation, form a part of what is called by authors, the villi of the stomach. Other vessels, perhaps absorbing as well as secretory, compose the remainder. That some portion of the villi form excretory ducts of the vessels, or glands, I have not the least doubt, from innumerable, ocular examinations of the process of secretion of gastric juice. The invariable effect of applying aliment to the internal, but exposed part of the gastric membrane, when in a healthy condition, has been the exudation of the solvent fluid, from the above mentioned papillae.[2]

By these precise observations Beaumont was providing, for the first time, clear and convincing evidence of the capacity of the body to regulate the activity of the alimentary system in accordance with the demands created by the entry of food. Previous workers had provided good evidence for dissolution of food within the stomach by a gastric fluid, but the insecure foundations of this view can be judged from some of the evidence that was brought against it. Beaumont mentions, for example, a certain M. Montegre, who, gifted with the power of vomiting at pleasure,

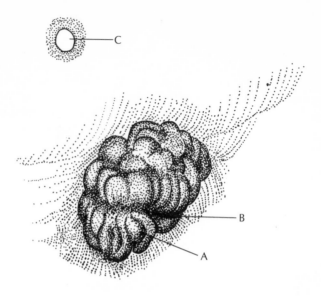

Fig. 2-5.   A portion of the stomach of Alexis St. Martin projecting through the fistula with the inner surface inverted. *A*, folds of the inner coats of the stomach; *B*, interstices filled with mucous substance; *C*, nipple. (From W. Beaumont, *Experiments and Observations on the Gastric Juice and the Physiology of Digestion*, 1833. Reprinted by Dover Publications, Inc., New York, p. 29.)

performed a series of experiments on the fluids of the stomach, obtained in this way, which induced him to come to a different conclusion of the subject of digestion. He conceives that what has been supposed to be the gastric juice, is, in fact, nothing but *saliva;* that it possesses no peculiar powers of acting on alimentary matter; that the principal use of the gastric juice is to dilute the food; and that the only action of the stomach consists in "une absorption vitale et elective," in which the absorbent vessels, in consequence of their peculiar sensibility, take up certain parts of the food and reject others. A complete refutation of the conclusions drawn from the experiments of Montegre, will be found in the fact, which has been tested by more than two hundred examinations and experiments, made by me, on the gastric cavity, that there never exists free gastric juice in the stomach, unless excited by aliment, or other stimulants. The fluid obtained by Montegre was, in all probability, a mixture of saliva (which had been unconsciously swallowed) and the mucus of the stomach. Neither of these secretions are capable of digesting aliment; nor could the peculiar products, generally obtained from the chemical analysis of the gastric juice, be found in them.[3]

Beaumont was perfectly correct in his interpretation of the results of Montegre; salivation is now known to be a normal accompaniment of vomiting. The confidence of Beaumont's assertions, and the clarification that he brought to this obscure field, are a tribute to the power of simple, but accurate, observation and experiment. His analysis of the functioning of the stomach paved the way for Pavlov's work, but, for evaluation of this, it will be convenient to concentrate attention mainly on the pancreas. For more than fifty years this organ has provided its investigators with perplexing problems, while at the same time it has formed a basis for fundamentally important advances in our knowledge of regulatory mechanisms.

■ NEURAL AND CHEMICAL FACTORS IN THE REGULATION OF DIGESTION

Pavlov was a great experimental physiologist, with a remarkable capacity for devising operative procedures that made the alimentary tract available for study without obstructing its normal mode of functioning. For his studies of the pancreas, he made use of dogs in which the pancreatic duct had been arranged to open to the exterior; the rate of secretion of the organ could thus be readily determined by counting the drops that fell from the opening. At the same time he exposed the vagus nerve in such a way that it could be stimulated without causing the animal discomfort. He rightly pointed out that the failures of earlier workers to achieve success with similar procedures were a consequence of the activities of the digestive system being inhibited by discomfort or pain experienced by the experimental animal. Pavlov perfected his own techniques to such a degree that he was able to demonstrate the responses of the animal before lecture audiences. His published lectures recapture something of the atmosphere of those heroic days of large-scale physiology, when the investigator, handicapped though he may have been by lack of modern, sophisticated equipment, had the advantage, nevertheless, of being concerned with the whole animal, rather than excised organs and tissues.

> The dog before you is provided with a permanent pancreatic fistula, made in the manner I have described in the first lecture. The animal has fully recovered from the operation and everything is healed. Four days ago the cervical vagus was divided on one side; the peripheral end of the nerve was laid bare, furnished with a ligature, and preserved under the skin. I now carefully remove the cutaneous sutures, and cautiously draw forward the ligature with the nerve, without causing appreciable discomfort to the dog. Observe that not a drop of juice flows from the metallic funnel, the wide end of which includes the part of the abdominal wall where the orifice of the pancreatic duct is situated. Now I begin to excite the nerve with an induction

current. As you see, the dog remains perfectly still without exhibiting the least sign of pain. Two minutes elapse without any result from the stimulus — this I ask you especially to bear in mind — and now, in the third minute, the first drop of juice makes its appearance, followed by others in quicker and quicker succession. After three minutes I interrupt the excitation, but the juice continues to flow spontaneously, and only stops at the end of four or five minutes from the cessation of the stimulus. I again apply the current, and obtain the same effect. This is the invariable result upon every dog. It must be added that the vagus nerve was stimulated by other workers with the same purpose in view, and yet what I can now publicly demonstrate was never seen. The reason of success lies in the nature of the preparations for the experiment.[4]

From this and other experiments, Pavlov drew a confident conclusion: the vagus was the secretory nerve of the pancreas. This, however, was only one step in Pavlov's analysis, for he had also made the important discovery that the entry of the gastric contents into the duodenum evoked a flow of juice from the previously quiescent pancreas. Moreover, he had shown that it was the acidity of the contents that was the actual stimulus, for secretion could also be evoked simply by introducing hydrochloric acid into the duodenum. At this time, in the closing years of the nineteenth century, it was generally supposed that the nervous system was responsible, through its reflex pathways, for bringing about such responses. This is indeed true of the salivary glands, and it was natural for Pavlov to conclude that the stimulating action of acid upon the pancreas was another example of such reflex behavior. The acid, it was thought, stimulated receptors in the duodenal lining; these receptors were thought to be linked with the pancreas through nerve fibers running into the brain and connecting with outgoing fibers of the vagus nerve.

Confirmation of this hypothesis by further experiment, however, proved more difficult. Two experiments may be cited. First, L. Popielski, one of Pavlov's co-workers, destroyed the most likely reflex pathways between the duodenum and the pancreas by cutting through the vagus and splanchnic nerves and destroying the medulla (through which the pathways would be expected to run). Nevertheless, he found that the introduction of acid into the duodenum still evoked an output of pancreatic secretion. Later, he removed the solar plexus and the spinal cord, but still the acid produced the same effect. Similar results were obtained in 1901 by E. Wertheimer and L. LePage in France. They prepared an animal in which a loop of the duodenum had been isolated from the rest of the alimentary tract and all nervous connections removed. When acid was introduced into the loop, pancreatic juice still flowed from the pancreas, a result difficult to explain in terms of reflex action.

In retrospect, it seems remarkable that these results did not cast doubt on the supposed activity of reflex pathways connecting the duodenum and pancreas. It was supposed, however, that denervation had not been complete. Popielski, in fact, was driven to rely upon a purely hypothetical assumption: that the response of the pancreas must depend upon local reflex pathways, separate from the main nerves and central nervous system but adequate to link the organ with the duodenum. This explanation, however, was difficult, if not impossible, to reconcile with the result of the experiments mentioned above, in which all possible nervous connections seemed to have been removed. In short, the problem needed thorough and fundamental reconsideration. This was provided by two English physiologists, W. M. Bayliss and E. H. Starling, who were drawn to the problem as a consequence of their studying the influence of local reflexes upon intestinal movements. Their interest led in an unforeseen way to the discovery of a new principle of adaptive organization.

Bayliss and Starling carried out their experiments on anesthetized dogs. A cannula was inserted in the pancreatic duct, so that the flow of secretion could be measured with a conventional drop recorder. Arrangements were made for injecting fluids into the blood stream and recording blood pressure. The results are best described in the investigators' own words.

III. THE EFFECT OF THE INJECTION OF ACID INTO THE DUODENUM AND JEJUNUM

It is unnecessary to describe at length the results obtained under this heading. We are able to confirm the statements made by our predecessors. The result of injecting from 30 to 50 c.c. of 0.4% hydrochloric acid into the lumen of the duodenum or jejunum is to produce, after a latent period of about two minutes, a marked flow of pancreatic juice. Further, this effect is still produced after section of both vagi, section of the spinal cord at the level of the foramen magnum, destruction of the spinal cord, section of the splanchnic nerves, or extirpation of the solar plexus, or any combination of these operations.

Fig. [2-6] will serve as an illustration of the fact. In this case the spinal cord was destroyed from the 6th thoracic vertebra downwards, and both vagi and splanchnic nerves were cut. At the period of time marked by the signal, 50 c.c. of acid were injected into the duodenum, about 2 minutes from the beginning of the injection the first drop of secretion is recorded, and a rapid series of drops commences at 4 minutes, to last for some 3 or 4 minutes and gradually cease after 11 or 12 minutes. . . .

Our experiments, therefore, confirm those of previous observers in so far as we find that after exclusion of all nerve-centres, except those in the pancreas itself, a secretion of pancreatic juice is obtained by the introduction of acid into the duodenum. But, as pointed out

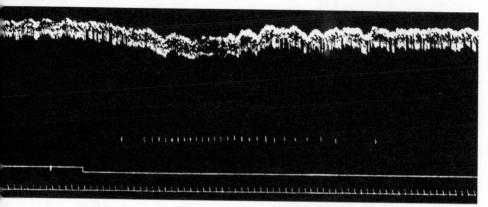

Fig. 2-6.   Effect of injection of acid into duodenum after destruction of cord. Upper curve, blood pressure. Uppermost of three lines — drops of pancreatic secretion. Middle line — signal marking injection of 50 ml of 0.4% HCl. Bottom line — time in 10 sec. Blood-pressure zero is at level of time marker. (From W. M. Bayliss and E. H. Starling, *Journal of Physiology*, 28 (1902), 328.)

above, the *experimentum crucis* of taking an isolated loop of intestine, dividing the mesenteric nerves supplying it, and then injecting acid into it, had not been performed.

It is plain that this experiment cannot be performed on the duodenum for anatomical reasons. Fortunately, however, as Wertheimer and Lepage have shown, the jejunum, separated by section from the duodenum, is also capable of exciting the pancreas to activity, when acid is introduced, and in this case the centre for the "reflex" must be in the coeliac or mesenteric ganglia. The possibility of our crucial experiment is given here, and the results are contained in the next section.

IV. THE CRUCIAL EXPERIMENT

On January 16th, 1902, a bitch of about 6 kilos weight, which had been fed about 18 hours previously, was given a hypodermic injection of morphia some 3 hours before the experiment, and during the experiment itself received A. C. E. in addition. The nervous masses around the superior mesenteric artery and coeliac axis were completely removed and both vagi cut. A loop of jejunum was tied at both ends and the mesenteric nerves supplying it were carefully dissected out and divided, so that the piece of intestine was connected to the body of the animal merely by its arteries and veins. A cannula was inserted in the large pancreatic duct and the drops of secretion recorded. The blood-pressure in the carotid was also recorded in the usual way. The animal was in the warm saline bath and under artificial respiration.

The introduction of 20 c.c. of 0.4% HCl into the duodenum produced a well-marked secretion of 1 drop every 20 secs. lasting for some 6 minutes; this result merely confirms previous work.

But, and this is the important point of the experiment, and the turning-point of the whole research, the introduction of 10 c.c. of the same acid into the enervated loop of jejunum produced a similar and equally well-marked effect.

Now, since this part of the intestine was completely cut off from nervous connection with the pancreas, the conclusion was inevitable that the effect was produced by some chemical substance finding its way into the veins of the loop of jejunum in question and being carried in the blood-stream to the pancreatic cells. Wertheimer and Lepage have shown, however, that acid introduced into the circulation has no effect on the pancreatic secretion, so that the body of which we were in search could not be the acid itself. But there is, between the lumen of the gut and the absorbent vessels, a layer of epithelium, whose cells are as we know endowed with numerous important functions. It seemed therefore possible that the action of acid on these cells would produce a body capable of exciting the pancreas to activity. The next step in our experiment was plain, viz., to cut out the loop of jejunum, scrape off the mucous membrane, rub it up with sand and 0.4% HCl in a mortar, filter through cotton-wool to get rid of lumps and sand, and inject the extract into a vein. The result is shown in *Fig.* [2-7]. The first effect is a considerable fall of blood-pressure, due, as we shall show later, to a body distinct from that acting on the pancreas, and, after a latent period of about 70 secs. a flow of pancreatic juice at more than twice the rate produced at the beginning of the experiment by introduction of acid into the duo-

Fig. 2-7.   Effect of injecting acid extract of jejunal mucous membrane into vein. Explanation as in Fig. 2-6. The steps on the drop-tracing are due to a gradual accumulation of secretion on the lever of the drop-recorder, which fluid falls off at intervals. Blood-pressure zero is at level of drop-recorder. (From W. M. Bayliss and E. H. Starling, *Journal of Physiology*, 28 (1902), 331.)

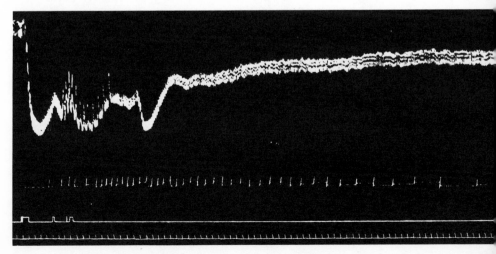

denum. We have already suggested the name "secretin" for this body, and as it has been accepted and made use of by subsequent workers it is as well to adhere to it.[5]

The initial experiments of Bayliss and Starling were completed in 1902; a preliminary report of them had been published in March, while the complete account, from which the above quotation is taken, appeared in September. By that time the authors were already referring to "subsequent workers" who had accepted the name secretin. This is an indication of the profound interest aroused by their work, for in their time research did not normally progress as rapidly and on so many fronts as it does today. Bayliss and Starling had demonstrated a new principle of physiological organization; they had shown that nervous pathways were not the only means by which coordination could be exercised. It was evident that the blood stream provided another route, through which circulation took place of chemical products that developed in one organ and were able to activate others.

For such chemical messengers Bayliss and Starling later suggested the term hormone, from the Greek, *hormaein*, meaning to impel or arouse to activity. The word is now familiar. In classical terms (which necessarily are extended in Chap. 4) a hormone is defined as a chemical substance produced in specialized secretory cells or glands and discharged directly into the blood; the blood stream carries it to other parts of the body, where it produces specific regulatory effects. The secretory process involved is called internal or endocrine secretion; the glands responsible are called endocrine glands. The latter are contrasted with exocrine glands, such as the enzyme-secreting tissue of the pancreas, which discharge their secretion externally on to a surface or into a cavity.

The discovery of secretin created a profound impression in Pavlov's laboratory, where all of the current work was based upon the concept that the activity of the alimentary tract and its glands was regulated exclusively through the nervous system. The reaction of Pavlov himself, however, was wholly in line with his greatness as an experimental scientist; he did not hesitate to modify his views, once he had convinced himself of the correctness of the new facts. The circumstances have been vividly described by B. P. Babkin, who was working in the laboratory at the time.

> I remember well the time when the preliminary communication on secretin by Bayliss and Starling appeared in 1902 in the *Physiologisches Centralblatt*, Volume 15, No. 23. Before the discovery of secretin the problem of the action of acid from the duodenum on the pancreas was made extremely complicated by Popielski and Wertheimer, who supposed the existence of different short reflex arcs connecting the duodenal mucosa with the secretory (acinous) cells of the pancreas.

The theory of humoral transmission of impulses from the intestine to the pancreas was not only new and startling; it also simplified at once the involved problem of the regulation of the pancreatic secretory activity. Bayliss and Starling's article produced almost a sensation in our laboratory. It shook the very foundation of the teaching of the exclusive nervous regulation of the secretory activity of the digestive glands, a concept which seemed to be established so solidly and supported by so many experimentally proved facts.

Pavlov's reaction to the discovery of a humoral regulation was that which one would expect from him. He did not give up at once the idea of the exclusive nervous regulation of pancreatic secretion but rather the reverse. He tried to confirm facts obtained by himself earlier on the secretory functions of the vagus and splanchnic nerves and to disprove Bayliss and Starling's hormonal theory.

Two of Pavlov's co-workers, Borisov and Walther, showed that (very crude) acid extracts of many organs (duodenum, small and large intestine, stomach, and even striated muscles) stimulated the secretion not only of the pancreatic juice but of saliva also. From this it was concluded that the acid extract of duodenal mucosa did not contain a specific pancreatic hormone but a substance or number of substances foreign to the body.

Very soon, however, Pavlov began to change his opinion. In the article in *Nagel's Handbuch* (2:742), published in 1907 but written by Pavlov in the summer of 1903, he again pointed out the presence of foreign substances in the extracts of the duodenal mucous membrane but added: "Thus there remain certain things, as a matter of fact but a very few, which have to be cleared up to make us absolutely sure of the participation of secretin in the normal mechanism of the action of acid on the pancreas."

Pavlov radically changed his opinion about the new fact discovered by the English physiologists probably in the fall or in the winter of 1902–3 after reading Bayliss and Starling's complete and excellent paper on secretin in the *Journal of Physiology* (1902). In this article Bayliss and Starling reported experiments with highly purified extracts of the duodenal mucosa which stimulated a profuse secretion of the pancreatic juice and produced hardly any side effects (e.g., fall of the blood pressure, etc.). Pavlov always bowed to facts, so he did not hesitate any longer to recognize the existence of a humoral mechanism of pancreatic secretion. I think it was in the fall of 1902 that Pavlov asked V. V. Savich to repeat the secretin experiment of Bayliss and Starling. The effect of secretin was self-evident. Pavlov and the rest of us watched the experiment in silence. Then, without a word, Pavlov disappeared into his study. He returned half an hour later and said, "Of course, they are right. It is clear that we did not take out an exclusive patent for the discovery of truth."[6]

It will be apparent from Babkin's account that the evidence considered thus far would not by itself have been adequate to establish fully and beyond any possibility of doubt the concept of secretin as a hormone. This situation was well known to Bayliss and Starling, who, along with many later workers, contributed further evidence. Indeed, even to this day the problems implicit in the discovery of secretin have not been wholly resolved. Yet the means by which further evidence was obtained merits close attention, for the principles that have governed research into the nature and mode of secretin action are relevant to the whole field of endocrinology; and the status of endocrinology as a major field of contemporary biological endeavor is the tribute of the second half of the twentieth century to the investigations of Bayliss, Starling, and other pioneers.

First, it must be realized that the presence of a biologically active substance in a tissue extract is not necessarily evidence that that substance is secreted from the tissue, or that it is active in the intact animal in normal physiological conditions. Rigid conditions of proof must be satisfied before the substance can be accepted as a hormone and the tissue as an endocrine gland. Admittedly, it may be impossible to satisfy all conditions, for technical difficulties may stand in the way. In such cases scientists must be content with satisfying only some conditions, bearing in mind that to this extent the evidence is weakened. Judgment must decide when the hypothesis of hormonal action is adequately established.

It is desirable first to identify the tissue or organ in which the hormone is being secreted. (In fact, discovery of the secreting tissue has sometimes been the first step in the identification of a hormonal mechanism.) Secretory granules, or stages in their formation, should be visible; and it should then be possible to correlate variation in the appearance of these secretory cells with variations in the output of the hormone or in the demands that are being made for the hormone in the rest of the body. Next, it should be possible to remove the secretory tissue, or to immobilize it, and to correlate this with the appearance in the body of clearly defined consequences of hormone deprivation. This may be achieved experimentally with animals in the laboratory; or, alternatively, clinical observations upon patients with some disturbance of endocrine function may provide comparable evidence. It should then be possible to carry out replacement therapy, which consists of the introduction into the body of either implants of the secretory tissue or injections of extracts prepared from this tissue. Such therapy should alleviate the symptoms resulting from the previous deficiency.

It is necessary also to demonstrate that the hormone is actually present in the blood stream in normal physiological conditions, and, ideally, to show that it is present in higher concentration in the venous blood leaving the gland than in the arterial blood entering it. Only then can it be shown quite beyond doubt that active materials present in a tissue are actually discharged from it into the blood stream. This demonstration, along with other aspects of these studies, will depend upon the devising of suitable assay methods, by which the amounts of the hormone present in the blood or in tissue extracts can be measured. Finally, it is desirable that the hormone should be subjected to detailed chemical analysis. It should be obtained in a pure form, its chemical composition should be precisely determined, and, ideally, this composition should be confirmed by synthesizing the substance in the laboratory. An important advantage accruing from this last step, of course, is that large quantities of the hormone may then become available for clinical use at much less cost than that involved in extraction from living tissue.

It is surprising and unfortunate that the cells producing secretin have never been identified. Moreover, it is impossible to carry out surgical removal and replacement therapy, since the hormone is produced by the part of the system that it is regulating. In other respects, however, the evidence for the hormonal status of secretin is very strong. Thus, although specific secretory cells were not identifiable, Bayliss and Starling were able to demonstrate that secretin was obtainable only from that part of the alimentary canal that came into contact with chyme, the normal acid stimulus for secretin release. It was present in the duodenum and the upper part of the following region of the intestine (jejunum) but not in the rest of the intestine. This made it reasonable to regard the presence of secretin as being adaptively related to the passage of gastric contents into the duodenum.

One criticism that Bayliss and Starling had to meet was that their postulated hormone was merely a nonspecific vasodilator substance. Such substances are known to be present in tissue extracts, and they certainly can increase the rate of glandular secretion by increasing the amount of blood that flows through the gland. Crude extracts of the duodenal wall admittedly have a vasodilator action; but Bayliss and Starling were well aware of this, as is evident from their own words (p. 55). They were able to show, however, that vasodilator material could be removed by further purification of the extracts, and the effect of the secretin remained unimpaired.

Other evidence of secretin being a hormone was added by later investigators. For example, it was convincingly demonstrated that secretin actually circulated in the blood under normal physiological conditions. This evidence was obtained by arranging two animals, so that the blood of one passed into the circulation of the other. Initially, no secretin could be demonstrated in the blood circulating in either animal; but it appeared in both when acid was injected into the duodenum of only one. The hormone, therefore, must have been traveling from the stimulated animal into the other through their common circulation.

Further and convincing evidence that communication between duodenum and pancreas was absolutely independent of nervous connections was obtained by ingenious operative procedures. Thus A. C. Ivy and his colleagues in the United States transplanted part of the pancreas and also loops of the jejunum of a dog into its body wall, where these organs eventually developed a new blood supply. The old vessels, together with any nerve fibers that might have been included in their walls, were then severed. Yet acid inserted into a duodenal loop still evoked secretion from the transplanted pancreas, under conditions in which the newly developed blood supply was the only possible means of communication between the two transplants.

As for chemical studies of the hormone, it was early recognized that injection of secretin might be a valuable way of detecting disorders of pancreatic function in man; certainly this has been a powerful motive for securing pure preparations of secretin. Several groups of investigators concentrated upon this problem, and in so doing they showed the advantages that may result from independent attacks upon the same problem. They showed also the advantages of the comparative method of study. In this instance the comparison of results obtained with two different preparations threw an unexpected light upon the nature of secretin and upon its mode of action.

To appreciate this development, it is necessary to look back to the work of Pavlov's school. They had established that nervous stimulation, acting through the vagus nerve, evoked pancreatic secretion. The discovery of secretin, however, had shown that there was a chemical stimulant, acting through the blood stream. It became necessary, therefore, to explain why the body needed two different mechanisms to regulate the pancreas.

A partial answer to this problem was achieved as a result of the independent development in different laboratories of two distinct methods of preparing secretin extracts. Bayliss and Starling had removed histamine (the vasodilator substance mentioned earlier) from the intestinal mucosa with absolute ethanol. They then extracted the hormone from the mucosa with 0.4 per cent hydrochloric acid and purified the extract by successive treatment with acetic acid and ethanol. Later, a group of American workers, following a French lead, precipitated the secretin, after the acid extraction, by saturation with sodium chloride. Subsequent treatment of the precipitate, based upon the use of ethanol and of trichloracetic acid, resulted in a powder called SI. This was highly active, although it was still far from being chemically pure. Meanwhile, J. Mellanby, in England, had developed a different extraction method. In this the secretin was initially extracted by absolute alcohol; it was then adsorbed on to precipitated bile salts and precipitated from aqueous solution by the addition of dilute acid. This, too, produced an active preparation.

It was from this point that controversy developed. Mellanby found that the pancreatic secretion evoked by his preparation of secretin contained only water and sodium bicarbonate. From this he concluded that there was a simple explanation of the existence of a dual control of the pancreas. The vagus, he suggested, was responsible for the discharge of the enzymes, for the pancreatic secretion that it evoked was known to be rich in these; secretin, by contrast, was responsible for the addition to these of the necessary water and bicarbonate. Unfortunately for what could have been a satisfactory interpretation, the experience of those who used the SI preparation was different; they found that this material evoked the secretion of enzymes, as well as fluid and bicarbonate.

The cause of this disagreement was revealed in 1943 by A. A. Harper and H. S. Raper in England. By comparing the products of the two methods of preparation, they showed that two hormones were actually concerned. Both were present in the SI material but only one in Mellanby's preparation. The one present in both was responsible for the discharge of water and bicarbonate; this they considered to be secretin in the strict sense. The other was responsible for the discharge of enzymes; this hormone, previously unrecognized, they called pancreozymin. Secretin and pancreozymin were both precipitated by saturation with sodium chloride, whereas secretin alone was adsorbed to bile salts. Thus the SI preparation contained both hormones, whereas in Mellanby's procedure the pancreozymin was lost in the supernatant. Both groups of investigators had been perfectly correct in their findings. It just happened that nature, as so often, had proved to be more subtle than had been foreseen.

It must be admitted, however, that the full extent of this subtlety still eludes satisfactory explanation. Pancreozymin and the vagus nerve both discharge enzymes from the pancreas, so that one is still left with two mechanisms producing the same result. It is not at all clear why this should be so. It is possible, however, that the stimulus of seeing food, or of eating it, acts through the vagus nerve to bring about a discharge of enzymes in advance of the arrival of the acid gastric contents in the duodenum. This could conceivably improve the efficiency of the intestinal phase of digestion.

Before leaving the subject of secretin, one should be aware of one other unexpected and illuminating development. By 1933 a group of Swedish investigators had prepared a crystalline, nontoxic material in which secretin (probably secretin in the strict sense) was associated with a picric acid complex. This was made available for clinical tests of pancreatic function, using the method of injecting a test dose and aspirating the juice through a tube. In the following year Ivy's group of workers also prepared a somewhat similar crystalline material. It now seemed that the problem of isolating secretin in pure form had been solved; yet, in fact, there were certain differences in the properties of the two preparations that can be seen in retrospect to have made this an overoptimistic conclusion. Once again the complexity of a situation had been underestimated, but it was not until 1949 that the problem was reopened by Swedish investigators.

> We were approached . . . by clinicians, who asked us to prepare secretin for clinical use, since it was not available commercially. We hesitated to do so, as there seemed to be nothing of scientific interest in preparing secretin. It had been crystallized in the form of picrolonates. Its molecular weight, isoionic point, amino acid composition and a variety of other properties were described in the literature. Moreover, the methods of preparation were cumbersome.
>
> However, in 1950, Friedman & Thomas described a fairly simple procedure for the preparation of secretin for clinical use. We then decided to prepare some material according to this method. Using a modification of it, we succeeded in preparing amorphous secretin with a potency comparable to that of the crystalline preparations described in the literature. Several factors indicated that our material was not homogeneous. This suggested that the secretin component of the crystalline material might not necessarily have been the pure hormone. Thus, it was possible that secretin — half a century after its discovery — had still not been isolated in pure form. Further work, by ourselves and by others, confirmed this supposition.[7]

It had long been apparent that secretin was probably a polypeptide, and these new chemical studies confirmed this. The pure polypeptide (of secretin in the strict sense) has at last been isolated; and, now, more than 60 years after the discovery of the chemical regulation of pancreatic secretion, the amino acid sequences in the molecule have been determined. Further discussion of this fundamentally important aspect of hormonal studies appears in Chapter 3.

Enough is now known of secretin and pancreozymin to justify the conclusion that they are both hormones of the alimentary tract; nor are they the only hormones present *(Fig. 2-8)*. By methods that closely parallel those used in the study of secretin, it has been well established that the mucosa of the stomach secretes a hormone called gastrin. This hormone, like secretin, is probably a polypeptide which operates in conjunction with the autonomic nervous system to regulate the secretion of gastric juice. Further, the secretory activity of the liver is also under chemical control. Secretin is believed to promote the flow of bile from liver cells, while contraction of the gall bladder is regulated by another hormone that is released into the blood from the duodenum when the latter receives protein or fatty

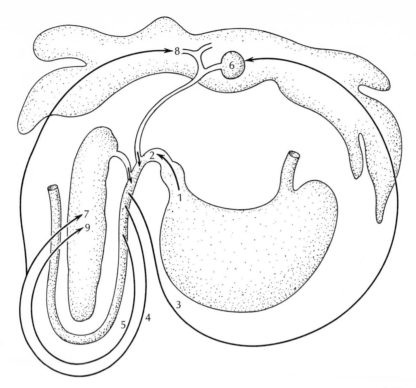

Fig. 2-8. Some of the endocrine pathways that regulate digestion in a mammal. The passage of gastric contents from the stomach (*1*) into the duodenum (*2*) evokes the release from the latter of three hormones, cholecystokinin (*3*), secretin (*4*), and pancreozymin (*5*). Cholecystokinin evokes contractions of the gall bladder (*6*); secretin stimulates the secretion of fluid from the pancreas (*7*), and of bile from the liver (*8*); while pancreozymin stimulates the secretion of the pancreatic enzymes (*9*). The secretions of the liver and pancreas are thus discharged into the duodenum (*2*) in appropriate quantities at the correct time. (From E. J. W. Barrington, *Hormones and Evolution*, London: English Universities Press Ltd., 1964, 20.)

material. The stimulating effect of fat is a particularly significant adaptation; for the bile salts, as mentioned earlier, play an important part in the digestion of fatty material. The hormone concerned has been named cholecystokinin, but it closely resembles pancreozymin in its chemical properties and may eventually prove to be identical with it.

From time to time it has been claimed that other hormones are secreted by the alimentary tract of mammals. Although the evidence is incomplete, scientists feel sure that more remains to be learned about the control of alimentary function in this group. A sense of incomplete knowledge is felt more strongly in the case of lower vertebrates, for present information in this field is exceedingly limited and fragmentary. Enough is known, however, to demonstrate the elegance and precision of control that can be achieved by the interaction of nervous and chemical factors. While this control became apparent in external respiration, in that instance the chemical agent, carbon dioxide, was no more than a product of the general metabolism of the body. In alimentary regulation the body secretes chemical substances that are designed, so to speak, for the express and specific purpose of regulation. This is a principle with immense possibilities that will be explored further in Chapters 3 and 4.

■ **SOME CHARACTERISTICS OF SCIENTIFIC RESEARCH**

Chapter 2 has dealt with the discovery of secretin and pancreozymin in some detail, in order to illuminate the ways in which scientific research progresses. Arthur Koestler, in a discussion of patterns of discovery, has written of this in more general terms.

> In the first place, a new synthesis never results from a mere adding together of two fully developed branches in biological or mental evolution. Each new departure, each reintegration of what has become separated, involves the breaking down of the rigid, ossified patterns of behaviour and thought. . . . A new evolutionary departure is only possible after a certain amount of de-differentiation, a cracking and thawing of the frozen structures resulting from isolated, over-specialized development.
>
> Most geniuses responsible for the major mutations in the history of thought seem o have certain features in common; on the one hand scepticism, often carried to the point of iconoclasm, in their attitude towards traditional ideas, axioms and dogmas, towards everything that is taken for granted; on the other hand, an open-mindedness that verges on naïve credulity towards new concepts which seem to hold out some promise to their instinctive gropings. Out of this combination results that crucial capacity of perceiving a familiar object, situation, problem, or collection of data, in a sudden new light or new context: of seeing a branch not as part of a tree, but as a potential weapon or tool; of associating the fall of an apple not with its ripeness, but with the motion of the moon. The discoverer perceives relational patterns of functional analogies where nobody saw them before, as the poet perceives the image of a camel in a drifting cloud. . . .
>
> Another pre-condition for basic discoveries to occur, and to be accepted, is what one might call the "ripeness" of the age. It is an elusive quality, for the "ripeness" of a science for a decisive change is not determined by the situation in that particular science alone, but by the general climate of the age. It was the philosophical climate of Greece after the Macedonian conquest that nipped in the bud Aristarchus' heliocentric concept of the universe; and astronomy went on

happily with its impossible epicycles, because that was the type of science that the medieval climate favoured.

Moreover, it *worked*. This ossified discipline, split off from reality, was capable of predicting eclipses and conjunctions with considerable precision, and of providing tables which were by and large adequate to the demand. On the other hand, the seventeenth century's "ripeness" for Newton, or the twentieth's for Einstein and Freud, was caused by a general mood of transition and awareness of crisis, which embraced the whole human spectrum of activities, social organization, religious beliefs, art, science, fashions.[8]

Those above principles are well exemplified in the history of the discovery of secretin. The work of Bayliss and Starling followed logically upon that of the Pavlov school, but to say no more than that would be to underestimate the significance of their discovery. The Russian workers had shown that pancreatic secretion could be evoked by direct stimulation of the vagus nerve, or by introducing acid into the duodenum; but it is misleading to say, as does one recent account, that in so doing they had discovered the dual mechanism of pancreatic secretion. Bayliss and Starling had established a new principle of regulation, had broken down an old pattern of thought, and had seen facts in a new context. This is the creative aspect of research. The difficulty of achieving it may be judged from the failure of Bayliss and Starling's contemporaries to take the same step forward. Wertheimer and LePage had shown the possibility of exciting pancreatic secretion by inserting acid into an isolated loop of jejunum, but it remained for Bayliss and Starling to act further on the suggested implications of this experiment and, in so doing, to discover secretin.

Remarkably enough, within a few weeks of the first announcement of the discovery of secretin (specifically, May 3, 1902), Wertheimer revealed how close he had come to making the same discovery. A collaborator had suggested to him exactly the same idea as had occurred to Bayliss and Starling: that acid might cause another substance to be released by the intestine. In much the same way that the English scientists had worked, Wertheimer introduced acid into the duodenum, removed the fluid after a few minutes, and injected the substance into the blood. Unfortunately, no pancreatic activity resulted, and he did not repeat the experiment. After Bayliss and Starling had published their own findings, he repeated his experiment on a number of dogs; in each case he now obtained a pancreatic secretion! This is an example (and there are many in the history of biological research) of contemporary workers developing similar ideas. It is natural for this to happen, for an individual's ideas are to some extent the product of the climate of opinion of his time. But we see that an idea, however good, is not enough; for conditions may be unsuitable

for securing satisfactory results at a first attempt. Boldness and resolution are no less essential in bringing an investigation to a successful
conclusion.

One other point made by Koestler deserves emphasis in this context. It is possible to see, in retrospect, that the time was ripe for discovery of the principle of endocrine regulation. Clinical studies during the nineteenth century had begun to establish the idea that certain
organs (the thyroid gland, for example) could influence parts of the
body that were far distant from them. Moreover, it had been discovered that extracts of the adrenal and pituitary glands could bring
about a substantial rise of blood pressure. The significance of these
findings remained obscure, and it was the discovery of secretin that
first clearly indicated the possibility of one organ influencing another
by release of a secretion that was specifically adapted to bring about
a particular result. In these respects Bayliss and Starling were clearly
fortunate. The climate of contemporary thought was ripe for the
generation of their idea; no less important, it was ripe also for the
reception of it.

■ THE BOUNDARIES OF OPEN SYSTEMS

At the completion of the coordinated digestive activity of the muscles
and glands of the mammalian alimentary tract, the food material still
lies, in effect, outside the body. Before the nutritive molecules can
be introduced into the animal's metabolism, they must pass through
the epithelium of the alimentary canal and on into the blood stream,
so that they can be transported to appropriate parts of the body. This
is the process called absorption. The absorptive properties of the alimentary epithelium, however, must be viewed as more than an aspect
of the physiology of nutrition. The epithelium is only one of several
barriers that are interposed between the animal and its external environment and that reflect the complexity of the task of maintaining
an open system. It is these barriers that make possible the conservation of the highly specific organization of the system and the maintenance of its level of free energy.

A familiar example of a barrier in the human body is the skin of the
body surface. Skin is constructed to be tough and impermeable, so
that the passage of material through it is reduced to the minimum
consonant with certain demands of temperature control (discussed
later). This, however, is only one type of barrier. The cells of the
body must have a free interchange of materials with the blood stream
and the body fluids by which they are bathed; in this instance, therefore, permeability is essential. Since the composition of living cells
differs from that of the medium surrounding them, the permeability
must be controlled so as to ensure the maintenance of this difference.

It is in this respect that the cell membrane is of critical importance, since it is endowed with remarkable properties that enable it to serve both as a barrier and as a medium of controlled exchange. By examining these properties, one can acquire both a basis for understanding other aspects of physiological regulation and, more specifically, knowledge of how the nutritive molecules of food are transported into the living substance of the body.

At the close of the nineteenth century, certain studies on the permeability of plant cells showed that the rate of penetration of many substances into cells was related to the solubility of those substances in lipid solvents, or, in modern terminology, to their oil-water partition coefficient. Those substances that were less soluble penetrated more slowly. It was suggested that this might be because the cell membrane was composed of lipids, an explanation that is now generally accepted as part of the truth. However, later studies showed that there were other factors to be taken into account. Lipids have a high surface tension, yet measurements of the surface tension of cell membranes showed that their values were very low—always below 2.0 dynes per cm and often below 0.2. This would be impossible if the membranes were purely lipoidal, but it can be accounted for if they contain a layer of protein adsorbed on to a lipid surface. Such an association is known to be able to produce a membrane with a low surface tension and the elasticity shown by experimental manipulation to be characteristic of the cell surface.

These considerations led J. F. Danielli to suggest that the cell membrane was constructed like the model illustrated in *Fig. 2-9*. This model has a sandwich structure, made up of a bimolecular lipid layer, which would be about 50 Å thick, with a protein layer adsorbed on each of its surfaces. Not only does the model satisfy some of the properties shown by the cell membrane, it has since been shown to agree remarkably well with the structure of the cell membrane as revealed by electron microscopy. The latter device shows that the membrane is typically about 75 Å thick, and that it has indeed a sandwich structure. Centrally there is a layer 35 Å thick, which corresponds with the expected dimensions of the postulated lipid component; while each external surface is formed of a separate layer about 20 Å thick, which corresponds equally well with the postulated protein component.

While the Danielli model in *Fig. 2-9* satisfies some of the required properties, there is now evidence that carbohydrate also contributes to the membrane. But in any case something more is needed; for the penetration of smaller molecules is not usually related to their oil-water partition coefficient but seems rather to be determined by their molecular size. The reason for this is not clear, but the implication is that there must be a lack of homogeneity in the lipid layer, or that there are definite pores in it. Danielli has suggested how a model with pores could account for this additional requirement *(Fig. 2-10)*. Glucose, for example, might possibly pass through a pore by adsorption or by combination with some component of the membrane to form complexes of the type discussed later in this chapter. Admittedly, much of the evidence upon which scientists base their interpretation of the structure of cell membranes is necessarily indirect. Since the problem is dealt with in more detail elsewhere in this series (Vols. II and III), this text confines its attention to the observed phenomena of transport through these membranes.

There are several ways in which materials can move passively into and out of a cell by purely physical processes that do not demand expenditure of metabolic energy. One of these is the diffusion of nonelectrolytes down a concentration gradient, the consequence of thermal movement of the molecules. If the substance concerned is passing into or out of a cell, then its rate of transfer will be proportional to the concentration gradient across the membrane. A second possibility is the passive transport of electrolytes, which can be effected by the movement of electrically charged ions down a gradient of electric potential. A third possibility depends upon the supposed existence of pores in biological membranes. Water can pass through these pores under the influence of hydrostatic or osmotic pressure and, in so doing, will influence the movement of solute particles, accelerating those that may be diffusing in the same direction as its

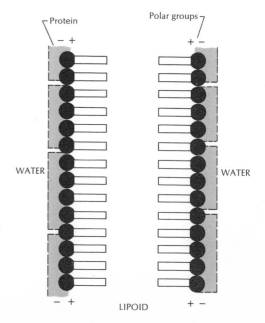

Fig. 2-9. Structure of the cell membrane as proposed by Danielli. (From H. Davson and J. F. Danielli, *The Permeability of Natural Membranes*, London: Cambridge University Press, 1943, p. 509.)

flow, and slowing down those that are diffusing in the opposite direction. This is the phenomenon known as solvent drag.

Passive diffusion certainly plays an important part in the relationships between an animal and its environment. For example, it provides for the transfer of oxygen and of carbon dioxide across the thin epithelium of the pulmonary alveoli. However, if one considers the whole field of metabolic exchange, the application of diffusion is limited, because it could not account for the complex chemical composition of the cell and for the characteristic differences existing between the contents of the cell and the fluids that surround it. In any case, passive movement of materials down a gradient involves a loss of organization and an increase of entropy. Thus in the general case of a solute unevenly concentrated over its field of distribution, the random movements of thermal agitation must eventually produce a homogeneous solution. Therefore, one is driven to suppose that solutes are also transported through cell membranes by some mechanism that maintains biological organization through the utilization of energy. This is called active transport.

■ ACTIVE TRANSPORT

The definition of active transport, as B. Andersen and H. H. Ussing point out, is essentially a negative one: active transport is said to occur when the pattern of transfer cannot be accounted for solely by physical forces but must involve also the expenditure of metabolic energy.

The mechanism of active transport is by no means fully understood. However, one much favored explanation rests on the hypothesis that certain carrier substances are present in the cell membrane, and that these are able to transport solutes after combining with them to form carrier-solute complexes. It is supposed that the combination takes place at one surface of the membrane, that the complex then moves across the membrane, and that the transported solute is eventually released at the other surface. This could, in theory, be achieved by the synthesis of a carrier substance at one surface and its breakdown at the other. Alternatively, the carrier substance might be free to combine with the solute at one surface but would be transformed at the other surface into a noncombinable form. In either case metabolic energy would be needed to maintain the gradient of a carrier-solute complex.

It must be appreciated that these suggested explanations of active transport are highly theoretical; indeed, they have been criticized, for example, on the grounds that the size of the carrier molecules and their attendant enzymes would have to be unduly large in relation to the size of the membranes across which they are supposed to move. Studies of bacterial genetics, however, have given greater

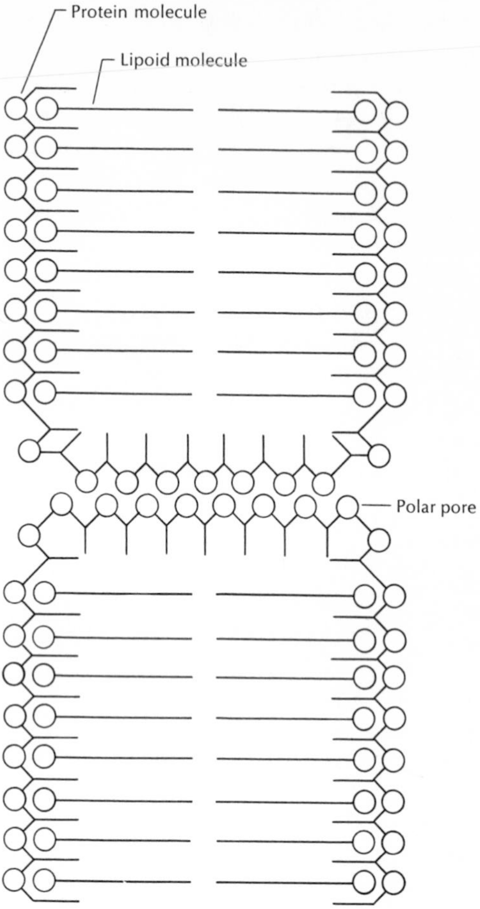

Fig. 2-10. Diagram of a possible structure of a porous membrane. (From J. F. Danielli, in *Recent Developments in Cell Physiology,* ed. J. A. Kitching, London: Butterworth & Co. Ltd., 1954, p. 8.)

reality to the idea that specific substances are involved as agents in membrane transport. *Escherichia coli* takes up galactose from the surrounding medium by means of a transport system that depends on the activity of a specific enzyme, galactoside permease. J. Monod, in the studies that have done so much to establish current ideas of the organization and regulation of genetic action, found mutant forms of this bacterium that were unable to concentrate this particular carbohydrate. The deficiency was ascribed to a mutant gene that was preventing the synthesis of the specific enzyme. But whatever the explanation of active transport may be, its occurrence is not in doubt, and is made evident by a number of well-defined characteristics.

One of the characteristics of active transport is that the solute moves against its concentration or electrochemical gradient. This provides an increase in free energy (defined at the beginning of

Chapter 1), and it is because of this that active transport is of paramount importance to the maintenance of living systems. Another characteristic is that the rate of this "uphill" movement is not necessarily a simple linear function of the difference in concentration of the solute on the two sides of the membrane. For example, at higher concentrations of solute the transport may be impeded, an effect that can be accounted for on the supposition that the carrier has become saturated by the solute. A third feature indicating the occurrence of active transport is that the rate of movement of one substance may differ greatly from that of another, even though the two may be closely related in molecular structure. For example, optical isomers may move at very different speeds. The naturally occurring *dextro*-xylose is absorbed more readily by the mammalian intestine than is the *levo*-isomer; while naturally occurring *levo*-amino acids are absorbed more readily than the *dextro*-acids. In these instances the transport process is adaptively organized to deal with naturally occurring food materials, presumably through the establishment of specialized relationships between the molecular conformations of the solute and of the carrier.

Another characteristic of active transport relates to temperature coefficients, which are the factors by which reaction velocities and biological processes are increased by a rise in temperature of 10°C (see Chapter 5). The significant fact here is that the temperature coefficient of the transport process may be high and of the same order usually associated with enzyme-controlled reactions. Associated with this is the phenomenon called competitive inhibition, in which the presence of one substance impedes the transport of another substance that is chemically similar to it. In this instance it is supposed that the inhibitor substance tends to saturate the carrier and thus to impede the combination of the chemically similar substance with it. Finally, active transport is inhibited by certain substances that are known to be enzyme poisons and that presumably impede the metabolic processes upon which the energy supply depends.

Two other possible modes of carrier-mediated transport have been postulated, both of them based upon the concept of active transport as outlined in this section. One of these is termed exchange diffusion. In this the combination or separation of carrier and solute is supposed to take place at either surface of the membrane. The particles of carrier-solute complex will move either way across the membrane under the influence of thermal agitation, and at either surface a bound solute particle may be exchanged for a free one taken up from the bathing solution. An essential requirement of this process is that neither the solute particles nor the carrier particles can diffuse alone. They move across the membrane only as a bound complex;

thus no net transfer of solute takes place, and the composition of the ambient solutions remains unaltered.

The other type of possible transport is termed facilitated diffusion. Here there is a net transfer; but the movement of the transported solute takes place down the concentration gradient, so that the equilibria attained are similar to those resulting from diffusion. The difference is that these equilibria are achieved more quickly than would be possible by unaided diffusion; the theoretical explanation of this is that the movement is facilitated by the formation of carrier-solute complexes. Facilitated diffusion, like active transport in the restricted sense, is sensitive to certain inhibitors, but with the difference that these are not specifically metabolic inhibitors. All three of these supposedly carrier-dependent processes can be referred to collectively as membrane transport.

So important is the occurrence of active transport that it is well to give a specific illustration of its established existence before considering its particular relevance to the absorptive process of the alimentary epithelium. For this purpose reference can be made to a work that, although comparatively recent, is already classical in the decisiveness of its conclusions. It is based upon studies of the frog's skin which differs from that of mammals in being highly permeable. This difference is associated with the use of the body surface of amphibians as an accessory respiratory membrane. Because of this, and because amphibians live in fresh water, they are subject to the loss of salts by diffusion through their skin, as well as by excretion in their urine. Such a loss is compensated for by the active uptake of sodium chloride through their skin, in association with other processes considered later when the ways in which vertebrates regulate the salt and water content of their bodies are examined (Chap. 4).

The frog's skin has long been known to possess remarkable physico-chemical properties. It was shown by E. H. Du Bois-Reymond in 1857 that there is a difference of electric potential between the two surfaces of the skin, the inside being positive to the outside. Much later (1937) it was found by A. Krogh that frogs can take up salt from the water around them, even if the concentration of sodium chloride is as low as 10^{-5} M. Krogh also found that this mechanism was specific to sodium; neither potassium nor calcium were taken up, although bromide and bicarbonate were able to substitute for chloride. Evidently this movement of sodium is indicative of active uptake, as it has just been defined; and Ussing has decisively demonstrated that it does, indeed, take place.

The potential difference between the negative outside and the positive inside of the skin amounts to some 60 mv. From this it can be calculated that if the movement of the positively charged sodium ion were due solely to passive diffusion down the electrochemical gradient, its outflow (efflux) should be 10 times its inflow (influx). However, as previously indicated, it is its influx that is higher, and sometimes by a factor of more than 10, so that it is clearly moving up the gradient. On the other hand, it is possible that passive diffusion might account for the flux of the negatively charged chloride ion, which could be moving down the gradient. Ussing was thus led to suggest that active transport of the sodium ion might be the sole source of the electric potential across the skin. He confirmed this hypothesis in the following way.

His procedure depended upon the fact that surviving frog skin can maintain its electric potential *in vitro* just like an electric battery and can continue to discharge electric current for many hours. Its electromotive force can be short-circuited, however, by connecting a battery across it. In these conditions, with the potential difference between the two sides of the skin maintained artificially at zero, any ionic fluxes must necessarily be due to active transport. Whether or not any ionic fluxes are actually occurring can then be determined by adding radioactive isotopes to the medium and detecting whether they move in one direction or the other.

It is clear that no net transfer of passive ions can take place if the skin is short-circuited, so that the potential drop over it is nil, and if, further, the bathing solutions on the two sides are identical. Ions which are subject to active transport will, on the other hand, flow faster one way than the other, and thus contribute to the total current flowing through the short-circuit. An experimental apparatus was therefore constructed by Dr. Zerahn and myself, making possible the simultaneous determination of short-circuit current and ionic fluxes. The transport rate of sodium across the skin is so low that the determination by chemical analysis of the current/active-transport relationship would meet with great difficulties. The tracer method, on the other hand, makes possible the determination of the transport rate with accuracy. The influx of sodium can be determined with ^{22}Na and the efflux with ^{24}Na, and this procedure is now being regularly used. It turned out, however, that the efflux was only a small fraction of the influx, so that it suffices in most cases to apply a suitable correction to the influx in order to obtain the net sodium transport.

The apparatus used is shown in *Fig.* [*2-11*]. The skin, S, is placed between two celluloid chambers, C, containing Ringer's solution. The potential differences across the skin is read on a potentiometer, P, which is connected through calomel electrodes to two agar-Ringer bridges, A and A', opening close to the skin. Another pair of agar-Ringer bridges, B and B', opening at a distance sufficient to give a homogeneous electric field at the level of the skin, are connected through silver/silver-chloride electrodes with a microammeter, M, and a battery, D. The current in this circuit is now adjusted by aid of

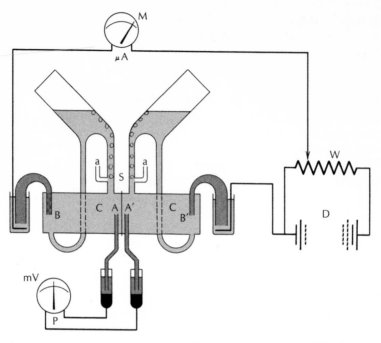

Fig. 2-11.   Diagram of apparatus used for determining Na flux and short-circuit current. *C*, celluloid chamber containing, on each side of the skin, 40 ml Ringer's fluid; *S*, skin; *a*, inlets for air; *A*, *A*[1], agar-Ringer bridges connecting outside and inside solutions, respectively, with calomel electrodes; *B*, *B*[1], agar-Ringer bridges used for applying outside e.m.f.; *D*, battery; *W*, potential divider; *M*, microammeter; *P*, tube potentiometer. (From H. H. Ussing, *Symposia of the Society for Experimental Biology*, 8 (1954), 415.)

a variable resistance, W, so that the potential drop across the skin is zero. It is obvious that this accomplishes a total short-circuit of the skin. The current generated is read on the microammeter. Table [2-1] shows the results of some of our first experiments. Influx and efflux were not determined simultaneously, but in parallel experiments. The figures are arranged so that those from influx experiments are to the left and those from the efflux experiments to the right. Both the flux values and the currents are expressed as millicoulombs/cm²/hr.

It is noticed that the efflux is always much smaller than the current, whereas the influx is identical with, or, in some cases, a little higher than, the current. On an average from a considerable number of runs, the influx is 5% higher than the current, whereas the efflux is very nearly 5% of the current. Thus, the net sodium flux is exactly equal to the short-circuit current. Consequently we arrive at the conclusion that the total current which can be drawn from the short-circuited frog skin comes from active sodium transport. . . .

One may ask the question whether the mechanism responsible for the active sodium transport is specific to this ion or whether we are dealing with a more or less unspecific cation-transporting system. As long as the bathing solutions are ordinary Ringer's, sodium is likely to dominate the picture compared to, say, potassium, simply due to its much higher concentration. Experiments which have recently been performed by Dr. Zerahn and myself indicate, however, that the transport mechanism prefers sodium to potassium to a remarkable extent. Table [2-2] shows some of the results. Instead of ordinary Ringer's, bathing solutions were used where, expressed on a molar basis, 35% of the total monovalent cation was potassium and the remaining 65% sodium. Influx and efflux of sodium were determined simultaneously with ^{22}Na and ^{24}Na, respectively. It is seen that even under these conditions the total current is accounted for by the net sodium flux, indicating that potassium contributes insignificantly, or not at all, to the short-circuit current.[9]

TABLE 2-1

Sodium Flux and Total Current Values Obtained in 1 Hr. Periods on Totally Shorted Normal Frog Skin. Group A Comprises Results from Five Influx Experiments, Group B Results from Six Efflux Experiments.[a]

A (influx)			B (efflux)		
	millicoulomb cm.$^{-2}$hr.$^{-1}$			millicoulomb cm.$^{-2}$hr.$^{-1}$	
Date	Na	Current	Date	Na	Current
26. iv	102	99	28. iv	9.7	130
	93	99		10.5	139
27. iv	177	174	2. v	5.3	111
	176	162		9.1	108
	124	123		13.0	108
				13.6	112
3. v	64	63			
	64	55	11. v	6.0	136
	57	49		5.6	124
4. v	248	253	8. vi	14.7	92
	260	224		13.2	100
	205	205			
			22. ix	2.6	164
23. ix	139	133		2.4	118
	118	112			
			4. x	0.8	102

[a] From H. H. Ussing, *Symposium of the Society for Experimental Biology*, 8(1954), 415.

TABLE 2-2

Showing That the Current Generated by the Short-circuited Frog Skin Is Carried by Sodium Ions, Even When One-third of the Sodium in the Bathing Solutions Is Replaced by Potassium. Area of Skin, 7·1 cm².[a]

	(K/Na) × 100 in solutions	Influx (μequiv. Na/hr.)	Efflux (μequiv. Na/hr.)	Na (μequiv./ hr.)	Na current (μamp.)	Total current (μamp.)
I	35.0	13.2	0.58	12.6	339	289
	35.0	9.4	0.81	8.6	230	236
II	35.0	5.80	0.38	5.42	145	157
	35.0	6.13	0.35	5.78	155	154
	35.0	5.50	0.41	5.09	136	143
III	35.0	4.05	1.04	3.01	81	85
	35.0	5.30	1.06	4.24	114	116
	35.0	5.35	0.94	4.41	118	121

[a] From H. H. Ussing, *Symposium of the Society of Experimental Biology*, 8 (1954), 416.

■ THE ABSORPTION OF MATERIAL FROM THE ALIMENTARY CANAL

It is necessary now to examine the degree to which these principles of solute movement can account for the transfer of nutritive materials into the interior of the body. Also, it should be asked to what extent they are adaptively deployed to facilitate the uptake of valuable components of the diet in preference to substances that are not of physiological significance. In mammals absorption takes place mainly in the upper region of the small intestine, where the surface of the epithelium is extended into innumerable small processes called villi *(Fig. 2-12)*. Within each of these are blood vessels and lymph vessels (lacteals). When the intestine is distended with food *(Fig. 2-13)*, it is apparent that this arrangement serves to increase enormously the area of close contact between the blood stream and the intestinal contents, an area that probably amounts to about 10 sq meters in man. This might seem to favor the occurrence of passive diffusion, but closer consideration shows that this process cannot be expected to account completely for nutritive uptake. One factor operating against it is that digestion results in the intestinal contents containing large amounts of substances of low molecular weights; these increase the osmotic pressure of the contents and so tend to create a flow of water into the intestinal lumen. Moreover, the hydrostatic pressure of the circulation tends to force water out of the blood into the intestine, although this effect is to some extent counterbalanced by the hydrostatic pressure of the intestinal contents which forces water in the opposite direction. The situation is thus complex, but it has proved possible to analyze it adequately by the application of a variety of techniques, including those already mentioned.

Simple diffusion does, in fact, play a role that is of great importance in medical practice. Both in the rat and in man, it has been established that certain drugs pass through the epithelium of the stomach and intestine by diffusion. In general, and for reasons indicated earlier, it is lipoid-soluble drugs that penetrate most readily. The process is affected by the electric charge carried on the particles, and it is the un-ionized forms to which the epithelium is mainly permeable. Therefore, salicylates and barbiturates, which are largely un-ionized in the stomach, are quickly absorbed, whereas highly ionized substances, such as quinine and ephedrine, are hardly taken up at all. One may suppose that diffusion functions in these examples partly because it is favored by the concentration gradient (for these substances are not, of course, normally present in the blood stream), and partly because the body has had no previous experience of these human contrivances. It is expected that during the course of evolution the body has become adapted to take up much of its essential

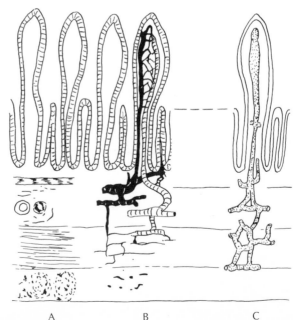

Fig. 2-12. Diagram of blood vessels and lymphatics of the small intestine of a mammal. *A*, structure of wall; *B*, blood vessels; *C*, lymphatics. (After Bailey, from E. E. Hewer, *Textbook of Histology for Medical Students*, 2nd edition, London: William Heinemann Medical Books Ltd., 1941, p. 223.)

A   B   C

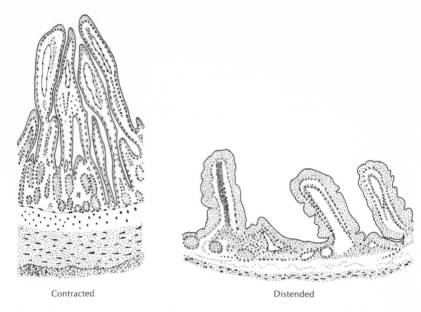

Contracted   Distended

Fig. 2-13. Structure of the small intestine when strongly contracted (left) and normally distended with food material (right). (After Johnson, courtesy of *American Journal of Anatomy.* From E. V. Cowdry, *A Textbook of Histology*, Philadelphia: Lea & Febiger, 1938, p. 298.)

requirements by active transport, so that it can take the fullest advantage of the supplies that become available in the intestinal contents. No such adaptation can have been established in relation to molecules that are not normally presented to it.

From this point of view, it is not surprising to find that the intestinal epithelium is capable of the active uptake of certain ions. The situation is comparable to that found in the frog's skin; indeed, in this respect the skin of the frog and the intestinal epithelium of the mammal are making somewhat similar contributions to the maintenance of the open system of the two animals. The difference, however, is that both sodium and chloride are actively absorbed against the concentration gradient (at least in the intestine of the rat); whereas in the skin of the frog, only the sodium is actively transported, the chloride ions moving with it along the gradient of electric potential created by the sodium flux. This dual transport system of the intestinal epithelium has not as yet been demonstrated in any other tissue.

Active transport through the intestinal epithelium is not confined to inorganic ions; many of the organic molecules released by digestion are also taken up in this way. This can be demonstrated by a number of procedures, of which a few examples follow. The active transport of amino acids in the small intestine of the turtle (*Testudo hermanni*) has been established by removing the epithelium from the underlying muscle and placing it in fluid in a Plexiglas frame, so that the fluid on one side is completely isolated from that on the other side. In principle the procedure is like that described above for the frog's skin. A short-circuit current is adjusted to abolish the potential difference between the outer and inner surfaces of the mucosa. In this way, and by using radioactive amino acids labeled with ^{14}C, it can be shown that a number of amino acids, including glycine, alanine, and tyrosine, are actively transported across the mucosa from its lumenal surface, in the absence of any electrochemical gradient. Some of the characteristics of active transport noted earlier become evident in these experiments. Competitive inhibition is detectable, for methionine inhibits the transport of tyrosine and glycine; the supposition is that all of these have a common carrier. It is found, too, that the transport mechanism is adaptively related to the molecular conformation of the amino acids; the naturally occurring L-isomers are the ones that are transported, whereas the D-isomers are not. Moreover, acid amides, which are much the same molecular size as amino acids but which are not naturally present in the diet, are absorbed much less readily than the acids. The adaptive organization of the active uptake process is thus clearly shown.

Certain carbohydrates are also moved by active transport. This conclusion follows from comparatively simple considerations based upon measurements of the rate of absorption of various molecules. For example, galactose and glucose, which are hexoses, are absorbed much more quickly than xylose and arabinose, which are pentoses. The latter have the smaller molecules, so that if only passive diffusion were concerned they would be expected to move more rapidly. Moreover, metabolic poisons reduce the rate of uptake of galactose and glucose but leave the rates of the others, including the hexose, fructose, relatively unaltered. It may be concluded, therefore, that glucose and galactose are taken up by active transport. In accord with this conclusion, the two substances show competitive inhibition; if glucose and galactose are fed together, there is a reduction in the absorption rate of both of them.

The absorption of carbohydrates has also been studied *in vitro* by various devices. Several of these depend upon removing a length of intestine (e.g., the small intestine of the rat) and suspending it as an isolated sac. In a much favored variant of this, the sac is inverted, so that the mucosa is now on the outside and the originally external surface (the serosa) on the inside. The inverted sac is suspended in the test fluid containing the substance that is being studied. The lumen of the sac is filled with fluid, but the volume of this is very small. Thus any uptake from the outer (now mucosal) surface into the fluid within the sac is readily measured, since it results in large

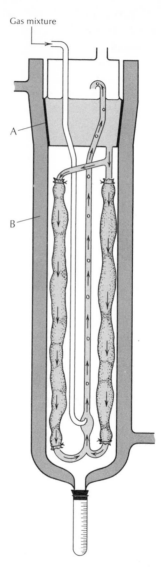

Fig. 2-14. Apparatus used for studying water transfer in the *in vitro* intestine. The part of the apparatus carrying the intestine is provided with a ground glass joint which fits into the outer water jacket at *A*. The loops of the intestine are suspended in air and the fluid transferred is collected in the graduated tube. For clarity only two loops of intestine are shown instead of the three normally used. Water at 38° C is circulated through the water jacket *B*. (From D. H. Smith and C. B. Taylor, *Journal of Physiology*, 136 (1957), 633.)

changes in concentration. The conditions of such experiments are far from those of the normal physiological functioning of the organ, but valuable results can be obtained if care is taken to maintain the mucosa in good condition. Another variant *(Fig. 2-14)* is to suspend the intestinal sac, without inversion, in air, with the test fluid placed in the lumen of the sac against the mucosal surface. Absorption results in drops of fluid appearing on the air-covered serosal surface; these drops can be collected in suitable vessels. In such ways it has been shown that glucose is actively transported against the concentration gradient, and that this movement is arrested by treatment with phlorizin, which is a metabolic inhibitor. It is of interest that the mammalian intestine has little capacity for the uptake of disaccharides and polysaccharides, a situation that is adaptively related to the fact that the body has only a limited capacity for metabolizing them.

The absorption of fats follows a different course and, indeed, has been the center of much controversy. The arguments involved fall outside the scope of the present discussion, so that it must be sufficient to state the situation in general terms. It is agreed that in normal circumstances digestion and absorption of these substances require the simultaneous presence within the intestine of both bile salts and pancreatic lipase. It is also known that the ingestion of olive oil is followed within a few hours by the appearance of minute fat droplets within the lacteals of the mammalian villi. One interpretation of this course of events is that the lipase, which is activated by the bile salts, breaks down the fats into fatty acids and monoglycerides. The complex mixture of fatty materials is then supposedly absorbed as the component droplets of a fine emulsion, the bile salts having the further function of stabilizing this emulsion. Finally the droplets are resynthesized within the intestinal cells, forming neutral fats which then pass into the lacteals.

The foregoing interpretation of fat absorption seems to be soundly based, but there are other aspects of this complex situation that should be considered. For example, it seems that some fat absorption may occur in the absence of either bile salts or lipase. One suggested explanation of this (supported by experimental evidence) is that fats may sometimes be directly absorbed into the intestinal epithelial cells without prior hydrolysis. It may well be that both mechanisms contribute to the normal uptake of this material into the mammalian open system.

1. From *A Way of Life and Other Selected Writings of William Osler*, Dover Publications, Inc., New York, 1951, pp. vii–viii. Reprinted through permission of the publisher.
2. W. Beaumont, *Experiments and Observations on the Gastric Juices and the Physiology of Digestion* (New York: Dover Publications, Inc., 1833), p. 104.

3. *Ibid.*, pp. 97–98.
4. Reproduced from *The Work of the Digestive Glands* by I. P. Pavlov, Charles Griffin and Co., Ltd., by permission of the publisher, p. 60.
5. W. M. Bayliss and E. H. Starling, "The Mechanism of Pancreatic Secretion," *Journal of Physiology*, 28 (1902), 328–333.
6. B. P. Babkin, *Pavlov, A Biography* (Chicago: University of Chicago Press, 1949), pp. 228–229. Copyright © 1949 by the University of Chicago. All rights reserved.
7. V. Mutt, "On the Preparation of Secretion," *Arkiv für Kemi*, 15 (1959), 76.
8. Arthur Koestler, *The Sleepwalkers* (London: Hutchinson & Co., 1959), pp. 518–520. Reprinted by permission of A. D. Peters & Co.
9. H. H. Ussing, "Active Transport of Inorganic Ions," *Symposia of the Society for Experimental Biology*, 8 (1954), 413–416.

CHAPTER 3 The Storage and
Release of Energy

■ CLAUDE BERNARD AND THE DISCOVERY OF GLYCOGEN

The passage of digestion products through the epithelium of the
alimentary canal makes them available at last for incorporation into
the living material of the body. In part, these products will serve the
growth of the organism and the maintenance of its structure; in part,
they will be stored as energy reserves, or, depending upon the organism's immediate needs, some of their contained energy may be
made available at once. All of these possibilities involve a complex
of interrelated metabolic activities, and the situation is further complicated by another requirement noted earlier. Life of the higher
vertebrates depends upon the maintenance of constancy in the composition of the body fluids in which the cells and tissues must function. Indeed, this principle operates in general throughout the animal kingdom, although probably nowhere else with such precision
as in birds and mammals. Periodic flooding of blood and lymph with
the products of digestion runs counter to this principle, so that the
entry of these substances into the body must be accompanied by complex regulatory reactions that serve to restore normality. It is necessary now to examine these events in some detail, for they occupy a
central position in adaptive organization.

If understanding of so wide-ranging a field can be said to derive
from any one starting point, one may ascribe to the great French
physiologist, Claude Bernard, the initiation of man's current knowledge of the deployment of energy-rich molecules within the mam-

malian body. He has left, in a vivid personal record, an account of
the development of his studies. It shows how dangerous it may be
to accept the simplest and most obvious explanation of the results
of an investigation and demonstrates no less clearly how important
it is for an investigator to be prepared to modify or even to reject a
hypothesis, when facts discordant with it begin to accumulate. Bernard concentrated particularly upon the fate of sugar within the
body, for it was easy to identify this substance chemically and thus
to follow its course in the blood stream. Moreover, he was hopeful
that this study might lead to an understanding of the cause of diabetes mellitus, a grave condition in man that was thought to be associated with some disorder in the handling of sugar by the body.

When Bernard began his work, it was supposed that the sugar present in animals came exclusively from their food and was destroyed
by oxidation. Sugar had thus gained the name of respiratory nutriment. Bernard's first objective was to discover in what organs the
sugar actually disappeared.

> To solve this problem, I had to hunt for sugar in the blood and follow
> it into the intestinal vessels which absorbed it, until I could note the
> place where it disappeared. To carry out my experiment, I gave a
> dog sweetened milk soup; then I sacrificed the animal during diges-
> tion and found that the blood in the superhepatic vessels (hepatic
> veins), which hold all the blood of the intestinal organs and the liver,
> contained sugar. It was quite natural and, as we say, logical to think
> that the sugar found in the superhepatic vessels was the same that I
> had given the animal in his soup. I am certain indeed that more than
> one experimenter would have stopped at that and would have con-
> sidered it superfluous, if not ridiculous, to make a comparative ex-
> periment. However, I made a comparative experiment, because I was
> convinced that we must always doubt in physiology, even in cases
> where doubt seems least allowable. However, I must add that a com-
> parative experiment was also required here by another circumstance,
> viz., that I used the reduction of copper as a test for sugar. This,
> however, is an empirical characteristic of sugar which might be shown
> by substances still unknown in the bodily economy. But, even apart
> from that, I repeat, a comparative experiment would have had to be
> made as an experimental necessity, for this very case proves that we
> can never foresee its importance.
>
> So for comparison with the dog fed on sugary soup, I took another
> dog to which I gave meat to eat, being careful moreover to exclude
> all sugary or starchy material from its diet; then I sacrificed the ani-
> mal during digestion and examined comparatively the blood in its
> superhepatic veins. Great was my astonishment at finding that the
> blood of the animal which had not eaten any also contained sugar.
>
> We therefore see that comparative experiment led me to the dis-
> covery that sugar is constantly present in the blood of the super-

hepatic veins, no matter what the animal's diet may be. You may imagine that I then abandoned all hypotheses about destruction of sugar, to follow this new and unexpected fact. I first excluded all doubt of its existence by repeated experiments, and I noted that sugar also existed in the blood of fasting animals.

Bernard quotes these researches as illustrating his dictum that

when we meet a fact which contradicts a prevailing theory, we must accept the fact and abandon the theory even when the theory is supported by great names and generally accepted.

The current theory

assumed that the vegetable kingdom alone had the power of creating the individual compounds which the animal kingdom is supposed to destroy. According to this theory, established and supported by the most illustrious chemists of our day, animals were incapable of producing sugar in their organs. If I had believed in this theory absolutely, I should have had to conclude that my experiment was vitiated by some inaccuracy; and less wary experimenters than I might have condemned it at once, and might not have tarried longer at an observation which could be theoretically suspected of including sources of error, since it showed sugar in the blood of animals on a diet that lacked starchy or sugary materials. But instead of being concerned about the theory, I concerned myself only with the fact whose reality I was trying to establish. By new experiments and by means of suitable counterproofs, I was thus led to confirm my first observation and to find that the liver is the organ in which animal sugar is formed in certain given circumstances, to spread later into the whole blood supply and into the tissues and fluids. . . .

After finding, as I said above, that there is sugar in the livers of animals in their normal state, and with every sort of nutriment, I wished to learn the proportion of this substance and its variation in certain physiological and pathological states. So I began to estimate the sugar in the livers of animals placed in various physiologically defined circumstances. I always made two determinations of carbohydrate for the same liver tissue. But pressed for time one day, it happened that I could not make my two analyses at the same moment; I quickly made one determination just after the animal's death and postponed the other analysis till next day. But then I found much larger amounts of sugar than those which I got the night before with the same material. I noticed, on the other hand, that the proportion of sugar, which I had found just after the animal's death the night before, was much smaller than I had found in the experiments which I had announced as giving the normal proportion of liver sugar. I did not know how to account for this singular variation, got with the same liver and the same method of analysis. What was to be done?

Should I consider two such discordant determinations as an unsuccessful experiment and take no account of them? Should I take the mean between these experiments? More than one experimenter might have chosen this expedient to get out of an awkward situation. But I disapprove of this kind of action. . . . Nothing is accidental, and what seems to us accident is only an unknown fact whose explanation may furnish the occasion for a more or less important discovery. So it proved in this case.

I wished, in fact, to learn the reason for my having found two such different values in the analysis of my rabbit's liver. . . . Without ascribing much importance to it, up to that time I had made my experiments a few hours after the animal's death; now for the first time I was in the situation of making one determination only a few minutes after death and postponing the other till next day, i.e., twenty-four hours later. In physiology, questions of time are always very important because organic matter passes through numerous and incessant changes. Some chemical change might therefore have taken place in the liver tissue. To make sure, I made a series of new experiments which dispelled every obscurity by showing me that liver tissue becomes more and more rich in sugar for some time after death. Thus we may have a very variable amount of sugar according to the moment when we make our examination. I was therefore led to correct my old determination and to discover the new fact that considerable amounts of sugar are produced in animals' livers after death. For instance, by forcibly injecting a current of cold water through the hepatic vessels and passing it through a liver that was still warm, just after an animal's death, I showed that the tissue was completely freed from the sugar which it contained; but next day or a few hours later, if we keep the washed liver at a mild temperature, we again find its tissue charged with a large amount of sugar produced after it was washed.

Once in possession of the first discovery that sugar is formed in animals after death as during life, I wished to carry my study of this singular phenomenon further; I was then led to find that sugar is produced in the liver with the help of an enzyme reacting on an amylaceous substance which I isolated and which I called *glycogenous matter*, so that I succeeded in proving in the most clear-cut way that sugar is formed in animals by a mechanism in every respect like the mechanism found in vegetables.[1]

Bernard would doubtless have agreed with the later dictum of Louis Pasteur, that chance favors the prepared mind. The researches described in this revealing self-analysis, aided by a powerful element of chance, had led him to results of fundamental importance. He had discovered glycogen, had described techniques for its extraction and purification, and had studied some of its reactions. He had shown that the sugar in animals could come from sources other than their food, and that animals could build as well as destroy carbohydrates.

Further, it was now clear that the liver had other functions beyond the secretion of bile, so that it had become necessary to look for complex functional interrelationships between the various organs of the body. The contrast between the discharging of bile into the alimentary tract and the discharging of sugar directly into the blood led him to the concept of internal secretion. Although this term is no longer applied to the passage of glucose into the blood, the concept itself has been immensely fruitful. It underlies the unraveling of the functioning of the endocrine glands and of the hormones that they secrete, and it may well have stimulated Bayliss and Starling to their discovery of secretin. Finally, Claude Bernard saw that the storage of glycogen, and its breakdown into a steady supply of glucose for distribution by the blood stream, was a device contributing to the maintenance of constancy in the composition of the body fluids. From this arose his great generalization that constancy of the internal environment is the essential condition for maintenance of free independent life.

■ THE CONCEPT OF HOMEOSTASIS

Homeostasis is a generalization of such fundamental importance that it needs further explanation. It arises out of Bernard's recognition of three forms of life, which he called *la vie latente, la vie oscillante,* and *la vie constante.* In his classification latent life was the life of spores and encysted microorganisms, in which the influence of the external environment is so dominant that the manifestations of life are arrested completely; oscillatory life was the life of poikilotherms (so-called cold-blooded animals, p. 186), in which activity varies in conformity with the external temperature; and constant life was the life of homoiotherms (warm-blooded animals), in which life is carried on at a constant temperature, seemingly independent of external conditions. One interpretation of the last situation held that the life of such animals was controlled in some way by an internal vital principle that was beyond the reach of scientific analysis. Such reasoning was a product of the philosophy already referred to as vitalism. Bernard's interpretation ran counter to this view. He believed that the constancy was a result of regulatory processes operating according to analyzable physiological principles and continuously maintaining this constancy by responding to the factors tending to upset it.

In the terminology used earlier, Bernard saw the life of the homoiotherm as dependent on the maintenance of a balanced equilibrium or steady state. This was a view that profoundly influenced the subsequent development of animal physiology, as can readily be seen in the writings of many later authorities, such as J. S. Haldane and Joseph Barcroft in England, Y. Henderson and W. B. Cannon in the

United States. Its application extends far beyond the field of Bernard's original investigations, for it is now understood that all organisms must to some extent maintain steady states, and that the complex and precisely controlled regulating mechanisms of higher vertebrates have developed from simpler mechanisms through the operation of natural selection. W. B. Cannon provides the classical exposition of this viewpoint:

> When we consider the extreme instability of our bodily structure, its readiness for disturbance by the slightest application of external forces and the rapid onset of its decomposition as soon as favoring circumstances are withdrawn, its persistence through many decades seems almost miraculous. The wonder increases when we realize that the system is open, engaging in free exchange with the outer world, and that the structure itself is not permanent but is being continuously broken down by the wear and tear of action, and as continuously built up again by processes of repair. . . .
>
> The perfection of the process of holding a stable state in spite of extensive shifts of outer circumstances is not a special gift bestowed upon the highest organisms but is the consequence of a gradual evolution. In the eons of time during which animals have developed on the earth probably many ways of protecting against the forces of the environment have been tried. Organisms have had large and varied experience in testing different devices for preserving stability in the face of agencies which are potent to upset and destroy it. As the construction of these organisms has become more and more complex and more and more sensitively poised, the need for more efficient stabilizing arrangements has become more imperative. Lower animals, which have not yet achieved the degree of control of stabilization seen in the more highly evolved forms, are limited in their activities and handicapped in the struggle for existence. Thus the frog, as a representative amphibian, has not acquired the means of preventing free evaporation of water from his body, nor has he an effective regulation of his temperature. In consequence he soon dries up if he leaves his home pool, and when cold weather comes he must sink to its muddy bottom and spend the winter in sluggish numbness. The reptiles, slightly more highly evolved, have developed protection against rapid loss of water and are therefore not confined in their movements to the neighbourhood of pools and streams; indeed, they may be found as inhabitants of arid deserts. But they, like the amphibians, are "cold-blooded" animals, that is, they have approximately the temperature of their surroundings [but see later, p. 225], and therefore during the winter months they must surrender their active existence. Only among the higher vertebrates, the birds and mammals, has there been acquired that freedom from limitations imposed by cold that permits activity even though the rigors of winter may be severe.
>
> The constant conditions which are maintained in the body might be termed *equilibria*. That word, however, has come to have fairly

exact meaning as applied to relatively simple physico-chemical states, in closed systems, where known forces are balanced. The coördinated physiological processes which maintain most of the steady states in the organism are so complex and so peculiar to living beings — involving, as they may, the brain and nerves, the heart, lungs, kidneys and spleen, all working coöperatively — that I have suggested a special designation for these states, *homeostasis*. The word does not imply something set and immobile, a stagnation. It means a condition — a condition which may vary, but which is relatively constant. [This definition may be compared with the later one quoted on p. 19.][2]

■ PATHWAYS OF CARBOHYDRATE METABOLISM

Claude Bernard was himself so ready to modify and discard hypotheses in the light of further studies that he would not have been surprised to learn that his own interpretations have undergone extensive transformation. This is especially true of his views on the mode of functioning of the liver. He had supposed that the increase in liver glycogen that followed a meal was a direct consequence of the ingested glucose being transformed within that organ into glycogen. This explanation, however, is only partly correct; the full course of events is very much more complex. It is necessary now to summarize these events in an outline sufficient to provide a basis for understanding the processes that regulate them and maintain the homeostasis of the body *(Fig. 3-1, p. 91).*

It is now known that much of the ingested glucose in the hepatic blood supply passes through the liver to be metabolized elsewhere. Nevertheless, some of it passes into the liver cells by membrane transport and there is converted into glycogen in the process called glycogenesis. This process has to be primed by energy stored in the phosphate donor, adenosine triphosphate (ATP), which phosphorylates the glucose in the presence of the enzyme hexokinase. Thus glucose-6-phosphate, which is converted into glucose-1-phosphate by the enzyme phosphoglucomutase, is formed. Glucose-1-phosphate is then converted into glycogen through the intermediate stage of uridine diphosphoglucose.

These pathways, however, account for only a small part of the total glycogen content of the liver; for this compound can be formed, in addition, from certain amino acids which, like glucose, are products of digestion. It can also be formed from lactic acid (produced in the muscles and passed in the blood to the liver) and, to a small extent, from fats. This formation of glycogen from noncarbohydrate sources is called gluconeogenesis. The amino acids concerned, which include glycine, alanine, serine, and cysteine, are known as glucogenic amino acids. The feeding of them to diabetic animals leads to the appearance of sugar in the urine (see below). As an example, alanine is degraded by transamination to pyruvate, which can either be oxidized through the activity of the citric acid cycle or transformed, through the fructose phosphate and glucose phosphate pathways, into glycogen.

$$
\begin{array}{cccc}
 & \text{COOH} & & \text{COOH} \\
 & | & & | \\
\text{CH}_3 & \text{CH}_2 & \text{CH}_3 & \text{CH}_2 \\
| & | & | & | \\
\text{CH (NH}_2) + \text{CH}_2 & \rightleftarrows & \text{CO} + & \text{CH}_2 \\
| & | & | & | \\
\text{COOH} & \text{CO} & \text{COOH} & \text{CH (NH}_2) \\
 & | & & | \\
 & \text{COOH} & & \text{COOH} \\
\end{array}
$$

| Alanine | α-Ketoglutaric acid | Pyruvic acid | Glutamic acid |

The metabolism of the lactate derived from muscular tissue follows the same pathways as shown above. The course of fat metabolism is less clear but need not concern the reader at this time. It will be sufficient to appreciate that the glycogen stored in liver is derived from several sources.

The other important function of the liver in the present context, and the one discovered by Bernard, is the enzymatic breakdown of its glycogen into glucose *(Fig. 3-1)*. This process, called glycogenolysis, is effected first by the agent of the enzyme phosphorylase, which breaks down the glycogen into glucose-1-phosphate. This is transformed into glucose-6-phosphate, which is then broken down by glucose-6-phosphatase into glucose and inorganic phosphate. The liver thus contributes in three important ways to the metabolism of carbohydrates and, in so doing, provides for the controlled storage of energy-rich molecules and their release into the blood stream.

No less important is the part played by the muscles, but their contribution differs from that of the liver. They are concerned with the oxidative release of energy and its manifestation as muscular work. Glucose released from the liver, and much of that derived directly from postdigestive absorption, passes into the muscle cells by membrane transport. Within the cells it is phosphorylated by the transfer of the terminal phosphate group from ATP, and the glucose-6-phosphate so formed comes under the influence of some of the same metabolic pathways that exist in the liver. Some glucose-6-phosphate is built up into glycogen; some, however, is directly metabolized with the release of energy. In due course the stored glycogen will also be broken down and used in this way.

Two stages can be recognized in the breakdown of glycogen. One, called glycolysis, consists of the anaerobic breakdown of glucose-6-

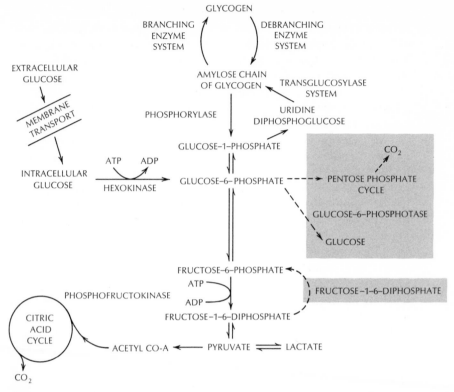

Fig. 3-1. The chief metabolic pathways for carbohydrate in liver and muscle. Reactions that occur mainly or only in the liver are shaded. (From F. G. Young, *Proceedings of the Royal Society of London, Series B*, 157 (1962), 9.)

phosphate to form pyruvate, which is then converted into either lactate or acetyl coenzyme A. The second stage, which is aerobic and depends, therefore, upon an adequate oxygen supply to the muscular tissue, involves the oxidative breakdown of the acetyl group of acetyl coenzyme A to carbon dioxide and water through the operation of the citric acid cycle. These processes occur also in the liver, the important difference between liver and muscle cells being that the latter lack glucose-6-phosphatase, which breaks down glucose-6-phosphate, and fructose-1-6-diphosphatase, which converts fructose-1-6-diphosphate to fructose-6-phosphate. Muscle cells, therefore, unlike liver cells, cannot convert glycogen to glucose, nor can they carry out gluconeogenesis.

The glucose in the blood stream is known as blood sugar. The homeostatic regulation of its concentration in man is well shown by studying the sequel to the ingestion of carbohydrates. An immediate result is a rise in the blood-sugar level, a condition known as hyper-glycemia, which is a normal sequel to a meal *(Fig. 3-2)*. Measurement of this rise and of the subsequent recovery constitutes the glucose tolerance test which is used in clinical practice in the investigation of abnormalities of carbohydrate metabolism. The person under investigation fasts for some eight hours and then drinks a solution of glucose. Blood samples are taken before the test and at 30-minute intervals thereafter and are examined for their glucose content. This can be determined either by some method based upon the capacity of this carbohydrate to reduce certain reagents, such as potassium ferrocyanide or copper salts, or by measuring the oxygen uptake when the glucose solution is treated with the enzyme glucose oxidase.

The results of such tests are shown in *Fig. 3-3*. It will be observed that the blood-sugar level, initially at about 90 mg per cent (i.e., 90 mg per 100 ml), rises rapidly to a maximum which is reached within 30–45 minutes. Thereafter, it falls again, to reach the normal resting value after about two hours. The initial rise is due to the flooding of the blood with glucose in advance of the capacity of the regulatory mechanism to deal with it. The subsequent fall results in part from oxidation of the glucose and in part from its conversion into glycogen within the tissues, particularly in the liver and muscles by the pathways outlined above.

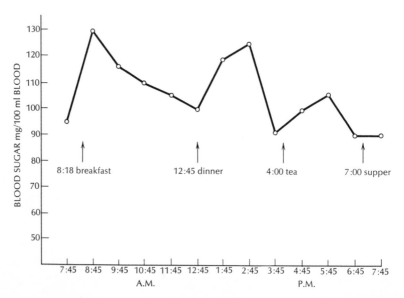

Fig. 3-2. Capillary blood-sugar concentration during twelve hours, showing the effect of meals in a healthy human subject. (From G. H. Bell, J. N. Davidson, and H. Scarborough, *Textbook of Physiology and Biochemistry*, 5th edition, Edinburgh: E. & S. Livingstone Ltd., 1963, p. 292.)

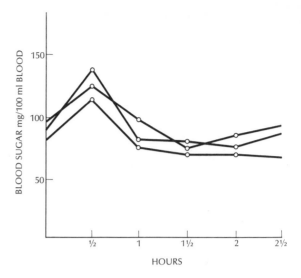

Fig. 3-3. Blood-sugar curves from three normal human subjects after the injection of 50 g glucose (glucose tolerance test). (From C. H. Bell, J. N. Davidson, and H. Scarborough, *Textbook of Physiology and Biochemistry*, 5th edition, Edinburgh: E. & S. Livingstone Ltd., 1963, p. 292.)

■ DIABETES MELLITUS AND THE DISCOVERY OF INSULIN

Thus far regulation of glucose concentration in the blood stream has been examined only in normal individuals; it illustrates the operation of a steady-state system, when the homeostatic regulatory mechanisms are functioning correctly. However, correct functioning may not always be possible, and it is the study of what happens in these circumstances that has led to the current understanding of the regulation of carbohydrate metabolism. *Figure 3-4* shows what happens when the glucose tolerance test is applied to patients with mild disturbance of this metabolism. The blood sugar of the fasting individuals is within the normal range, but the rise after ingestion of glucose is greater and more prolonged than normal. The effects of this are detectable in the urine. In normal people glucose in the blood is filtered into the kidney tubules through the glomeruli of the tubules; but it is resorbed further down the tubules by active uptake, so that the urine is free from sugar. If, however, the level of blood sugar rises beyond a certain critical point, the tubules are unable to reabsorb all the glucose that is presented to them, so that some of the sugar passes out in the urine. In consequence, the fluid tastes sweet, a characteristic that gives the name of diabetes mellitus (*mellitus,* sweetened with honey) to this disturbed condition. The critical point is reached at a blood concentration of about 160 mg per cent. This level is exceeded by both individuals illustrated (*Fig. 3-4*, p. 94), and the broken lines indicate the periods during which some of the glucose was excreted in the urine. In such individuals there is clearly some malfunctioning of the homeostatic mechanism.

Diabetes mellitus, however, is much more than a matter of passing some glucose in the urine. It arises from a profound disturbance of metabolism, with consequences so wide-ranging and clearly defined and, until recently, so difficult to control, that its existence has been recognized for many centuries. A number of the symptoms in mammals are known to result from a departure from the normal course of carbohydrate metabolism. The blood-sugar level is unusually high, and there is a corresponding reduction in glycogen content of the muscles and, more particularly, of the liver. In the terminology outlined earlier, glycogenesis is reduced, liver glycogenolysis is increased, and there is a decrease in the ability to oxidize glucose, which in its turn leads to general muscular weakness.

The high blood-sugar level leads to a great deal of glucose being passed in the urine, sometimes over 100 g per day. This is accompanied by excessive urination (polyuria), because much water has to be excreted in order to keep the glucose in solution in the urine; it is to this that the term diabetes (*diabainein*, to pass through) refers. The need for fuel in the tissues and the need to replace the lost water lead to hunger and thirst. The hunger is increased by the body turning to an increase in gluconeogenesis as an adaptive response to meet the continuing demand for fuel; this, however, is of no avail, because the glucose formed is lost through increased glycogenolysis. Gluconeogenesis involves a breaking down of protein. Thus there is an inevitable loss of nitrogen, and the body is said to be in negative nitrogen balance, a condition characteristic of diabetes mellitus. Further,

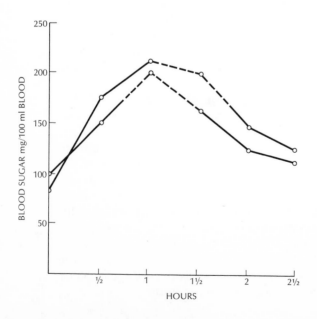

Fig. 3-4. Blood-sugar curves from two mildly diabetic patients. The dotted lines indicate glucosuria. Although the fasting blood sugar is nearly normal, the response to 50 g glucose is abnormal. Compare with the normal curves in Fig. 3-3. (From C. H. Bell, J. N. Davidson, and H. Scarborough, *Textbook of Physiology and Biochemistry*, 5th edition, Edinburgh: E. & S. Livingstone Ltd., 1963, p. 311.)

a fall in the respiratory quotient toward 0.7 reflects a transference of oxidative metabolism from carbohydrates to fats and proteins; these latter substances are drawn upon, through the pathways already mentioned, and the tissues begin to waste away. An impairment of fatty acid metabolism leads to the accumulation of ketone bodies, giving a characteristic smell of acetone in the breath; while there is also a disturbance of the electrolyte content of the body fluids.

Not surprisingly, the development of diabetes mellitus commonly resulted in premature death, until the events of 1921, to be mentioned below, led dramatically to the discovery of a means of alleviating the condition. Generations of investigators had devoted their best efforts to the study of the disease, but this was one of the situations in which the physiological organization of animals proved to be of a complexity surpassing anything that had been foreseen. Because of this, the unraveling of the nature of the condition had to proceed along more than one front and through stages that did not, at the time, seem to be at all closely connected.

It can now be seen that one essential step toward diabetes control was the discovery in 1869, by a twenty-two-year-old medical student, of a peculiar feature of the microanatomy of the mammalian pancreas. This organ consists predominantly of cells that secrete the digestive enzymes of the pancreatic fluid, but the student in reference, Paul Langerhans, showed the presence of many small islands or groups of cells that are readily distinguishable from the zymogen tissue. Although he was unable to determine the function of these cells, later investigators showed them to be of profound importance in relation to carbohydrate metabolism. They have been appropriately named the islets of Langerhans.

A second essential step was the discovery of a way of producing diabetes experimentally in laboratory animals. This was successfully achieved in 1889 as an accidental by-product of investigations of digestive physiology carried out by Oscar Minkowski and J. Von Mering. Thirty-seven years later, in 1926, Minkowski sent a letter, giving an exact account of the way in which the discovery was made, to a pupil of Von Mering who had suggested that the latter's contribution had been unduly minimized. This letter is a document of unusual interest, for it brings out clearly the element of chance that has already been shown to contribute to important discoveries. Also, the letter indicates the importance of informal discussions which take place in and around the laboratory and the delicacy of the personal relationships that sometimes underlie cooperative work.

You know I worked in the laboratory of the Medical Clinic at Strassburg while Von Mering was working at Hoppe-Seyler's Institute when you were an assistant there. One day in April 1889 I went over to your

Institute to consult some chemical periodicals in your library, which were not available in our Clinic, and there I met von Mering, who shortly before had recommended "Lipanin," an oil with 6 per cent free fatty acids, as a substitute for cod liver oil in the belief that its favourable therapeutic effects might be due to its free fatty acid content.

"Do you use Lipanin frequently in your clinic?" von Mering asked me.

"Oh, no," I answered. "We give our patients only good fresh butter, not rancid oil."

"Don't scoff," he replied. "Healthy men must split fats before absorbing them. If, however, the pancreas does not function properly, fats already split must be given."

"Have you proved this experimentally?" I asked.

"That is not so easy," he answered, "since pancreatic lipolytic enzymes pass into the gut even if one ties the pancreatic duct."

"Well, then," I said, "remove the whole pancreas!"

"That is an impossible operation," he replied.

As I did not know that Claude Bernard had stated that animals could not be kept alive after total pancreatectomy, and my youth led me to presumptuous overestimations of the results I had already obtained in my surgical experiments, I exclaimed:

"Bah! there are no impossible operations; pancreatectomy cannot be more difficult than hepatectomy; give me a dog and I will remove its pancreas today."

"Good, I have a dog which I can let you have now. So try it."

That same afternoon in Naunyn's laboratory, with von Mering's help, I took out his dog's pancreas. Perhaps, as a lucky coincidence, that particular animal possessed especially favorable anatomical conditions; they vary considerably in different animals. The whole gland was removed and the abdominal wall sutured; the animal remained alive and apparently well for nearly four weeks. I intended to return it to von Mering for his experiments on the utilization of fats, so I did not bother much about it; but because there was no suitable cage available it was kept tied up in one part of the laboratory. The day after the operation, von Mering had to go to Colmar urgently because his father-in-law was seriously ill with pneumonia. He had to stay there over a week. Meanwhile the dog, which was house-trained, very often micturated in the laboratory. I scolded the servant for not letting it out frequently enough, but he said: "I do, but the animal is queer; as soon as it comes back it passes water again even if it has just done so outside."

This observation induced me to collect some of the urine in a pipette and do a Tommer's test. Finding the urine reduced strongly, I made a 10 per cent solution with 1.5 cc. I still had in the pipette and found it contained 12 per cent sugar.

I thought at first that the glycosuria might be due to the fact that von Mering had treated his dog for a long time with phloridzin. So I immediately pancreatectomized three more dogs with no sugar in their urine previous to the operation. The second and third animals died two days later of necrosis of the duodenum, but both had glycosuria before they died. The fourth animal survived and from the second day after pancreatectomy had a persistent diabetes just like the first animal's.

It was then von Mering returned, but did not come at once to the laboratory. I met him again on the first of May, the Anniversary of the foundation of Strassburg University, at the festival celebration in the auditorium. Purely by chance, I was sitting behind him and I said over his shoulder, "Do you know, von Mering, that all pancreatectomized dogs become diabetic?"

"That's interesting," he replied, "we must follow up this question."

I then operated on a whole series of dogs, assisted sometimes, but not always, by von Mering. Once he tried to operate, but the animal died of hemorrhage on the operating table so he gave up trying. . . .

Naunyn, who was in a position to judge, considered I had shared too much with von Mering in not keeping the work on diabetes for myself and leaving him to follow up the further work on fat absorption. I knew, however, that I owed the discovery of diabetes to a lucky accident, and that I had not, any more than von Mering, imagined until then the importance the pancreas had in carbohydrate metabolism. Moreover, perhaps I would never have tried the extirpation of the pancreas if that conversation with von Mering had not taken place. I thought it only decent to invite him to collaborate in the work on diabetes, and I have never omitted to place his name together with mine even in recent times, as for example in my report on insulin in the Kissington Congress of 1924. . . .

I do not intend to publish this information. I shall, however, leave a copy of this letter in a suitable place, for at some future time a student of the history of diabetes may be interested in the true facts. . . .[3]

The observations of Langerhans, Von Mering, and Minkowski were gradually brought into association as a consequence of the development of the idea of internal secretion, already formulated by Bernard, and the realization that some organs were able, in ways not then understood, to have far-reaching effects on the functioning of the body. The association of malfunctioning of the thyroid gland with cretinism and myxedema (p. 121) are examples of this, as is the role of secretin in digestive physiology. Repetition and extension of the pancreatectomy experiments of Von Mering and Minkowski showed that the presence of the pancreas was necessary for the maintenance of normal carbohydrate metabolism, but at first it was not clear whether or not the islet tissue was functionally distinct from the zymogen tissue. It was suggested, quite plausibly, that the former was simply a modification of the latter; but decisive evidence against this view was obtained by experiments in which the pancreatic duct was tied off in otherwise intact animals. The result of this was that the zymogen tissue degenerated and was replaced by fibrous tissue, whereas the islet cells were unaffected. Not only did this establish the independence of the two tissues, it also suggested the involvement of the islets in the control of carbohydrate metabolism. As long as they were intact, there was no glycosuria; but if they too began to degenerate, as they sometimes did, then glucose began to appear in the urine.

So probable did it seem that the islets were producing an internal secretion, that in 1901 the supposed secretion was named insuline (*insula*, island), although it had still not been shown to exist! It was known that myxedema could be alleviated by feeding thyroid gland to the afflicted patient; it seemed likely, therefore, that diabetics might benefit equally well by having pancreatic tissue fed to them. Yet experiments of this type repeatedly failed, not was any success gained by attempts to prepare beneficial extracts from the organ.

Work on diabetes progressed no further until 2 A.M. on the morning of November 1, 1920, when a Canadian general practitioner, Frederick Banting, who was also employed as a university instructor in Toronto and was at that hour preparing a lecture, suddenly was struck by the significance of the experiments in which the pancreatic duct had been ligated. It occurred to him that during the preparation of extracts of the whole pancreas, the supposed hormone might be digested by the pancreatic enzymes. If, however, the duct was first ligated so that the zymogen tissue degenerated, it might be possible to extract the hormone unharmed. He did not know that others also had had this idea and had abandoned it because of the great technical difficulties involved. Indeed, he is reported to have said that he would never himself have undertaken this investigation, had he known how much had already been published in the field. His experience is a classical demonstration of the importance of refusing to be depressed by the weight of previous work in any promising field of research; for Banting, in collaboration with C. H. Best, succeeded in preparing extracts that could alleviate the diabetic condition. Thus these two investigators established the existence of a hormone, now known as insulin, which is responsible for the regulation of carbohydrate metabolism.

In 1922 Banting and Best were able to report in detail the results of their experiments with dogs *(Fig. 3-5)*. They had tied off the pancreatic duct and had found that "the pancreatic tissue removed after seven to ten weeks' degeneration shows an abundance of healthy islets, and a complete replacement of the acini with fibrous tissue."[4] They went on to summarize the results:

> In the course of our experiments we have administered over seventy-five doses of extract from degenerated pancreatic tissue to ten dif-

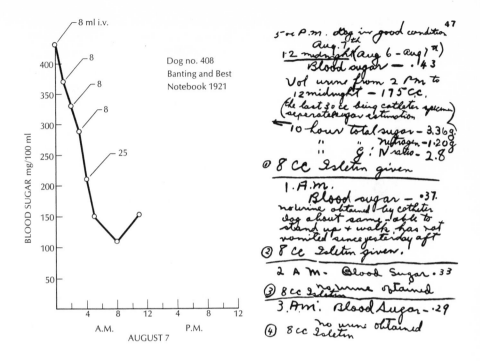

Fig. 3-5. Left. Redrawn from an early graph from the experiments of Banting and Best showing the effect of injection of a cold saline extract made from dog pancreas removed after the pancreatic duct had been ligated and the pancreas had degenerated. The dog into which the injections were made was rendered diabetic by removal of its pancreas. Its blood sugar when injections began was greatly above normal. The moment of each injection is indicated by an arrow. The time scale is along the bottom line. The blood sugar fell to normal within eight hours. *Right.* One of the pages from the original notes of this experiment which ran through the nights of August 6-7, 1921. The extract is referred to as Isletin. (From G. A. Wrenshall, G. Hetenyi, and W. R. Feasby, *The Story of Insulin.* London: The Bodley Head Ltd., 1962, p. 67.)

ferent diabetic animals. Since the extract has always produced a reduction of the percentage sugar of the blood [*Fig. 3-6*] and of the sugar excreted in the urine, we feel justified in stating that this extract contains the internal secretion of the pancreas. Some of our more recent experiments, which are not yet completed, give, in addition to still more conclusive evidence regarding the sugar retaining power of diabetic animals treated with extract, some interesting facts regarding the chemical nature of the active principle of the internal secretion.[4]

The immediate importance of the discovery of insulin was that it provided a means of preparing pancreatic extracts that could be administered to human patients; these extracts had the power to alleviate the diabetic condition and thus to save the lives of those who might otherwise have died. In a broader biological context, however, the discovery can be seen to have shown that the regulatory capacity of the alimentary tract and its derivatives is not confined to the chemical control of its own activities; it was now clear that its field of action extends throughout the body.

■ THE MOLECULAR BIOLOGY OF ISLET TISSUE

The production of insulin within the pancreatic islet tissue has been amply documented and is now accepted as a fundamental feature of vertebrates ranging from fish to mammals and probably including the cyclostomes. Justification for this conclusion rests upon a close histological analysis of the tissue and the correlation of its appearance with variations in the state of carbohydrate metabolism. This analysis has also shown, however, that the composition and mode of functioning of the islet tissue is more complex than earlier envisaged.

The actual source of the insulin is now well established. Two types of cell, termed A (or α) and B (or β) cells, have long been known to

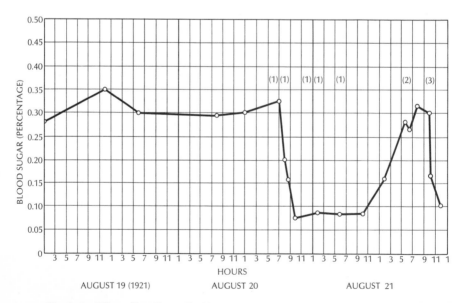

Fig. 3-6. Effect of insulin on the blood-sugar curve of a depancreatized dog (redrawn from Banting and Best). (1) Injection of extract of degenerated pancreas; (2) extract after incubation with pancreatic juice; (3) extract incubated without pancreatic juice. Note that the trypsin of the pancreatic juice destroys the hormone. (From C. H. Best and N. B. Taylor, *Physiological Basis of Medical Practice*, 2nd edition, Baltimore: The Williams and Wilkins Co., 1940, p. 935.)

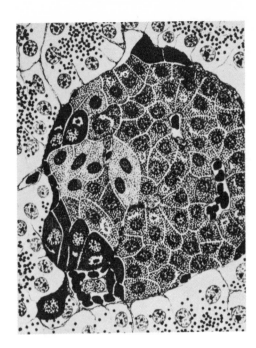

Fig. 3-7. Islet of Langerhans of a rabbit. The cell types are indicated schematically: the A-cells are black; the B-cells have dark granulation; the D-cells have light granulation. Zymogen cells surround the islet. (From T. B. Thomas, *American Journal of Anatomy*, 62 (1937), 55.)

exist in the islets of mammals. B cells alone are present in cyclostomes (lampreys and hagfish), which are primitive jawless vertebrates, at a lower evolutionary level than fish. Both A and B cells, however, are probably present in the pancreatic tissue of all groups of vertebrates from fish upwards. Moreover, it is now thought probable that there is often a third type, termed the D or A_1 cell *(Fig. 3-7)*. It is agreed that of these three types, which are distinguishable from each other by their reactions to stains, histochemical tests, and experimental treatment, it is only the B cells that secrete insulin. One reason for this conclusion is that B cells contain granules which react positively to histochemical tests for sulfhydryl groups; such groups, as shall be seen later, are known to be present in the insulin molecule. Further, the injection of large amounts of glucose into the blood stream of experimental animals results in the B cells becoming degranulated and vacuolated; whereas the same treatment leaves the other two types of cell unaffected. Such a glucose load, as it is called, creates a heavy demand for insulin; and the resultant appearance of the B cells is just what would be expected, if they were secreting large amounts of the hormone. Their response is not regulated by the nervous system but appears rather to be a direct reaction of the cells to the increased level of glucose in the circulating blood. One other line of evidence is obtained from experiments in which animals receive injections of alloxan, a substance that selectively destroys the B cells while leaving the other types relatively undisturbed. Animals treated in this way pass into a diabetic condition, the result one would expect from the destruction of the insulin source.

Man's ability to identify the cells which secrete insulin stands in marked contrast to his inability to name the source of secretin and other digestive hormones, which arise from what are currently unidentified cells in the wall of the alimentary tract. The islet tissue, however, is also of alimentary origin; for it differentiates within the pancreatic rudiment that grows out from the developing alimentary canal of the vertebrate embryo. It would seem, therefore, that secretions of the islet tissue may be closely related to the digestive hormones, although more specialized in their mode of production and more wide-ranging in their fields of action. This conclusion is borne out by other considerations. As noted above, cells like the B cells of higher form, are present in the earlier evolved cyclostomes. These animals, however, do not possess a differentiated enzyme-secreting pancreas; instead, the zymogen cells are still located wholly within the intestinal epithelium. This is clearly a primitive character, and equally primitive is the anatomical development of the insulin-secreting cells, particularly in lampreys. In these animals such cells lie within the submucosa of the intestinal wall; and in the ammocoete larva of the lamprey they can be clearly seen to differentiate out of the intestinal mucosa, forming groups of cells that have been called the follicles of Langerhans.

It seems likely that the site of the insulin-secreting cells in cyclostomes reflects the evolutionary origin of islet tissue. As E. N. Willmer has pointed out, it is the wall of the digestive tract that first experiences fluctuations in the uptake of nutrients from the intestinal lumen. It would seem logical for certain cells within the intestinal wall to become sensitive to these variations and to respond to them by corresponding fluctuations in the discharge of their own metabolites. Such might well have been the origin of the type of chemical regulation that insulin now exerts on the levels of nutrients circulating through the body. Moreover, another consideration that links this hormone with the digestive hormones is found in its chemical composition. Reasons for supposing that digestive hormones are polypeptides have been mentioned earlier. Thanks to the brilliant work of Frederick Sanger in elucidating the structure of the insulin molecule, it is now known that insulin too is a polypeptide.

Insulin was isolated in crystalline form by J. J. Abel in 1926. It was known at that time to be a protein, but the problem of proceeding from that point to a determination of its chemical constitution presented formidable difficulties. Protein molecules were known to be highly complex in their composition, but the principles underlying their structure were not understood. It seemed likely that their properties might be determined by the specific order or arrangement of the amino acid residues along the polypeptide chain; but the hypothesis was impossible to test, because no methods had been worked out for establishing this order in any protein molecule.

Up to 1945 little new knowledge was gained. Yet, within the succeeding ten years, the work of Sanger at Cambridge University established the complete chemical structure of the insulin molecule. F. G. Young has written of this achievement:

> To many it is particularly pleasing that in these days when the importance of individual, as opposed to group, activity is sometimes in danger of neglect, the complete chemical structure of insulin should have been elucidated not by a large "team" of research workers "headed" by somebody but by one who may reasonably be described as a modest individualist — Frederick Sanger, whose researches were pursued in co-operation with no more than one or two junior colleagues at a time. That this investigation should have been brought to a successful conclusion within a period of about ten years (1945-1955) is truly astonishing and a great tribute to Sanger's foresight, persistence, and experimental ability. This research involved an immense amount of painstaking manipulative work at the laboratory bench, the plan of which rested upon hard logical thinking with careful preliminary consideration of experimental possibilities and subsequent critical interpretation of results.[5]

It is impossible to describe Sanger's studies in detail here. In principle, they depended upon partial but controlled hydrolysis of the insulin molecule — with acid or with proteolytic enzymes (cf. *Fig. 3-14*, p. 119) — into small fragments of the original chains. Each fragment might contain four or five amino acid residues, which could be separated and identified by using various methods such as paper chromatography and ion-exchange of chromatography. In this way, and by determining which were the terminal residues in the fragments, it was possible to establish the relative positions of the residues and to show how the fragment could be put together. The result is shown in *Fig. 3-8*. The insulin molecule is seen to have a molecular weight of 6000 and to be composed of two polypeptide chains, an A-chain and a B-chain, of which the A-chain is the shorter. These two chains are joined at two places by the disulfide bridges of cysteine residues, while two parts of the A-chain are connected together by a third disulfide bridge which thus forms an intra-chain bridge.

The results of this structural analysis, to quote Sanger,

> showed that proteins are definite chemical substances possessing a unique structure in which each position in the chain is occupied by one, and only one, amino acid residue. Examination of the sequences

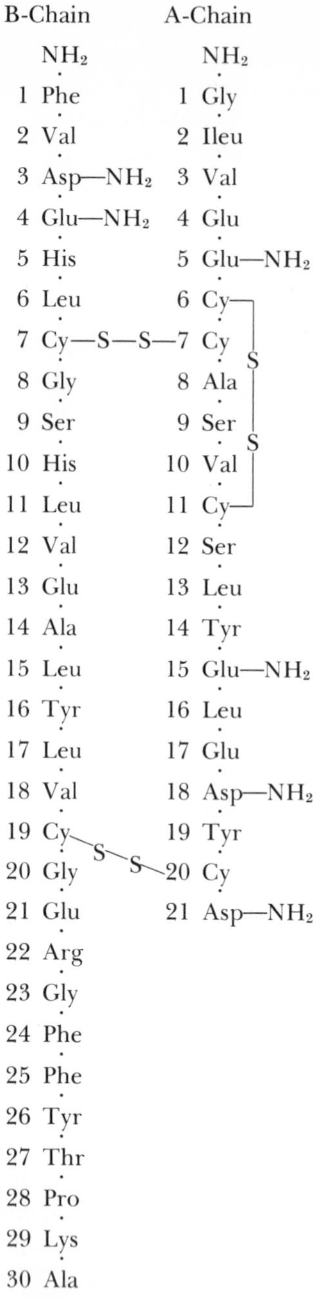

B-Chain	A-Chain
NH₂	NH₂

B-Chain A-Chain

NH₂   NH₂

1 Phe   1 Gly

2 Val   2 Ileu

3 Asp—NH₂   3 Val

4 Glu—NH₂   4 Glu

5 His   5 Glu—NH₂

6 Leu   6 Cy⌐

7 Cy—S—S—7 Cy ⌉ S

8 Gly   8 Ala

9 Ser   9 Ser ⌋ S

10 His   10 Val

11 Leu   11 Cy⌐

12 Val   12 Ser

13 Glu   13 Leu

14 Ala   14 Tyr

15 Leu   15 Glu—NH₂

16 Tyr   16 Leu

17 Leu   17 Glu

18 Val   18 Asp—NH₂

19 Cy   19 Tyr

20 Gly   20 Cy

21 Glu   21 Asp—NH₂

22 Arg

23 Gly

24 Phe

25 Phe

26 Tyr

27 Thr

28 Pro

29 Lys

30 Ala

Fig. 3-8. The structure of insulin from ox pancreas. (Based on F. Sanger and F. G. Young in *Comparative Endocrinology, 1*, U. S. von Euler and H. Heller, ed., New York: Academic Press, 1963, p. 372.)

of the two chains reveals no evidence of periodicity of any kind, nor does there seem to be any basic principle which determines the arrangement of the residues. They seem to be put together in an order that is random, but nevertheless unique and most significant, since on it must depend the important physiological action of the hormone.[6]

Earlier it was said that B cells and the insulin they secrete are a basic feature of vertebrate physiological organization. As a result of Sanger's work, however, it is now known that the insulin molecule, while always possessing, according to present knowledge, the characteristic property of being able to lower the level of blood sugar and to achieve other effects that go with that action, is by no means uniform in its chemical structure. Even within mammals there occur variations in this structure (Table 3-1); these, however, do not seem to be matched by any significant variation in the biological potency of the molecules. Many of these variations occur within the length of the A-chain that is covered by the intra-chain disulfide bridge, but different variations are also known in other parts of this chain and also in the B-chain. It is evident that the variations consist of the substitution of one amino acid residue by another. The assumption is that these substitutions are the result of genetic mutations that modify the programming of the secretion of the hormone in ways that do not affect the ultimate ability of the molecule to influence carbohydrate metabolism. It is very possible that each such substitution is the expression of a single mutation.

TABLE 3-1

Variations in the Amino Acid Sequence of Mammalian Insulins[a]

	A-Chain				B-Chain		
	4	8	9	10	3	29	30
Ox*	Glu	Ala	Ser	Val	Asp.NH$_2$	Lys	Ala
Sheep†	Glu	Ala	Gly	Val	Asp.NH$_2$	Lys	Ala
Horse‡	Glu	Thr	Gly	Ileu	Asp.NH$_2$	Lys	Ala
Sei whale§	Glu	Ala	Ser	Thr	Asp.NH$_2$	Lys	Ala
Pig†	Glu	Thr	Ser	Ileu	Asp.NH$_2$	Lys	Ala
Sperm whale‡	Glu	Thr	Ser	Ileu	Asp.NH$_2$	Lys	Ala
Dog‖	Glu	Thr	Ser	Ileu	Asp.NH$_2$	Lys	Ala
Human¶	Glu	Thr	Ser	Ileu	Asp.NH$_2$	Lys	Thr
Rabbit‖	Glu	Thr	Ser	Ileu	Asp.NH$_2$	Lys	Ser
Rat 1‖	Asp	Thr	Ser	Ileu	Lys	Lys	Ser
Rat 2‖	Asp	Thr	Ser	Ileu	Lys	Met	Ser

* Sanger & Tuppy (1951*a*, *b*), Sanger & Thompson (1953).
† Brown, Sanger & Kitai (1955).
‡ Harris, Sanger & Naughton (1956).
§ Ishihara, Seito, Ito & Fujino (1958).
‖ L. F. Smith—unpublished.
¶ Nicol & Smith (1960).
[a]Data collected from various authors by F. G. Young, *Proceedings of the Royal Society of London, B*, 157 (1962) 2.

Even more pronounced differences exist between the amino acid composition of the insulins of two species of teleost fish—the cod (*Gadus callarias*) and the bonito (*Gymnosarda alleterata*)—and between these and the insulin of the ox (Table 3-2). In the A-chains, in particular, the differences are sufficient to imply marked differences in the corresponding amino acid sequences. Yet, just as with the different mammalian insulins, when these various products are assayed on the rat, there proves to be very little difference in their biological activity.

Insulins of various species do differ, however, in respect to another biological property. Insulin, being a protein, can act as an antigen; this means that if the insulin of one species is injected into another species, it may evoke the production of antibodies in the blood of the latter. For example, ox insulin can evoke an antibody in the horse. The serum of a horse containing this antibody will then be able to neutralize the biological activity of the ox serum under certain experimental conditions. Using this principle, the immunological behavior of ox insulin can be compared, for example, with that of cod insulin, using their respective horse antibodies as a basis for the comparison. It can thus be shown that the amount of horse antibody-to-ox-insulin needed to neutralize one biological unit of cod insulin is forty times the amount needed to neutralize one biological unit of ox insulin.

From these figures and other data, certain general conclusions can be postulated which are applicable to other protein molecules as well as to insulin. The serial arrangement of the amino acid residues in the polypeptide chain of a protein molecule constitutes what is termed the primary structure of the molecule. Because of the complexity of the protein molecule, however, these constituent chains may be coiled, giving the molecule a secondary structure; while the coils themselves may be folded and joined together to give a tertiary structure. It may be assumed that it is the total structure or configuration

TABLE 3-2

Amino Acid Composition of Separated A- and B-Chains of Insulin From Ox, Cod and Bonito (Bonito Insulin II)[a]

Amino acid	A-Chain			B-Chain		
	Ox	Cod*	Bonito†	Ox	Cod*	Bonito†
Ala	1	*0*	*0*	2	2	*3*
Arg	0	*1*	0	1	1	1
Asp	2	*5*	*3*	1	*3*	1
Cys	4	4	4	2	2	2
Glu	4	*2*	4	3	*2*	3
Gly	1	1	1	3	3	3
His	0	*1*	*2*	2	2	2
Ileu	1	*2‡*	1	0	0	0
Leu	2	*1‡*	2	4	4	4
Lys	0	0	*1*	1	1	1
Met	0	0	0	0	*1*	0
Phe	0	*1*	*1*	3	*2*	*2*
Pro	0	*1*	*1*	1	*3*	*2*
Ser	2	*0*	*0*	1	1	1
Thr	0	0	0	1	*0*	*0*
Try	0	0	*0?*	0	0	*0?*
Tyr	2	*1*	*1*	2	2	2
Val	2	*1*	*0*	3	*2*	*2*
Total	21	21	21	30	*31*	*29*

(Figures which differ from those for ox insulin are in italics.)
* Wilson & Dixon (1961).
† Kotaki (1961).
‡ These figures have been corrected from table 1 of Wilson & Dixon (1961) as the result of correspondence with Dr. G. H. Dixon.
[a] Data collected from various authors by F. G. Young, *Proceedings of the Royal Society of London, B,* 157 (1962) 3.

of the molecule that determines the totality of its properties. But, if this is so, it is conceivable that only a small part of the molecule may be responsible for the specific activity manifested in a particular regulatory response. This small part can be thought of as an "active site," with the rest of the molecule concerned with other properties, such as the antigen reactions just mentioned. In the present state of our knowledge, this concept is highly theoretical; and, for this reason, it will not be discussed further. However, the concept does provide a possible explanation of why amino acid substitutions can occur without modifying the fundamental biological activity of the molecule. According to this hypothesis, they could be regarded as occurring in parts of the molecule that do not contain the active site. However, one still is forced to conclude that in the particular case of insulin the parts of the molecule that determine its immunological properties must differ from those determining its metabolic activities. This follows from the occurrence of immunological differences between molecules that are similar in metabolic activities.

It is to be expected that the establishment of some relationship between the molecular structure of a hormone and its biological activity would lead to an understanding of the means by which the hormone achieves its effects. This problem, which raises the fundamental question of the nature of the relationship between a biologically active molecule and the cells which it influences, is an absorbing one; for it is fundamental to man's understanding of the organization of living systems. At present, there is still virtually everything to learn about this matter; yet in recent years some progress has been made, and scientists are at least beginning to see how to frame some of the necessary investigations.

It is important here to distinguish between the gross physiological effects of a regulatory agent and the means by which these effects are initiated within the responding cells. In regard to the former, the most obvious effects of the administration of insulin to a diabetic animal are a fall in the level of blood sugar and an increase in the glycogen content of the skeletal muscle. The organism recovers its ability to store carbohydrate and to release energy from it. Many other effects can also be discerned, but it is generally supposed that most of these are secondary results of the restoration of normal carbohydrate metabolism, being consequential upon the interrelationships of the relevant metabolic pathways. It is believed, however, that insulin does have a direct action on protein metabolism and nitrogen retention.

All of the foregoing information tells one nothing of the means by which the insulin molecule brings about these effects, for any understanding of this demands extension of the analysis to the cellular level. Here one must begin with the fact that treatment with insulin of intact normal animals enables their muscular tissue to take in more

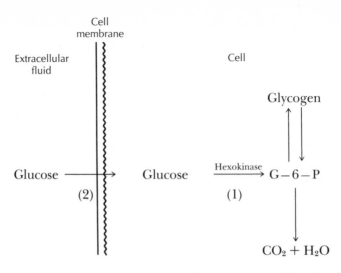

Fig. 3-9. Diagram to illustrate the possibility of a reaction at the cell surface (2) which precedes the first phosphorylation of glucose (1) and is concerned with the transfer of the sugar into the cell interior from the extracellular compartment. (From Rachmiel Levine and Maurice S. Goldstein, *Recent Progress in Hormone Research*, 11 (1955), 350.)

glucose from the blood. That this is so is implied in what was said earlier regarding the fall in blood sugar and the increase in muscle glycogen, and it has been clearly proven in direct experimental observations. If a rabbit is given glucose at the rate of 1.5 g/kg/hr for six hours, its blood sugar is markedly elevated. Administration of insulin during this period results in a considerable increase in muscle glycogen, while the liver glycogen steadily declines during the insulin treatment. Even more convincing is evidence obtained from experiments in which the isolated diaphragms of rats are maintained *in vitro*. If glucose labeled with radioactive carbon is added to the medium surrounding the diaphragm, it is possible to study the uptake of the glucose into the tissue, since this is reflected in the increasing radioactivity of the tissue. In this way it can be shown that the presence of insulin in the medium stimulates both glucose uptake and also glycogenesis in the diaphragm.

To explain how insulin produces these effects, it is necessary to find some stage in glucose uptake or metabolism that is specifically stimulated by the hormone. Many of the steps outlined in *Fig. 3-1*, p. 91 can be eliminated from consideration. For example, the complete removal of the pancreas does not impair glycolysis, nor does it have any consistent effect on the oxidation of pyruvate and citrate through the citric acid cycle. It is logical to conclude, therefore, that insulin must influence carbohydrate metabolism in the muscle cell at a very early stage, prior to the divergence of the several metabolic pathways.

One suggestion that has been thoroughly investigated is that insulin may stimulate the formation of glucose-6-phosphate by increasing the activity of the enzyme hexokinase which catalyzes that process. This hypothesis, however, has failed to gain support from experimental evidence and is no longer considered to provide the correct explanation. An alternative possibility is that insulin facilitates the membrane transport of glucose into the muscle cell, so that more is made available for glycogenesis (*Fig. 3-9*). This view, which has been argued particularly by R. Levine, has now been supported by substantial evidence, and, in light of our present knowledge, affords at least an acceptable working hypothesis to account for the action of insulin on carbohydrate metabolism. Whether it accounts equally well for the action of the hormone on protein synthesis is less clear, for there is no evidence that insulin stimulates the movement of amino acids into cells. In this instance it may be that the hormone acts directly on the ribosomes. But, in any case, it would be premature to suppose that a final picture of the mode of insulin action, or, indeed, of any other hormone has been drawn. Even in the particular case of carbohydrate metabolism, it is doubtful whether the influence of insulin is exerted solely upon membrane transport, for there is some evidence that it also exerts a direct stimulating action upon glycogenesis.

So far only the product of B cells has been considered. As mentioned earlier, these are present throughout vertebrates from cyclostomes to man, and their function may be regarded as thoroughly well established. However, this does not account for the existence of A cells, which are identifiable from fish upwards, although they are probably absent from cyclostomes. For a long time the significance of A cells was in doubt; but it is now believed that they produce a substance called glucagon, which has a hyperglycemic (blood-sugar-raising) effect that opposes (antagonizes) the hypoglycemic effect of insulin. Its influence is thought to be shown in the transient hyperglycemic effect that an intravenous injection of commercial insulin may produce prior to the main hypoglycemic effect (*Fig. 3-10*). It is supposed that the reason for this is that glucagon is commonly present as a contaminant in such extracts.

The existence of glucagon is not, however, a matter of hypothesis alone. It has been obtained as a crystalline polypeptide, with a molecular weight of 3485. The application of Sanger's methods to its study has shown that it, like insulin, is a polypeptide with highly characteristic properties. Its molecule is smaller than that of insulin, consisting of a single chain of 29 amino acids with its own chemical characteristics. It possesses tryptophan, which is absent from insulin;

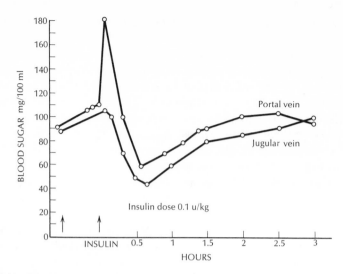

Fig. 3-10. Blood-sugar changes after intravenous injection of insulin. (From P. P. Foa, *The Hormones*, Volume 4, G. Pincus, K. V. Thiman, and E. B. Astwood, ed., New York: Academic Press, 1964, p. 532.)

but it lacks the cysteine residues that are present in the latter. Like the insulin molecule, however, it may be held to have evolved out of the polypeptide-secreting capacity of the wall of the vertebrate alimentary tract. The evidence that glucagon is secreted by A cells rests partly on the fact that it can be extracted from the pancreas when the zymogen-secreting tissue has been destroyed by ligation of the pancreatic duct and the B cells have been destroyed by alloxan. Further evidence can be derived from its chemical characteristics, for A cells contain granules that react positively to histochemical tests for tryptophan but negatively to tests for the sulfhydryl groups of cysteine residues.

To understand the supposed mode of action of glucagon, it is necessary to recall that the breakdown of glycogen to glucose in the liver takes place in three stages (cf. *Fig. 3-1*, p. 91):

1. glycogen + inorganic phosphate → glucose-1-phosphate
2. glucose-1-phosphate → glucose-6-phosphate
3. glucose-6-phosphate → glucose + inorganic phosphate

The first of these reactions is catalyzed by phosphorylase, and it is this reaction that is the slowest of the three. The rate of release of glucose from the liver will thus depend upon the concentration of active phosphorylase present in its cells. It is here that glucagon is believed to exert its effect by increasing the concentration of active enzyme. Part of the cellular content of the enzyme is present in inactive form; it becomes active on being phosphorylated, a process stimulated by glucagon. Thus the action of glucagon decreases liver glycogen and raises the level of the blood sugar. In addition, it appears to stimulate gluconeogenesis, so that it increases the total amount of carbohydrate available for release.

Because of these facts, it is believed by some workers that glucagon is a true hormone secreted in response to a lowering of the level of blood sugar. Unfortunately, however, knowledge of the behavior of glucagon in intact animals, under normal physiological conditions, falls far short of knowledge of its chemical constitution and its biochemical action. Its real significance, therefore, remains obscure; and it cannot yet be stated that it is a true hormone. As for the D (A_1) cells and any secretion they may produce, there is as yet no basis for any useful interpretation. One can only say that here, as in other components of the endocrine system, advances in knowledge are revealing depths of complexity that were earlier unsuspected.

■ HORMONAL INTERACTIONS IN THE REGULATION OF METABOLISM

Data from experiments with glucagon suggest that insulin may not be acting in isolation. Yet so far this chapter has discussed its action largely as though it were being exerted independently. In addition, insulin has been treated in the somewhat abstract environment of a mammal of unspecified size and age. It is necessary now to view both it and the mammalian body in a more realistic perspective.

The fully grown animal maintains itself in working order and at a fixed size by securing a delicately poised balance between catabolic and anabolic reactions. The former are concerned with the release of energy and general wear and tear of the body. The anabolic reactions are concerned with the building up of reserves, the maintenance of organization, and the replacement of worn parts of the machinery. Because there is a limit to the body's capacity for replacement, catabolism eventually predominates, and death results. However, this limitation, seen by man as the fundamental human predicament, is matched during the earlier part of life by a phase in which anabolism predominates. This is known as the growth phase, in which the body develops from a fertilized egg to its mature size. Growth, of course, is accompanied by differentiation, the progressive unfolding of organization; but this topic will not be considered here.

It is not easy to arrive at a satisfactory definition of growth, although man may feel that he readily understands the meaning of the term. It has been succinctly defined as "increase in size." "Growing," writes G. R. de Beer, "implies getting bigger and this increase in size is what should strictly be termed growth."[7] Another definition is that of J. Z. Young, for whom "growth is the addition of material to that which is already organized into a living pattern."[8] A. E. Needham, in a close analysis of these matters, points out that this last definition has the advantage of accepting that growth processes are not only concerned with increase in size but also provide for maintenance and repair. It may be that growth processes are to some extent qualitatively different from those involved in maintenance, but it seems likely that in many respects the metabolism of the fully grown animal differs from that of the growing juvenile primarily in the delicately adjusted balance of its anabolic and catabolic components.

The fact that one can talk at all of fully grown animals is an expression of a fundamental characteristic of growth in size. This process is multiplicative, in the sense P. B. Medawar expresses when he writes, "What results from growth is itself typically capable of growth."[9] This, indeed, is a corollary of Young's definition, since the ability to grow is inherent in living material. In mathematical terms, this means that growth is an exponential process which would proceed to infinity, were it not subject to appropriate checks. Ultimately, these checks are genetically determined, a consequence of natural selection having established an optimal maximum size that is appropriate to the organization and mode of life of a particular species. In general, therefore, one can say that size is an expression of adaptation, as J. B. S. Haldane showed in an entertaining essay.

> In a large textbook of zoology before me I find no indication that the eagle is larger than the sparrow, or the hippopotamus bigger than the hare, though some grudging admissions are made in the case of the mouse and the whale. But yet it is easy to show that a hare could not be as large as a hippopotamus, or a whale as small as a herring. For every type of animal there is a most convenient size, and a large change in size inevitably carries with it a change of form.
>
> Let us take the most obvious of possible cases, and consider a giant man sixty feet high — about the height of Giant Pope and Giant Pagan in the illustrated *Pilgrim's Progress* of my childhood. These monsters were not only ten times as high as Christian, but ten times as wide and ten times as thick, so that their total weight was a thousand times his, or about eighty to ninety tons. Unfortunately the cross sections of their bones were only a hundred times those of Christian, so that every square inch of giant bone had to support ten times the weight borne by a square inch of human bone. As the human thigh-bone breaks under about ten times the human weight, Pope and Pagan would have broken their thighs every time they took a step. This was doubtless why they were sitting down in the picture I remember. But it lessens one's respect for Christian and Jack the Giant Killer.
>
> To turn to zoology, suppose that a gazelle, a graceful little creature with long thin legs, is to become large, it will break its bones unless it does one of two things. It may make its legs short and thick, like

the rhinoceros, so that every pound of weight has still about the same area of bone to support it. Or it can compress its body and stretch out its legs obliquely to gain stability, like the giraffe. I mention these two beasts because they happen to belong to the same order as the gazelle, and both are quite successful mechanically, being remarkably fast runners.[10]

Many other factors, in addition to genetic adaptation, are involved in the determination of optimum size. One of these emerges from the earlier discussion of respiratory mechanisms. Insects, despite their possession of a blood system, rely upon tracheae for conducting oxygen through their body (see Chap. 1). While such a system works efficiently in small animals, it cannot possibly do so in large ones, because ventilation movements can circulate the air through only the more peripheral parts of the tracheal system. The passage of oxygen to the cells through the finer tubules depends ultimately upon diffusion, which can provide for effective oxygenation only when the distances it traverses are very short. It is significant that crustaceans, which carry oxygen in their blood stream, have reached sizes many times larger than the largest of insects.

Other factors that determine optimal size appear in Chapters 4 and 5 which consider the influence of temperature on animal life. It will be sufficient for the present, however, to appreciate that growth must be adaptively regulated. Thus it tends to proceed at a maximal rate at an early stage and then to slow down to a point at which catabolism begins to match anabolism. Growth processes are still operating, but they are now being regulated to ensure the maintenance of the genetically determined optimal size. Bear in mind that regulation is necessarily more subtle and complex than this simple statement suggests; one reason for this is that the phase of maximal size is likely to be the phase at which heavy anabolic demands are being made by the processes involved in sexual reproduction. Indeed, the metabolic demands of reproduction provide one reason why growth must eventually become slower. Growth and reproduction tend to be competitive processes making demands on nutrition that the animal may be unable to satisfy simultaneously.

The situation is clearly illustrated in the life history of the shore-dwelling polychaete worm, *Nereis diversicolor*. Spawning of this species takes place in early spring, and rapid growth sets in after hatching in February. The young worms increase in length at a rate of 1-2 cm each month, to reach a length of about 10 cm by October. Since the monthly increment remains constant, despite the increase in total body length, there is, in effect, a slowing of the growth rate. This sinks virtually to zero during the winter, at which time the germ cells enter upon a rapid growth phase in readiness for the spring spawn-

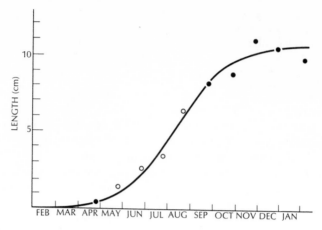

Fig. 3-11. Growth of young *Nereis diversicolor*. Empty circles represent estimated values; filled circles represent values calculated directly from the data. (From R. P. Dales, *Biological Bulletin*, 101 (1951), 137.)

ing. Thus the growth of these worms, plotted as size against time, follows a sigmoid curve (*Fig. 3-11*). Such a curve is commonly obtained from all such growth measurements, whether of parts of the body or of the whole animal.

A similar pattern applies equally to the specialized aspect of growth known as regeneration—the replacement of lost parts of the body, such as occurs when a worm replaces lost hind segments with new ones. This is illustrated in *Fig. 3-12*, which shows that the rate of growth of the regenerating hind end of an earthworm provides a curve similar to that obtained from whole specimens of *Nereis*. The growth of the regenerating part, plotted as size against time, follows the same sigmoid form. *Figure 3-12* also includes an analysis of the basis of this sigmoid form. It is seen to result from the fact that the plot of the daily increment of length (dL/dt) rises to a peak and falls away again; while the specific growth rate (which is the daily increment per unit of existing length) follows an exponential curve, its rate of decline becoming progressively less steep.

One is now in a position to examine the wider implications of the influence of insulin on carbohydrate and protein metabolism. The foregoing discussion leads to the conclusion that insulin cannot possibly be functioning in isolation. It is regulating metabolic reactions that must be adaptively adjusted in accordance with demands that vary during the life of the animal, not only in relation to the growth process, but also in relation to constantly fluctuating demands that are imposed by diverse environmental stresses. One would expect insulin to form part of a more complex regulating system, and this expectation is certainly justified by what is now known of the regulation of mammalian metabolism.

The hormones with which insulin forms an interrelationship in its regulation of metabolism arise in endocrine glands that are anatomically quite unrelated to islet tissue. One well-established example is given by the growth hormone of the pituitary gland of vertebrates. The control of growth, inasmuch as it demands the exertion of control throughout the body over a long period of time, is peculiarly well suited to hormonal regulation. Not surprisingly, therefore, such hormonal control is found to operate independently in widely separated groups of animals. For example, growth and regeneration in *Nereis* is known to be regulated by a hormone secreted by certain cells of the brain, an example of the phenomenon of neurosecretion which will be examined later in some detail (Chap. 4). This growth hormone

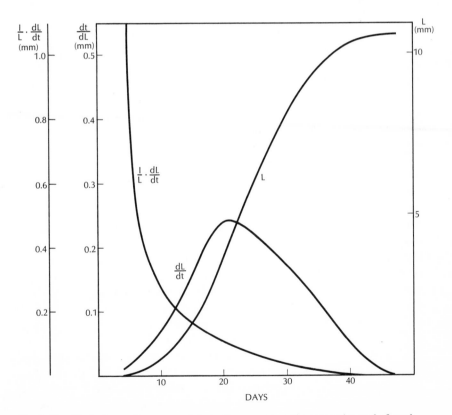

Fig. 3-12. Typical growth curve and derivatives: regenerating posterior end of earthworm. *Eisenia. L*, length of regenerate; *dL/dt*, first derivative, i.e., daily increment; *I/L · dL/dt*, specific growth rate, i.e., daily increment per unit of existing length. All are plotted as a function of time. (From A. E. Needham, *The Growth Process in Animals*, London: Sir Isaac Pitman and Sons Ltd., 1964, p. 12.)

is plentifully produced in young worms, but its production falls off in older specimens in correlation with their reduced growth rate. Further evidence for the existence of this hormone is seen in the fact that removal of the brain from young worms abolishes their capacity to regenerate; this capacity is restored, however, if the brains of other young worms are implanted into the bodies of the brainless specimens.

More complex and very much more fully documented examples are found in insects, where growth is regulated by a hormone called ecdysone, which is secreted by the prothoracic glands. This hormone is not a neurosecretion, but its output is controlled by a neurosecretory hormone that originates in the brain and is stored in the corpora cardiaca before being released into the blood stream (*Fig. 3-13*). In insects, with their firm exoskeleton, growth is rhythmic, associated with the process of molting, in which the old exoskeleton is discarded and a new one secreted to accommodate the enlarged body. It is the control of the prothoracic gland by the brain hormone that underlies this rhythmicity. For example, in the bug *Rhodnius,* subject of the classical studies of V. B. Wigglesworth, the molting process derives ultimately from the stimulus provided by the ingestion of a meal of blood. Nerve impulses from the alimentary tract pass to the brain and evoke secretion and release of the brain hormone, which in its turn evokes the release of ecdysone. Such, at least, is the principle of this complex regulatory sequence, stated here in its simplest terms.

The story is complicated, however, by the intervention of a third hormone, the juvenile hormone, which is secreted by the corpus allatum (*Fig. 3-13*). This hormone promotes larval development, so that when it is present at the molt the insect remains juvenile. At the final molt of the life cycle, the juvenile hormone is not secreted; and thus the insect metamorphoses into the adult (see Vol. IV of this series). The corpus allatum, like the prothoracic gland, is not a neurosecretory organ. However, it is innervated by the brain; and its activity is probably controlled in part by a neurosecretion from that organ, although other factors are also involved.

The growth hormone of the pituitary gland is also not a neurosecretion. Reference is made later to the organization of this gland (*Fig. 3-14*, p. 119), but for the present it is sufficient to note that the hormone arises in that part of the gland known as the pars distalis. Pituitary growth hormones are present throughout the vertebrates from fish upwards, although it is still uncertain whether or not one is present in the cyclostomes. Their presence is readily demonstrated by the results of removing the pituitary gland from young animals. This treatment commonly reduces or abolishes further growth, while normal growth rate can be restored by subsequent injection of appro-

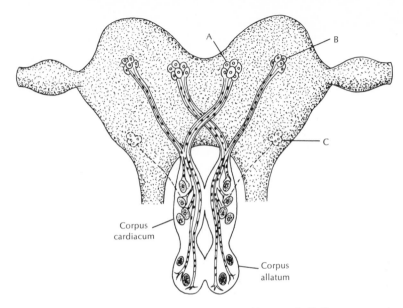

Fig. 3-13. Diagram of the neurosecretory system of insects. A, B, C, neurosecretory cell groups in brain. (From F. G. W. Knowles, in *Comparative Endocrinology,* 2, U. S. von Euler and H. Heller, ed., New York: Academic Press, 1963, p. 54.)

priate pituitary extracts. Disturbances in the output of the hormone produce startling consequences in man. A reduced output in early life results in dwarfism, whereas too great an output produces a giant with overgrown long bones and weak joints. Particularly distressing are the results of an increase in output beginning in later life, after the normal form of the skeleton has been fixed by the fusion of the epiphyses with the shafts of the long bones and by closure of the sutures. The result is the condition called acromegaly, expressed in a progressively distorted overgrowth of the skeleton.

The pituitary growth hormone has been isolated in pure form from a number of mammalian species and also from teleosts. It is now known to be a complex protein, showing specific differences in molecular constitution comparable to those found in the insulin molecule. These differences probably account for the fact that mammalian growth hormones can promote growth in teleosts, whereas the teleostean hormone is without effect in mammals. More recently, knowledge of the hormone has been greatly advanced by C. H. Li and his colleagues at Berkeley, who have succeeded in determining the complete amino acid sequence of the molecule of the human hormone. This is a remarkable achievement, for the molecule, with a molecular weight of 21,500, is very much larger than that of insulin. Its constitution is illustrated in *Fig. 3-14.* Among its characteristics are a single tryptophan at position 25, two disulfide bridges at 68–162 and 179–186, and three histidines at positions 33, 36, and 148.

Growth, as the foregoing discussion has indicated, is an adaptively regulated process, in which anabolism predominates over catabolism. More particularly, it must include the building-up of protein into the permanent structure of the animal. This is nitrogen retention, a process already seen to be influenced by insulin; it will not be surprising, therefore, to find some degree of interaction between the two hormones. This interaction was first demonstrated in experiments carried out in the 1920's by B. A. Houssay in Buenos Aires. He showed that removal of the pituitary gland from dogs made diabetic through pancreas removal reduced the intensity of the diabetic symptoms. If extracts of the pituitary gland were then injected into such animals, the severity of their diabetes was increased toward what would be expected in animals that had simply had the pancreas removed. These experiments, taken in conjunction with others, clearly showed that the pituitary gland (or, more specifically, the pars distalis) must secrete a substance that had effects opposed to those of insulin. This substance was initially referred to as the diabetogenic factor of the pituitary gland; later it was shown to be the growth hormone itself.

The growth hormone is now known to act in several ways to influence the integrated metabolic pathways already outlined (*Fig. 3-1*, p. 91). It promotes protein anabolism, as would be expected, and also increases the oxidation of fat. In addition, it depresses the rate of uptake of glucose by muscular tissues and thus restrains their utilization of carbohydrate. By reducing the metabolism of carbohydrate, the action of growth hormone tends to produce an elevation of blood-sugar level, and to this extent it is diabetogenic.

Another illustration of this diabetogenic action is seen if growth hormone is continuously injected into intact animals. This creates a large demand for insulin, with the result that the islet tissue may become exhausted. The animals are now truly diabetic, in that they suffer from a shortage of insulin. The diabetes differs, however, from that produced by the removal of the pancreas; for the excess of growth hormone will encourage nitrogen retention, whereas pancreatectomy leads to the breaking down of protein reserves with a consequent rise in nitrogen excretion. In any case, these are probably not the only effects of growth hormone upon metabolism. It is believed, for example, that the hormone exerts a stimulatory action upon both the A and B cells, and that this leads to an increase in the amount of insulin present in the pancreas. Again, a situation of great complexity exists, one that is far from being fully understood, and one that is the subject of continuing research.

Fig. 3-14. Amino acid sequence of human pituitary growth hormone. Numbers below the lines indicate the position of the amino acid residues from the amino terminus; ↑ indicates points of tryptic attack; ↓ indicates points of chymotryptic attack; ⇡ indicates points of peptic attack; ⇓ indicates points of attack by cyanogen bromide. (From Choh Hao Li, Wan-Kyng Liu, and Jonathan S. Dixon, *Journal of the American Chemical Society*, 88:9 (1966), 2050.

Two other components of the vertebrate endocrine system interact closely with insulin in the regulation of metabolic pathways. One is the adrenocortical tissue, which in mammals forms the outer substance, or cortex, of the adrenal gland. From this tissue are secreted several hormones (the adrenocortical hormones) that have diverse effects upon the metabolism of carbohydrates, water, and electrolytes, and that are essential for the maintenance of life. They will be considered further in Chapter 4. For the present, one may note that certain of these hormones (cortisol is an example) resemble growth hormone, in that they restrain the metabolism of carbohydrate by muscular tissue. Because of this action upon carbohydrates, they are called glucocorticoids. The action differs from that of growth hormone, in that it brings about a decrease in the uptake of amino acids by the cells. This difference is believed to be due to the fact that the glucocorticoids stimulate gluconeogenesis in the liver and thus promote the transfer of protein to that organ from other sites. Probably, therefore, the wastage of protein that is so characteristic of the diabetic animal is due, at least in part, to this action of the glucocorticoid hormones.

The second component acting in close association with insulin is the adrenal medulla. This tissue, which forms the central part of the adrenal gland of mammals, is functionally quite distinct from the adrenocortical tissue that surrounds it and, indeed, is spatially separated from it in many fish. It secretes two hormones, adrenaline and noradrenaline, often called the catechol hormones, because their structure is based upon the catechol grouping *(Fig. 3-15).* These can be said in a general way to exert actions that tend to mobilize the resources of the body, when heavy demands are being made upon them (cf. 150). For example, both hormones evoke an increase in blood pressure, while adrenaline, in particular, increases the output of the heart and stimulates glycogenolysis in the liver, so that there is a rise in blood-sugar level. In this last respect the action of adrenaline resembles that of glucagon, in that it is brought about through an increase of phosphorylase activity in the liver. As a result of it, there is a fall in liver glycogen. Further, there is an increased output of lactic acid from the muscles, for adrenaline makes another contribution to the mobilization of the animal's activity by encouraging glycolysis in the muscle cells.

The whole complex of events may be thought of as an emergency response, brought about by a temporary distortion of carbohydrate metabolism. For restoration of normal conditions and for maintenance of metabolic homeostasis, the animal must rely upon the other controlling mechanisms already mentioned. Nevertheless, the actions of the adrenal medulla at times of emergency serve to emphasize the total dependence of the vertebrate upon the regulation of the metabolic pathways that transfer energy into the tissues from the outside world. It is not surprising that the complexity of these controlling mechanisms, which are central to the very survival of vertebrate life in its hostile environment, should still baffle scientists in many ways.

There are still other hormones with important effects upon growth and metabolism that have not yet been mentioned. Among them are the two hormones secreted by the thyroid gland—thyroxine and triiodothyronine. The latter has been discovered only comparatively recently, so more is known about thyroxine. In principle, however, their effects are similar, although not necessarily identical. Absence of the thyroid gland, or underproduction of its hormones, result in impaired growth in mammals. A well-known illustration of this is the human cretin. Cretins, unless treated with thyroid extract, remain dwarfs, differing from pituitary dwarfs in the impaired development of the brain.

There is, however, a complication in interpreting the significance of the growth-promoting effect of the thyroid gland; this arises from the stimulating influence that its hormones exert upon the basal metabolic rate in the higher vertebrates. Oxygen consumption shows a marked decline after removal of the gland from experimental mammals, and it is low in cretins. It is low also in patients suffering from myxedema, which is a condition resembling premature senility, resulting from the development of thyroid deficiency in adults. In all such situations and, indeed, in normal mammals also, the injection of thyroid hormones brings about prompt elevation of metabolic rate. Thus there is an obvious possibility that the influence of the thyroid gland on growth may be secondary to its influence upon metabolism; thus the stunted growth of the cretin, for example, may be a consequence of lower metabolic rate. No doubt the two effects are, indeed, closely linked, but it is now accepted that the thyroid hormones do have specific effects upon growth processes.

One line of evidence supporting this conclusion emerges from studies of fish. The thyroid hormones do not increase basal metabo-

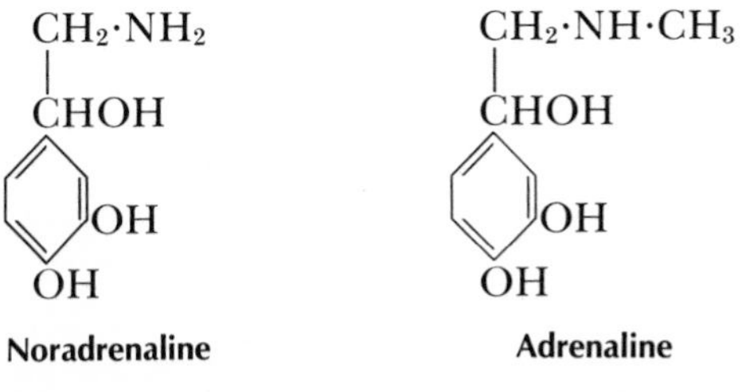

$$CH_2 \cdot NH_2 \qquad\qquad CH_2 \cdot NH \cdot CH_3$$
$$|\qquad\qquad\qquad\qquad |$$
$$CHOH \qquad\qquad\qquad CHOH$$

OH · · · OH

OH · · · OH

Noradrenaline · · · **Adrenaline**

Fig. 3-15. The catechol hormones, noradrenaline and adrenaline (norepinephrin and epinephrin).

lism in these animals as they do in mammals, a difference seen in Chapter 5 to be related to the difference in the temperature relationships of the two groups. But the growth of teleost fish is certainly increased if the animals are treated with thyroid hormones, while destruction of the thyroid gland slows down their growth and produces a condition that has been described as closely resembling that found in human cretins. Here, therefore, growth effects are clearly being evoked in the absence of any significant change in basal metabolic rate.

No less convincing is evidence from quite a different source, obtained from studies of the intracellular enzyme systems of the liver of rats. J. R. Tata has found in the course of these studies that injection of thyroxine over a period of three weeks increases the basal metabolic rate of the whole animal by 45–75 per cent, as would be expected; but he was able to define the action of the hormone more precisely by studying the enzyme activities in homogenates of liver tissue. He concluded that the hormone had a particularly marked stimulatory effect upon the production of enzymes concerned with the metabolic pathways of growth and maturation. In this instance, and in contrast to current views of the mode of action of insulin upon cell membranes, the hormone is presumably operating within the cell. Yet the situation may not be so very different in principle, although the exact mode of action of the hormone is unknown.

Tata noted that the enzymes that are particularly affected by thyroxine are those believed to be bound to structural elements within the cell, such as the mitochondria. This supports one view of the mode of action of the thyroid hormones, which supposes that they become incorporated into structural membranes and thereby alter their permeability. Alternatively, they might influence the activity of other molecules that normally function as part of the structures concerned. It is commonly thought that the integrated action of intracellular metabolic pathways depends upon the orderly arrangement of enzymes and their associated molecules within structural membranes. If this is so, profound effects might well be produced by hormonal molecules that were able to act upon these organized structures.

This foregoing discussion does not exhaust the list of hormones that are involved in one way or another in metabolic regulation. One could add parathormone, secreted by the parathyroid gland and concerned with the regulation of calcium metabolism. And, of course, there are the sex hormones, the androgens and estrogens secreted by the testes and ovaries respectively. These specifically stimulate the growth of parts of the reproductive system of the appropriate sex, so that in this respect they are clearly growth hormones. Their effects, however, range beyond these primary targets. Thus the androgens seem to promote the growth of the body in general and, in correlation with this, to favor nitrogen retention. Estrogens are not so obviously growth-promoting; in fact, they have a repressing action upon the growth of the skeleton.

Space does not permit pursuing these matters further. As this discussion has proceeded, it has grown further and further away from the starting point, which was the influence of insulin upon carbohydrate metabolism. This is a salutary lesson, illustrating the impossibility of applying arbitrary limits to biological phenomena. This is particularly so, when one is dealing with the control of metabolism; for metabolism is central to the very survival of life in its hostile environment, and one must expect that in the most highly evolved animals the regulating mechanisms will be of the utmost complexity.

From this point of view, one can see that the importance attached to insulin is to some extent artificial, a product of historical accident and of its exceptional importance in medical practice. No doubt it is, of all the vertebrate hormones, the one that is most closely and completely concerned with metabolic activity, yet it no longer holds quite its old primacy. It is now seen as part of a hormonal complex, operating through a series of checks and balances to contribute to the homeostasis of the body. It may be well to emphasize, however, that scientists can speak with assurance of the situation only as it is found in mammals. The hormones to which the text has referred are mostly present throughout the vertebrates, from the cyclostomes upwards (parathormone and glucagon—assuming that the latter is a hormone—are two exceptions); but one cannot assume that in the lower forms their functions follow the mammalian pattern. Indeed, it would be surprising if this were so.

Homeostasis, so exquisitely organized in birds and mammals, must be the end result of a long evolutionary history, during which natural selection has acted to improve the precision of the nervous and endocrine regulation upon which it depends. It may well be, then, that in lower vertebrates the hormones support physiological activities without demonstrating the precision exercised in the higher forms. The reader will see something of the way in which homeostatic mechanisms have evolved in Chapters 5 and 6, which examine some of the problems of temperature regulation in the vertebrates. At present, unfortunately, too little of the regulation of metabolism in lower vertebrates is known to permit useful comment on the history of this aspect of adaptive mechanisms. One can, however, avoid the trap of approaching the study of lower forms with mammalian preconceptions. Instead, one must expect to find in lower forms their own characteristic patterns of adaptive organization, different from those of mammals, perhaps, but fully adequate to ensure survival in the normal circumstances of their lives.

1. Claude Bernard, *An Introduction to the Study of Experimental Medicine* (New York: Dover Publications, Inc., 1957), pp. 181–182, 164, 165–167.

2. W. B. Cannon, *The Wisdom of the Body* (New York: W. W. Norton & Co., Inc., 1963), pp. 20, 23–24.

3. B. A. Houssay, "The Discovery of Pancreatic Diabetes. The Role of Oscar Minkowski," *Diabetes*, 1 (1952), 113–114.

4. F. Banting and C. H. Best, "The Internal Secretion of the Pancreas," *Journal of Laboratory and Clinical Medicine*, 7 (1922), 69.

5. F. G. Young, "Insulin and Diabetes," *British Medical Bulletin*, 16 (1960), 176–177.

6. F. Sanger, "Chemistry of Insulin," *British Medical Bulletin*, 16 (1960), 187.

7. G. R. deBeer, *Growth* (London: Edward Arnold, Ltd., 1924), p. 1.

8. J. Z. Young, *The Life of Vertebrates* (Oxford: The Clarendon Press, 1950), p. 6.

9. P. B. Medawar, in *Essays on Growth and Form*, ed. W. E. LeGros Clark and P. B. Medawar (Oxford: The Clarendon Press, 1945), p. 166.

10. J. B. S. Haldane, *Possible Worlds* (London: Chatto and Windus, Ltd., 1932), p. 187. By permission of the publishers, Chatto and Windus, Ltd., London, and Harper & Row, Publishers, New York.

CHAPTER 4   Water
and Ions

■ THE DEPENDENCE OF LIFE UPON WATER

Maintenance of animal life depends not only upon oxygen and
energy-rich food, but also upon a supply of water; for this is the
medium in which the chemical reactions of metabolism take place.
Water constitutes some 70 per cent of the total weight in most animals and in some (jelly-fish, for example) may reach as high a proportion as 95 per cent. This dependence upon water merits closer
analysis, for it is one of the most striking aspects of the way in which
living organisms are adapted to the physical and chemical properties
of the environment in which they must live. One cannot do better in
this connection than recall the classical analysis of L. J. Henderson.
He developed the argument that the fitness of water, carbonic acid,
hydrogen, and oxygen made up a unique complex of properties, in
the absence of which life could never have been established on this
earth. Much of his discussion of water was devoted to its thermal
properties, which will be considered in the next chapter; but he recognized that these were not the only considerations. He emphasized
also the significance of water's other physical properties, including
the solvent and ionizing powers with which this chapter is concerned.

> As a solvent there is literally nothing to compare with water. In truth
> its qualifications are on this point so unique and obvious that nobody
> seems to have taken the trouble to gather together the evidence, and,
> accordingly, beyond the bare assertion, a brief statement of the facts

is not easy. In the first place the solubility in water of acids, bases, and salts, the most familiar classes of inorganic substances, is almost universal. Relatively few of these bodies are highly soluble; very many are exceedingly soluble in water. Apart from their electrolytic dissociation and hydrolysis, which will be later discussed, the chemical changes wrought upon such dissolved substances in solution are commonly very unimportant. For chemical inertness, depending upon great stability, is a most significant characteristic of water, and undoubtedly a highly advantageous one as well. . . .

It has been calculated by Murray that the total yearly run off of all the rivers of the earth is about 6500 cubic miles, carrying nearly 5,000,000,000 tons of dissolved mineral matter and prodigious quantities of sediment. . . .

It is, of course, almost exclusively to these constant accessions that the ocean owes its salinity, which in the course of time has reached well-nigh inconceivable magnitude. The common salt alone in the oceans of all the earth amounts to not less than 35,000,000,000,000,000 tons. Quite as significant of the solvent power of water is the variety of elements whose presence in sea water can be demonstrated, thus proving that the total store of them is in any case enormous. They include hydrogen, oxygen, nitrogen, carbon, chlorine, sodium, magnesium, sulphur, phosphorus, which are easily demonstrated; further, arsenic, caesium, gold, lithium, rubidium, barium, lead, boron, fluorine, iron, iodine, bromine, potassium, cobalt, copper, manganese, nickel, silver, silicon, zinc, aluminium, calcium, and strontium.

Equally striking is the evidence in regard to the first stages of this geological process. Under the action of water, aided, to be sure, in many cases by dissolved carbonic acid, every species of rock suffers slow destruction. All substances yield *in situ* to the solvent work of water, and the dissolved parts may all be found in the great final reservoir, the ocean. It has been proved that nearly every one of the substances which are thus set in motion upon the face of the earth are placed under contribution by life, for biochemical analysis reveals them as constituents of living organisms, absorbed either on their way down from the mountain tops to the ocean or by the marine flora and fauna. . . .

If, therefore, aqueous solutions are, apparently of necessity, the very basis of the life processes, the state of substances when in this condition, and also when in contact with water, is of vital importance. . . .

There can be no doubt that ionization plays a great part in determining the characteristics of solutions of acids, bases, and salts, and in bringing about the reactions which occur among them, and between them and other substances. . . . and it is certain that the extent and variety of ionization in water far surpass what is possible in any other solvent. One reason for this is most simple. The ionizing substances are so very much more often soluble in water than in any other solvent, and when soluble are in general so much more highly soluble, that the opportunity for ionization in water is quite unparalleled.

Further, ionization in solution unquestionably depends upon the dielectric constant of the solvent, in accordance with the principle first stated by Nernst that the greater the dielectric capacity of the solvent, the greater is the degree of electrolytic dissociation of substances dissolved in it, when the conditions are otherwise the same. This is the case because the tendency of the electrically charged ions to reunite and form electrically neutral molecules must be less the greater the dielectric constant of the solvent. Now the dielectric constant of water is nearly the highest at present known, and therefore ionization in water is on that account also more extensive than in almost any other solvent.[1]

For the reasons given by Henderson and other reasons that will be examined later, the conservation and regulation of the water content of the body is a fundamental requirement of physiological organization. This requirement is met partly by behavioral adaptations, an example of which is seen in the arthropod, *Peripatus*. In some respects, *Peripatus* is the most primitive member of its group. Its cuticle, unlike that of most other arthropods, is still soft and permeable, so that water is readily lost through it by evaporation. Further loss takes place through the tracheal system, which opens at stigmata that lack closing mechanisms of the type found in many insects. The consequent danger of desiccation is overcome in *Peripatus* by a behavior pattern that takes the animal into damp microhabitats, such as concealed cavities within logs, where it is safe from water loss. Manton's analysis shows this to be an instructive example of economy in adaptation; for by behaving in this way, the animal is taking positive advantage of the primitive form of its cuticle. The flexibility of this outer layer gives the body a capacity for deformation that enables it to penetrate through cracks that would not admit predators with more rigid body surfaces. It is thus safe from pursuit as well as from desiccation. Ironically, however, this mode of escape from desiccation creates the danger of encountering too much water as a result of the flooding of the confined spaces of these sheltered habitats. Such a danger is overcome in *Peripatus*, as in many other small arthropods, by the development over the body of a waxy layer that repels water. This hydrofuge property, as it is called, can protect the animal from drowning by leaving the body surface free to continue respiratory exchange.

Water loss may also be reduced by biochemical adaptations, and this again is illustrated by *Peripatus*. Aquatic animals commonly excrete their waste nitrogen in the form of ammonia. This substance is poisonous; but, given abundant water in the environment, it can be readily washed away. *Peripatus*, which is obviously unable to do this, excretes most of its, nitrogen as uric acid, which is passed out of the digestive epithelium into the lumen of the intestine and expelled at regular intervals through the anus. Uricotely, as this form of excretion is called, is also found in many other terrestrial animals that need to conserve water; these include insects and certain gastropod mollusks among the invertebrates, and birds and certain reptiles among the vertebrates.

The advantage of uric acid in this connection is that it is relatively insoluble, so that little water need be used in expelling it from the body. Thus at first it seems surprising that mammals, which also need to economize in the use of water, do not practice uricotely. Instead, they excrete their nitrogen largely as urea, a process called ureotely. This is probably associated with their viviparous mode of development; the fetus excretes its nitrogen as urea into the maternal blood stream, and, once established, this pattern of excretion persists in the adult. This is because urea, unlike ammonia, can be safely excreted in solution, and, as will be pointed out later, mammals are well able to produce a relatively concentrated urine.

These patterns of nitrogen excretion are examples of analogy in physiological mechanisms. The uricotely of vertebrates has certainly evolved independently of that of *Peripatus*. Nor is uricotely the only possible solution of the problem. Spiders, for example, excrete their nitrogenous wastes largely as guanine, obtaining from this an advantage similar to that obtained by other terrestrial arthropods from the excretion of uric acid. Such adaptations provide continuous resistance to the normal range of hazards encountered by the animals concerned. Often, however, they are supplemented by regulating devices that respond to the fluctuations of the environment. Just as the activities of the mammalian alimentary tract, for example, are continuously monitored and regulated in accordance with the intake and passage of food material, so the appropriate organ systems can be brought into adaptive relationship with the varying needs of the body for water. This is a field of activity in which endocrine control is particularly well suited. We know it to operate in vertebrates, and there is evidence that analogous processes operate in arthropods; but the former group is better understood at the present time, and, therefore, examples will be selected from it.

■ ANIMALS AS "SEA BEASTS"

Regulation of body water cannot be considered in isolation from the solutes that are present in water. These solutes, which include chlorides, sulfates, phosphates and carbonates of sodium, potassium, calcium, and magnesium, confer upon the body fluids a level of osmotic pressure that is characteristic of particular groups but that is by no means constant throughout the animal kingdom. Many marine invertebrates do not regulate their internal osmotic pressure;

this remains similar to that of the water surrounding them, rising and falling in conformity with variations in the salt content of the latter. Such animals (the crab *Maia squinado, Fig. 4-1*, is an example) are said to be in osmotic equilibrium with the sea, or to be isosmotic with it. Because they lack the power of osmo-regulation, they are termed osmo-conformers. Osmotic equilibrium is a consequence of their being open systems, in which part, at least, of the body surface is permeable and, therefore, allows respiratory exchange to take place.

The survival of osmo-conformers in sea waters of different salinities is a function of the ability of their body tissues to continue operating in the resultant internal medium. In practice, this ability is strictly limited, for changes in osmotic pressure of the body fluids bring about disturbing alterations in the internal osmotic pressure of the cells that are bathed by these fluids. Osmo-conformers, therefore, are restricted to a narrow range of salinity and are said, in consequence, to be stenohaline.

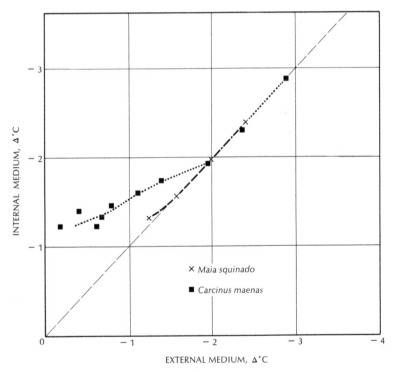

× Maia squinado

■ Carcinus maenas

Fig. 4-1. Osmotic pressures (expressed as depressions of freezing points) of the blood of the crabs *Maia squinado* and *Carcinus maenas* as a function of the external medium. (From W. T. W. Potts and G. Perry, *Osmotic and Ionic Regulation in Animals.* Oxford: Pergamon Press Limited, 1964; also from M. Duval, *Annales de l'Institut Océanographique,* tome II, fasc. 3 (1925). 232-407.)

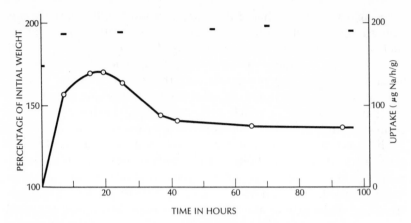

Fig. 4-2.   Uptake of sodium per hour (per gram wet weight) by *Nereis diversicolor* during the period of weight regulation when transferred from sea water of 35‰ salinity to that of 9‰ salinity. Continuous line indicates weight regulation, and dashes indicate sodium uptake. (From V. Fretter, *Journal of the Marine Biological Association, U. K.*, Council of the Marine Biological Association of the U. K., 34 (1955), 157.)

Some marine invertebrates, notably those that are adapted for estuarine conditions, can withstand a wider range of salinity; they are osmo-regulators and are said to be euryhaline. One example is the brackish-water shore crab, *Carcinus maenas. Figure 4-1* shows that this animal, in contrast to *Maia*, can maintain the concentration of its blood above that of the medium, as the osmotic pressure of the latter falls. However, for reasons that cannot be discussed here, there are limiting factors that lead to some fall in the blood concentration. Osmo-regulatory capacity is shown by the fact that this fall occurs more slowly than the fall in concentration of the medium.

Another example of an osmo-regulator is the polychaete worm *Nereis diversicolor*. In normal sea water this animal is in isosmotic equilibrium. If it is transferred to dilute sea water, it first gains weight as a result of osmotic uptake of water (*Fig. 4-2*). It can be shown by direct chemical determination that during this phase it loses salt, so that there is a fall in its internal osmotic pressure. This phase is followed by a phase of accommodation, during which there is a loss of water and a consequent reduction in weight. Finally, and provided that the medium is not too dilute, the worm becomes fully adapted at a new level of equilibrium. It is now hypertonic (that is, its internal osmotic pressure is now greater than the external), while its water balance is modified so that its weight is higher than its starting weight, although lower than the maximum previously attained (*Fig. 4-2*). This new equilibrium can be maintained indefinitely, as a result of the worm's active regulation of its water and salt content.

During the maintenance of equilibrium, there is no direct chemical evidence of salt flux either into or out of the animal. Such evidence, or lack of it, however, is often misleading. An appearance of static equilibrium may, in fact, be a net result of both inward and outward fluxes. As seen in considering ionic fluxes in the frog's skin, the use of radioactive isotopes enables scientists to obtain a more complete picture of such a situation. By adding these isotopes to the surrounding medium in small (tracer) doses and measuring the subsequent changes in radioactivity of the worm and of the medium, it is possible to follow molecular and ionic movements into and out of the body.

This technique has clearly shown that chloride and sodium ions do indeed pass into the body of *Nereis diversicolor,* partly as a result of passive exchange of ions with the medium and partly because of active uptake. In normal sea water (salinity 35%oo) the influx of Na^{24} may amount to 240–275 μg/hr/g wet weight (*Fig. 4-3*). This, according to V. Fretter's analysis, is a result of passive exchange. At small dilutions (e.g., 33.5%oo) the influx is proportional to the degree of dilution, but in more dilute sea water the influx is higher than would be expected if the worm was behaving as a simple osmometer. For example, if the external salinity is reduced by one half, the uptake of accommodating worms is 160 μg, while at a salinity of 9%oo it actually rises to 180 μg. These values remain much the same after the animals have equilibrated. The conclusion is that active uptake is taking place continuously against the concentration (electrochemical) gradient; this is why the influx does not fall in proportion to the fall in salinity. Loss of salt is inevitable from an open and permeable system; but the worm remains in net chemical equilibrium with the external medium, because this loss is being balanced by the active

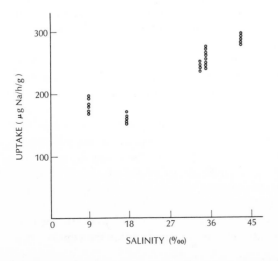

Fig. 4-3. Rate of uptake of sodium by *Nereis diversicolor* in sea water of different salinities, expressed as micrograms of sodium per hour, per gram wet weight. (From V. Fretter, *Journal of the Marine Biological Association, U. K.,* Council of the Marine Biological Association of the U. K., 34 (1955), 154.)

TABLE 4-1

Analysis of Plasma of Nephrops norvegicus
(Norwegian lobster)[a]

	Mg/g Water						Mg/ml	
	Na	K	Ca	Mg	Cl	SO₄	Protein	H₂O
Original (freshly drawn) plasma	11.90	0.296	0.555	0.216	18.40	1.780	33	961
Plasma after dialysis	10.54	0.384	0.448	1.297	18.59	2.572	33	961
Sea water	10.43	0.378	0.399	1.258	18.80	2.624	–	983

[a] From J. D. Robertson, *Journal of Experimental Biology,* 26 (1949), 190.

uptake. In regard to the site of the uptake, it has been shown that no change in flux results if the anus is closed by ligature; it would thus seem that the exchange must be taking place through the body surface and not through the intestine. It is known that in arthropods the excretory organs play an important part in similar exchanges; and one may assume, although it is not known, that the nephridia play a part in *Nereis,* for they open at the surface at segmental nephridiopores.

The situation in *Nereis diversicolor,* although stated in general terms only, will be worth bearing in mind, for it provides a model which is helpful in understanding the osmotic relationships of vertebrates. However, just as it is impossible to discuss water regulation without taking osmotic pressure into consideration, so discussion of osmotic pressure demands considerations of the ionic composition of the body fluids. Throughout the animal kingdom this composition resembles in a remarkable way the ionic composition of sea water. This, indeed, is one of the main reasons for the common supposition that life first arose in the sea. There are other reasons, also, for believing this to be so. For example, almost every major group of the animal kingdom has marine representatives; and it is usual to find that within any one group it is the marine forms that are the more primitive, while the fresh-water and terrestrial forms are the more specialized. One may conclude that the sea provides a medium that is exceptionally favorable for life, while fresh water and dry land present obstacles that can only be surmounted by the development of special adaptations. It is from this point of view that the composition of body fluids takes on a particular significance, for it suggests that life is adapted to the detailed chemical composition of the medium in which it originates.

While this view is, in principle, sound, it needs very careful evaluation in order to relate it satisfactorily to present-day concepts of the regulation of the composition of body fluids. One complicating factor is that the ionic composition of these fluids, even in isosmotic marine invertebrates, is by no means precisely the same as that of the sea. There are two main reasons for this. First, body fluids, unlike sea water, commonly contain considerable amounts of proteins which contribute to the total osmotic pressure. And second, these proteins are indiffusible and tend to form complexes with calcium, so that the ionic composition of body fluids is bound to differ in detail from that of sea water, even if they are in passive equilibrium with it. This, however, cannot fully account for the observed differences in ionic composition.

Evidence that another factor is involved is found in experiments in which the ionic composition of a sample of freshly drawn body fluid from a particular species is compared with another sample that has first been placed within a collodion sac and dialyzed against sea water. After dialysis, the fluid within the sac will be in passive ionic equilibrium with the sea water surrounding it. If the composition of the freshly drawn fluid is identical with that of the dialyzed sample, it follows that the animal is maintaining its body fluid in passive equilibrium with the sea water. If, however, there are differences between the samples, then it follows that the animal must be maintaining these differences by some active process of its own. The data of Table 4-1 show that *Nephrops* is certainly involved in an active process of maintaining body fluids, for there are marked differences between the freshly drawn plasma and the plasma after dialysis.

The results of a number of such analyses are given in a different form in Table 4-2. They show that in none of the species examined is the ionic composition of the freshly drawn fluid identical with that of the dialyzed fluid. In many species the differences are slight, but they are none the less significant, notably the tendency for the potas-

TABLE 4-2

Ionic Regulation in Some Marine Invertebrates[a]*

	Na	K	Ca	Mg	Cl	SO₄
Aurelia aurita	99	106	96	97	104	47
Arenicola marina	100	104	100	100	100	92
Maia squinado	100	125	122	81	102	66
Nephrops norvegicus	113	77	124	17	99	69
Sepia officinalis	93	205	91	98	105	22

[a] From J. D. Robertson, in *Recent Advances in Invertebrate Physiology*, ed. B. T. Sheer, (Eugene, Oregon: University of Oregon Press, 1957), 230.

* Concentration in plasma or coelomic fluid as per cent of concentration in body fluid dialyzed against sea water.

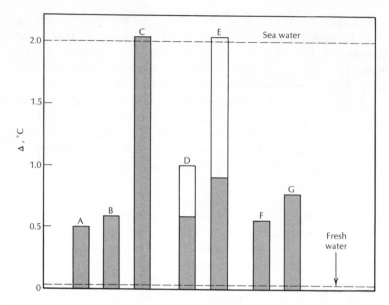

Fig. 4-4. Osmotic pressures (expressed as depressions of freezing point) of bloods of cyclostomes and fishes compared with those of fresh and sea waters. *A.* lamprey in fresh water; *B.* lamprey in sea water; *C.* hagfish; *D.* fresh water elasmobranch; *E.* marine elasmobranch; *F.* fresh water teleost; *G.* marine teleost. Base line sections of bars represent salts; top sections represent urea. (Adapted from E. Baldwin and V. S. Black, in *The Physiology of Fishes*, M. Brown, ed., New York: Academic Press, 1957, p. 187.)

sium concentration in the body fluid to be higher than the passive equilibrium value. In the highly specialized decapod crustaceans, however, and in *Sepia,* the differences are considerable and may involve every ion. Sodium and chloride are the least affected, presumably because they form such a large proportion of the total ions present. A high sodium value (as in *Nephrops*) apparently balances a low magnesium value and thus maintains a balance in the osmotic pressure and in the distribution of cations. Similarly, a high chloride value may balance a low sulfate value, as in *Sepia.* These differences exemplify the phenomenon of ionic regulation, which may be defined, following J. D. Robertson, as the maintenance in a body fluid of concentrations of ions differing from those of a passive equilibrium with the external medium.

Ionic regulation in vertebrates calls for particular notice, because it introduces a third reason why there may be differences between the body fluids and the sea. Variation in ionic ratios among vertebrates as a whole is actually less than in invertebrates, and less even than in the single class of insects. But the osmotic pressure of vertebrate blood (*Fig. 4-4*) is markedly lower than that of sea water, even in groups that live in the sea (with two exceptions, the myxinoid cyclostomes and the elasmobranchs, to be discussed below). Moreover, all vertebrates, regardless of their habitat, have lower concentrations of magnesium, potassium, and sulfate in their plasma than do marine invertebrates.

An explanation of these facts, logical, if to some extent hypothetical, can be derived from a consideration of the probable course of vertebrate evolution. It appears almost certain that vertebrates arose from marine filter-feeding ancestors, descendants of which are represented today by the protochordate ascidians and amphioxus. The evidence for this and the unraveling of the course of the transition raises difficult issues that cannot be considered here; but at least there is good geological evidence that the first vertebrates arose in the sea, probably in inshore waters. It would be expected, from what is known of the body fluids of marine invertebrates, that at one stage the body fluids of the earliest vertebrates must have been isosmotic with the sea. Remarkably enough, this is actually the condition today in the hagfish (*Fig. 4-4*); and it seems very likely that these myxinoid cyclostomes, alone among living vertebrates, preserve that ancient and primitive condition.

At an early stage vertebrates must have entered fresh water by penetrating into estuaries and moving on into rivers. It is reasonable to assume that their subsequent adaptation to fresh-water life would have involved a reduction in the osmotic pressure of their body fluids, for the text has pointed out an analogous (although temporary) lowering of osmotic pressure in *Nereis diversicolor*, while a similar condition is characteristic of the body fluids of estuarine and fresh-water crustaceans. Thus one can account for the fact that the osmotic pressure of the body fluids of vertebrates is substantially below that of the sea (*Fig. 4-4*) despite their ultimate marine origin. (Hagfish are exceptions to this, and marine elasmobranchs for reasons that will appear later.) Nevertheless, that origin is still reflected in the general balance of ions in the body fluids of all the higher vertebrates, even of those that have become fully terrestrial. It is sufficiently reminiscent of the composition of sea water to justify J. B. S. Haldane's description of man as being a "sea beast" (Table 4-3).

The type of body fluid thus established in vertebrates imposes problems of regulation which are readily apparent in fish. For fresh-water teleosts (*Fig. 4-5*) it results in an osmotic influx of water, so that in a sense these animals are in continuous danger of drowning. They solve the problem by removing the excess water through the kidney as a dilute urine which is hypotonic to the body fluids. Discharge of copious excretion necessarily involves a loss of the salt dissolved in it, but this is compensated for by an active uptake of sodium through the gills, with chlorine passively following the sodium. This adapta-

TABLE 4-3

*Concentrations of Ions (in mM/1) in Blood
of Vertebrates, Compared with Sea Water*[a]

	Na	K	Ca	Mg	Cl	SO₄
Sea water	459	9.78	10.05	52.5	538	26.55
Myxine (hagfish)	558	9.6	6.25	19.4	576	6.6
Rhinobatus	143	12.8	7.3	2	143.6	
Lophuis (angler fish)	185–200	5	6	5	153	
Man	145	5.1	2.5	1.2	103	2.5

[a] Data from C. L. Prosser and F. A. Brown, Jr., *Comparative Animal Physiology*, 2nd ed. (London: W. B. Saunders Co., 1961), pp. 60-61.

tion is not, of course, peculiar to vertebrates. It has been pointed out that active uptake occurs in *Nereis diversicolor* when it is adjusted to living in dilute sea water; under similar conditions it occurs also in *Carcinus*, as well as in fresh-water crayfish, to name only two other examples.

Modern fresh-water teleosts are probably direct descendants of early fresh-water bony fish. Some of the latter, however, later returned to the sea, where they encountered a different osmotic problem. The marine teleosts (*Fig. 4-6*) of today retain body fluids similar to those of their fresh-water relatives. Their internal osmotic pressure is, therefore, below that of the external medium, so that there is an osmotic efflux of water. This is compensated for by the drinking of sea water, which is absorbed, with its contained monovalent ions,

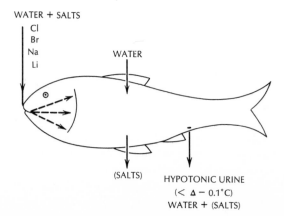

Fig. 4-5. Osmotic regulation in fresh water teleost fishes. (Adapted from E. Baldwin and V. S. Black, in *The Physiology of Fishes*, Vol. I, M. Brown, ed., New York: Academic Press, 1957, p. 178.)

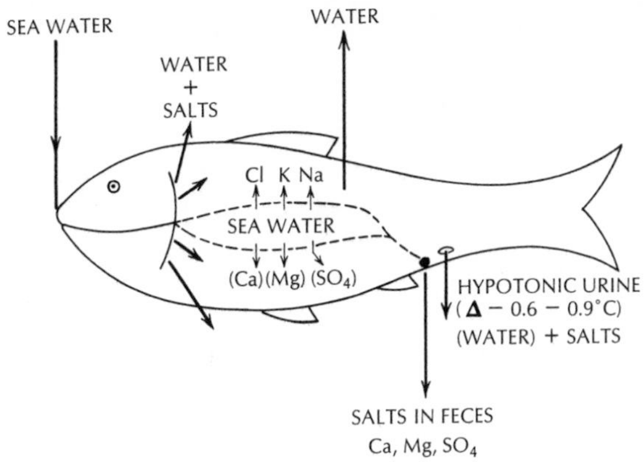

Fig. 4-6. Osmotic regulation in marine teleost fishes. (Adapted from E. Baldwin and V. S. Black, in *The Physiology of Fishes,* Vol. I, M. Brown, ed., New York: Academic Press, 1957, p. 185.)

from the intestine. The resultant excess of ions is lost through the gills, chloride being passed out actively with sodium passively accompanying it. Most of the divalent ions remain in the intestinal lumen and are lost in the faeces; such small amounts as may be absorbed are excreted in the urine. Migratory teleosts like the euryhaline salmon and eel, which pass from fresh water to the sea or vice versa, use the method of osmoregulation appropriate to the medium in which they are existing at any particular phase; the migratory lamprey follows the same pattern, which in this respect resembles the teleost rather than the hagfish.

The situation in elasmobranchs is quite different. Their history has been independent of that of the teleosts, and they are now almost exclusively a marine group. The ionic composition of their body fluids (e.g., *Rhinobatus,* Table 4-3) is in principle like that of teleosts, but they raise their internal osmotic pressure to that of the sea by accumulating urea in their blood (*Fig. 4-4*). In this way they avoid the osmotic stress encountered by the marine teleosts. Few elasmobranchs enter fresh water and then not very far. Those that do so have a lower content of urea than do their marine relatives; but this substance is not entirely lost, so that they are at some disadvantage as compared with fresh-water teleosts. They are committed, as a group, to marine conditions in a way that teleosts are certainly not.

The suggested course of events outlined above, with which few students of the subject would now disagree in principle, presupposes that the earliest vertebrates must have been able to regulate the composition of their body fluids. This assumption has become more easily acceptable by the knowledge that ionic regulation is widespread throughout the animal kingdom: such regulation exists even in the most primitive of invertebrates and probably also in the protozoa. It may truly be said that in this sense the adaptation of animals to marine conditions was a preadaptation to fresh-water life. Had animals not possessed the capacity for ionic regulation and limited osmotic regulation, as exemplified in *Nereis diversicolor*, it is difficult indeed to see how any of them could ever have entered into fresh-water habitats or have come to exploit the immense potentialities of terrestrial life. It is not surprising that man himself is a "sea beast"; he could not possibly be anything else. The following section examines how man's physiological mechanisms deal with this situation.

■ THE REGULATION OF BODY WATER IN MAMMALS

It is an impressive fact that man and other mammals can maintain a constant composition of body fluids in an environment in which there are continuous fluctuations in the availability of water. This constancy, a major feature of mammalian homeostasis, is largely under the control of two entirely separate endocrine secretions. One of these is released from, although not actually secreted by, the pituitary gland, while the other is secreted by the cortex of the adrenal gland. The contribution of the pituitary gland will be considered first.

The pituitary gland (*Fig. 4-7A*) consists of two components, the adenohypophysis (comprising the pars tuberalis, pars distalis, and pars intermedia) and the neurohypophysis (comprising, in higher vertebrates, the median eminence, the infundibular stalk, and the infundibular process or neural lobe).* These two components are separate in their embryological origin, but they become closely associated at an early stage of development. Such association, which reflects a close functional interrelationship of the two, must be accounted a fundamental feature of vertebrate organization, for it is already clearly established in the cyclostomes.

The adenohypophysis, which develops from the embryonic buccal cavity as an outgrowth called Rathke's pouch, consists of a number of distinct types of secretory cell responsible for the production of at least seven hormones. It will be mentioned in more detail later in this chapter. The immediate concern of this section is with the neurohypophysis. The peculiar part played by this component in the vertebrate endocrine system is a result of its development as a downgrowth (the infundibulum) of the floor of the diencephalon, which is the posterior part of the forebrain. The diencephalon plays a major part in the regulatory mechanisms of vertebrates. One reason for this is that its floor and the lower parts of its lateral wall constitute the region called the hypothalamus (*Fig. 4-8*), which earlier was described as the cerebral center of the parasympathetic and sympa-

---

* The pars intermedia and the neural lobe constitute together the posterior lobe, but this term is now passing out of use as the two regions are functionally distinct from each other.

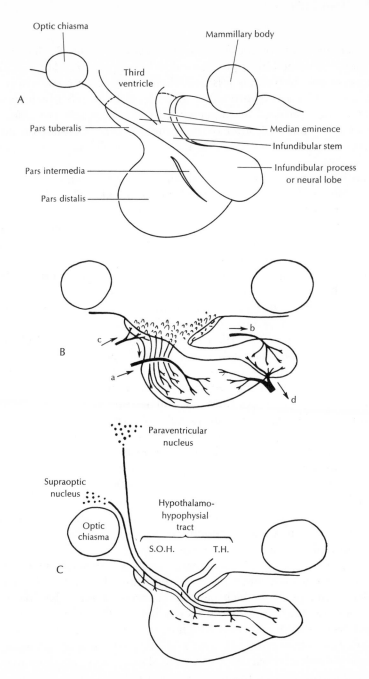

Fig. 4-7. Diagrams to show *A*, the nomenclature, *B*, the blood supply, and *C*, the inner-vation of the mammalian pituitary gland. *S.O.H.* supraopticohypophyseal tract; *T.H.* tubero-hypophyseal tract; *a.* vessel from internal carotid artery to pars distalis; *b.* vessel from internal carotid to neural lobe; *c.* vessels from internal carotid artery to primary plexus from which portal vessels drain down into the pars distalis; *d.* venous drainage into surrounding venous sinuses. (From G. W. Harris, *Neural Control of the Pituitary Gland.* London: E. J. Arnold & Son, Ltd., 1955, pp. 7, 17, 15.)

thetic components of the autonomic nervous system. Evidence for this can be obtained by applying localized electrical stimulation to the hypothalamus. In this way it is possible to bring about responses such as a rise in blood pressure and a dilation of the pupils which would normally be produced by the action of the sympathetic component. Similar stimulation of other parts of the diencephalon may produce effects normally associated with the action of the parasympathetic component.

Another significant fact, to be discussed later in Chapter 4, is that the presence of this region of the brain is essential if animals are to carry out the complex visceral responses involved in the regulation of body temperatures. It is thus probable that many of the nerve impulses traveling through the autonomic system originate in the neurons of the hypothalamus.

The neurohypophysis is linked with this center of visceral control in the following way. Existing in the hypothalamus are certain nerve cells that differ from typical neurons in being a larger size and containing a secretory product that is readily seen with the light microscope after the use of certain staining techniques. These cells are found in the mammalian hypothalamus in two paired groupings (*Fig. 4-7B*) called the supraoptic nuclei and the paraventricular nuclei (the term "nucleus" being used here in the neurological sense of an association of nerve cells fulfilling similar functions). The secretory product of these cells arises in the cell body (perikaryon) and passes down the axon to its ending. Since the secretory product remains readily stainable as it passes down, it is possible to trace the course of the nerve fibers with precision. In this way it can be shown that many of the fibers pass into the neural lobe, where their endings are closely related to blood vessels in such a way that their secretion can be released into the blood stream. Thus the neural lobe is not a gland. It is an organ in which secretion can be stored within nerve fibers and eventually released into the circulation.

Probably not all of the fibers travel as far as the neural lobe; some are thought to discharge their contents into blood vessels of the median eminence, to which later reference is made. That many of the fibers do reach the neural lobe is demonstrable experimentally as well as by direct observation of normal glands. It is possible to cut the pituitary stalk across (cf. *Fig. 4-7C*) and to insert at the point of section an artificial barrier, such as a plastic sheet, which will completely obstruct communication between the hypothalamic nuclei and the neural lobe. When this is done, the secretion slowly disappears from the neural lobe as a result of discharge into the blood stream, while freshly formed secretion accumulates on the hypothalamic side of the barrier. This is clear evidence that normally the secretion moves down the axons into the neural lobe.

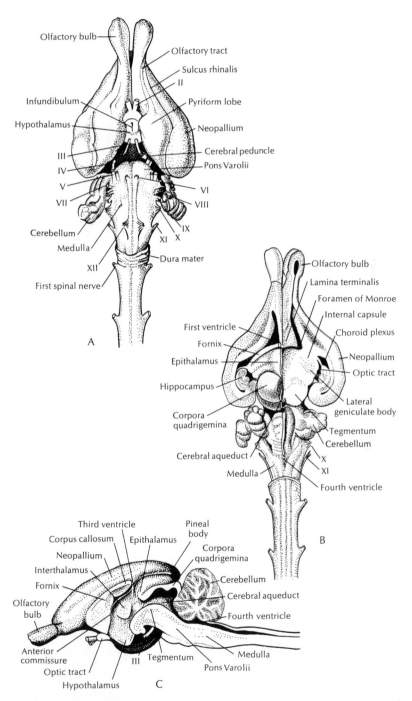

Fig. 4-8. Views of the brain of the rabbit. *A*, ventral; *B*, partially dissected from dorsal surface; *C*, sagittal section. (From J. Z. Young, *The Life of Mammals*. Oxford: The Clarendon Press, 1957, p. 372.)

No less important is the fact that when extracts are prepared from the tissues on the two sides of the barrier, it can be shown that the presence of stainable material can be precisely correlated with the presence of specific hormones, which are considered below. As the secretion disappears from the neural lobe after sectioning of the stalk, so also does the hormonal activity. The latter, however, remains detectable on the hypothalamus side of the point of section, where the secretion can also be seen to accumulate. This does not mean, however, that the stainable material is simply the hormones themselves. Electron microscopy shows that the latter are contained in vesicles, about 2000 Å in diameter, bounded by membranes. The secretion that is seen with the light microscope consists of accumulations of these vesicles, together with a carrier substance in which they are enclosed. This substance does not itself pass into the blood stream. In some way the hormonal material is released from the carrier and the vesicles and passes into the blood as molecules that are far below the limit of visibility with the light microscope.

The particular form of hormonal secretion outlined above is not confined to vertebrates. It is found, within a different pattern of anatomical structure, in invertebrate groups also, as already seen in *Nereis* and *Rhodnius*. It represents, in fact, a fundamental principle of endocrine organization. Hormones secreted in this way are called neurohormones, because they are secreted by what may be considered modified nerve cells. The cells themselves are called neurosecretory cells, but it must be emphasized that this term can be properly applied only when the cells have been established as actually secreting hormones. When this condition has been satisfied, it is legitimate to refer to the stainable product within the cells as neurosecretion. Finally, the association of neurosecretory nerve endings and blood vessels, adapted for the release of the secretion, forms what is called a neurohemal organ. The neural lobe of the pituitary gland is an example of such an organ, as also is the corpus cardiacum of insects (*Fig. 3-13*, p. 117) described earlier.

The discussion must now turn to the part played by the hypothalamic neurosecretion in the regulation of water metabolism of the mammal. Accumulating evidence indicates that the regulatory functions of the hypothalamus are expressed through the endocrine system as well as through the autonomic nervous system. That extracts of the neural lobe can influence bodily functions was first revealed toward the end of the nineteenth century with the discovery that injections of such extracts could produce a marked rise in the blood pressure of man and other mammals. Comparatively large doses, however, are required to produce this effect; and for this reason it is now doubted that it is a truly physiological reaction. More likely it is a pharmacological effect, produced in experimental conditions but not operative in the normal animal. Three other effects can also be produced in mammals by these extracts, however; and these are truly physiological responses, evoked, as is now known, by two distinct hormones, each of which is a polypeptide. The remarkable advances in man's knowledge of the structure of polypeptides, arising out of Sanger's studies of the insulin molecule, have made it possible not only to determine the precise constitution of these two hormones, but also, thanks to the work of V. du Vigneaud, to synthesize them in the laboratory. This places the following discussion on very firm ground.

The two hormones of mammals are called oxytocin and vasopressin. Each has a wide range of action in these animals and also in other vertebrates, actions that can be assayed quantitatively in the laboratory and expressed in terms of a pharmacological spectrum of the particular compound concerned. Examination of Table 4-4 will show that the field of action of the two hormones overlap, but that each hormone is characterized by having within its spectrum of activity certain outstanding potencies. Thus oxytocin stimulates particularly contractions of the smooth muscle of the uterus and of the alveoli of the mammary glands; the former (oxytocic) action aids parturition, while the latter brings about ejection of milk. Oxytocin is associated, therefore, with specialized features of mammalian reproduction. It has also been shown to have a depressant effect on blood pressure in the chicken.

The other hormone, vasopressin, restricts the secretion of urine from the kidney and for this reason is often referred to as the antidiuretic hormone, or ADH. It also evokes contraction of the oviduct of the hen and is responsible for the vasopressor effect in mammals.

TABLE 4-4

*Activities (Pharmacological Spectra) of Highly Purified
Mammalian Neurohypophyseal (Hypothalamic Polypeptide) Hormones,
Expressed as Units/Mg Peptide.[a]*

	Rat vaso-pressin	Rat anti-diuretic	Dog anti-diuretic	Isolated rat uterus	Rabbit milk ejection	Chicken vaso-pressin	Hen oviduct	Frog bladder
Arginine Vasopressin	400	400	400	12	51	56	320	26
Lysine Vasopressin	270	150	50	7.5	42	4.2	15–65	7.5
Oxytocin	4–7	4.5	4	420	370	430	34	420

[a] Data collected from various authors by H. Heller, in *Comparative Endocrinology,* Vol. 1, ed. U. S. von Euler and H. Heller (New York: Academic Press, Inc., 1963), p. 33.

144

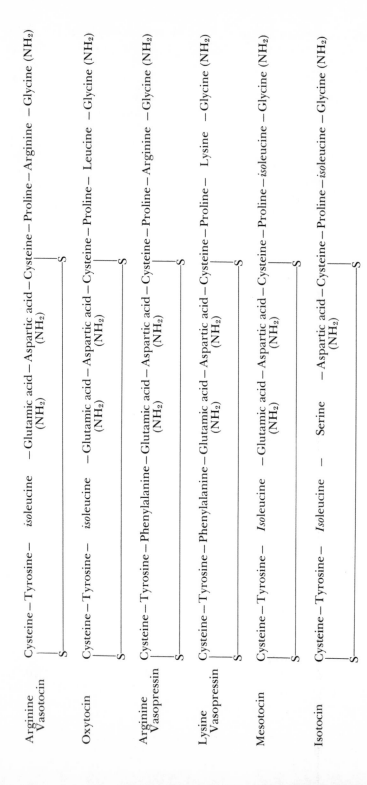

Fig. 4-9. Structural formulas of hypothalamic polypeptide hormones.

The oxytocic, milk-ejection, and antidiuretic actions are the three mammalian physiological responses mentioned above. They are evoked by small dosages and may be regarded as the normal and adaptively significant action of the hormones.

The structural formulas of these hormones are shown in *Fig. 4-9*. From this it will be seen that each consists of nine amino acid residues, with the disulfide bonds of the two cysteine residues united to form a ring. It will also be seen that vasopressin differs from oxytocin simply in the substitution of phenylalanine at position three and arginine at position eight. Further, vasopressin exists in two forms. One of these, arginine vasopressin, has an arginine residue at position eight, while the other, lysine vasopressin, has a lysine residue at that point. The significance of these substitutions, and of the other polypeptides shown in the figure, are matters that shall be considered later. For the moment, it is sufficient to note that the situation is a clear demonstration of the way in which the biological properties of molecules can be changed by small alterations in structure. Not only does oxytocin differ from the vasopressins in its properties; the two vasopressins also differ significantly from each other in their effects. Both arginine and lysine vasopressin, however, have as a primary property an action upon diuresis, so that in this context they can be conveniently referred to as one hormone: vasopressin.

The section is concerned primarily with the antidiuretic effect of vasopressin. This is dramatically shown in human patients suffering from diabetes insipidus, a condition in which large quantities of urine are produced without the sweet taste of that produced as a result of diabetes mellitus (hence the difference in the name). Diabetes insipidus results from a lack of vasopressin. The absence of the antidiuretic influence of this hormone leads to the production of so much urine that as much as thirty liters of water must be drunk per day to replace the wasted fluid. The condition can be promptly alleviated by the administration of the hormone in the form, for example, of snuff prepared from the neural lobe of the pituitary gland. Another illustration of the action of the hormone is seen in dogs. If their urine output is measured over a period of time during which a sudden noise is created near them, it is found that the shock results in a brief reduction of their urine production; this can be proved to be the consequence of a release of vasopressin in response to the stimulus.

The hormone produces its antidiuretic effect by an action upon the urinary tubules of the kidney. These tubules (*Fig. 4-10*) consist in mammals of a capsule into which is invaginated a cluster of blood vessels called the glomerulus. From the capsule there extends a long tubule, divided into a proximal convoluted tubule, a loop of Henle, and a distal convoluted tubule, the last-named opening proceeding with other tubules into a collecting duct. A filtrate from the blood in the glomerulus passes into the capsule; the filtrate is similar in composition to the blood itself except for its absence of protein, which is unable to pass through the filtering pores of the glomerular membrane. In the proximal convoluted tubule there is considerable concentration of urine, resulting, among other things, from the active uptake of sodium accompanied by a passive uptake of water along the resulting osmotic gradient.

Uptake of sodium continues in other regions of the tubule and probably also in the collecting ducts, but these regions seem relatively impermeable to water. It is in them that vasopressin is thought to act. It has no effect upon the proximal tubule, so that considerable concentration of urine takes place there even in its absence. This illustrates the general proposition that hormones commonly act by regulating activities that would take place to some extent, even if less efficiently, in their absence. What this hormone can do is increase the uptake of water in the distal tubule perhaps, it is thought, by enlarging the size of membrane pores and so facilitating the passage of water back into the blood stream. In this way the antidiuretic action of vasopressin is believed to be exerted. It would appear from the drastic results of its absence in man that it is always exerting some

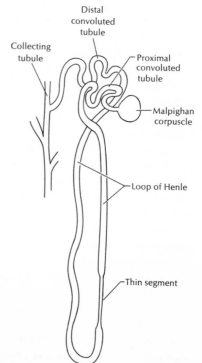

Fig. 4-10. Diagram of a nephron from the cortex of a mammalian kidney. (From E. J. W. Barrington, *Introduction to General and Comparative Endocrinology*. Oxford: The Clarendon Press, 1963, p. 81.)

influence upon the tubules, and that the amount secreted is increased or diminished in accordance with the requirements of the body for conserving its water content or for discharging surplus. It will be observed that what vasopressin is doing is facilitating the passive movement of water along an osmotic gradient. This is the limit of its powers in mammals; it exerts no influence upon active transport. The regulated release of this hormone, however, makes it possible for mammals to adjust their urine output to the availability of water. If they have drunk a great deal, then the urine will be correspondingly dilute. If, on the contrary, water is scarce, or if much is being lost in sweat (Chapter 6), then they can produce a concentrated urine that is markedly hyperosmotic to the blood.

■ **CORTICOSTEROIDS AND THE REGULATION OF ION METABOLISM IN MAMMALS**

The other important factor regulating homeostasis of the body fluids is the secretion of the cortex of the adrenal gland. This secretion is largely responsible for the control of ionic fluxes in mammals, although the secretion of the parathyroid gland, by virtue of its effect upon bone formation, has some influence upon the calcium and phosphate content of the blood. The cortex of the adrenal gland is a complex of secretory tissue that surrounds the medullary tissue, from which are secreted the catechol hormones, adrenaline and noradrenaline. Contained in the adrenocortical secretion are a number of hormones (*Fig. 4-11*), all of which are steroids, with a molecular structure based upon the four-membered ring that characterizes this group of compounds. Among these corticosteroids, as they are called, are hormones that have been seen to regulate certain metabolic pathways: cortisone, cortisol, and corticosterone. These three compounds are referred to as glucocorticoids, because their effects are exerted particularly upon carbohydrate metabolism. This restriction of action, however, is not complete; they also have some influence upon ion metabolism. The hormone principally concerned with the latter is another corticosteroid called aldosterone. It is, therefore, referred to as a mineralocorticoid, but again the distinction is not absolute. In any case, it is a distinction that is meaningful only in mammals; the present state of our knowledge gives no justification for classifying the various components of the adrenocortical secretion of lower vertebrates in this way.

The adrenal cortex is essential for life in mammals, as can be demonstrated by removing it from experimental animals. Their failure to survive may partly reflect deprivation of glucocorticoids, but mineralocorticoid deprivation, with its effects upon ion balance, is probably the more deadly. The primary effect is a reduced retention

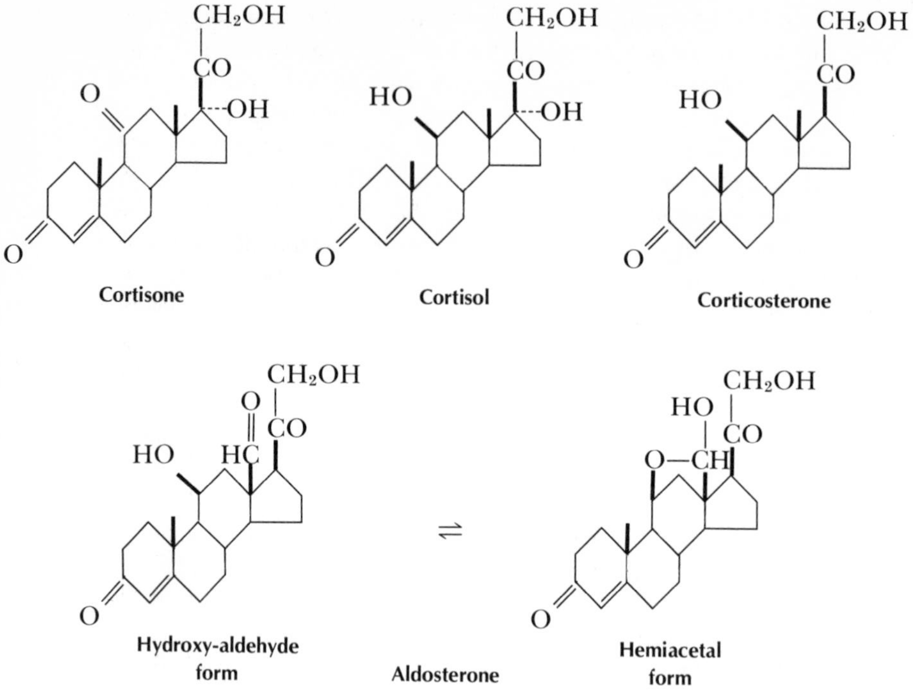

Fig. 4-11. Steroid hormones of the adrenocortical tissue (corticosteroids).

of sodium within the body, shown by increased excretion of this ion in the urine. The level of blood sodium falls, and with it there is a fall in chloride and bicarbonate and some rise in the blood potassium level. Associated with these ionic changes is an increased loss of water in the urine accompanying the passage of sodium. Consequently, there is a rise in the concentration of the components of the blood, and it is this increased hemoconcentration that is believed to be the primary cause of death.

Effects comparable to these have long been recognized in the human patient in the syndrome (complex of symptoms) that characterizes Addison's disease. This is named after the English physician Thomas Addison, who first described the condition in 1849, and who correctly ascribed it to chronic disorder of the adrenal glands. Later, it was specifically related to disorder of the cortical tissue. Among the symptoms are muscular weakness, associated in large measure with deprivation of glycogen, and a disturbed balance of ions in the blood. All of these conditions, both in human patients and in experimental animals, can be controlled by the injection of adrenocortical extracts and, more particularly, by treatment with aldosterone.

Clearly, the actions of the adrenocortical hormones, involved as they are with the water content of the body fluids as well as with their ionic composition, cannot be wholly dissociated from the actions of the hypothalamic polypeptides. Nevertheless, the sites of action of these two groups of hormones are different, at least as far as mammals are concerned. As previously noted, the polypeptides act by facilitating the passive movement of water down osmotic gradients. The corticosteroids, by contrast, act by facilitating the active transport of sodium. In mammals this action is exerted mainly upon the kidney tubule, which has been seen to be a major site of active transport, but the composition of the sweat is also affected. Of the several hormones involved, it is aldosterone, which is in any case the chief mineralocorticoid, that acts especially upon sodium uptake. Others, and in particular cortisol, are thought to have a direct action upon the sodium/potassium ratio in the body fluids rather than upon sodium uptake alone. Doubtless, there are complications here that still await clarification.

For the present analysis, however, it is adequate to think of the mineralocorticoids as influencing ionic fluxes, and the movements of water that are passively associated with them, in the epithelial tissues that are specialized for carrying out these transfers. In mammals the reacting tissues are primarily the kidney tubules. But, it is common to find, as comparative studies develop, that the target tissues of hormones in one group may differ from the target tissues of the corresponding hormones in another group, the differences being correlated with the adaptive organization of the groups concerned. It will be seen that this principle is certainly illustrated by the varying effects of the corticosteroids in different vertebrate groups, and it is for this reason that reference is made to epithelial tissues rather than specifically to the kidney tubules. Before this matter is considered further, however, there is another aspect of these hormones that demands attention.

■ THE CONCEPT OF STRESS

One of the most important requirements of regulating mechanisms is that they should provide for resistance to the wide range of stresses imposed upon animals by the searching hostility of their environment. Man's ideas relating to this owe much to the writings of Walter Cannon. His views on the importance of homeostasis and the mechanisms by which this regulation is maintained have already been quoted. It was a logical step for him to pass from these to the concept of the animal possessing adaptive mechanisms that enable it to muster all of its reserves to meet sudden crises that threaten its survival, mechanisms manifested in what have been called the responses of fright, flight, or a fight.

At the time when Cannon was writing, little was known of the function of the adrenal cortex; but he had himself contributed much to scientists' understanding of the function of the adrenal medulla, and it was on this that he concentrated his argument. The association of the cortical and medullary tissues in one gland in mammals is a peculiar feature of organization that still cannot be explained. Not the least of the difficulties involved here is that in lower vertebrates the degree of association is far less uniform; indeed, in fish and cyclostomes the two components are more or less separate from each other. However, there is certainly some overlap in the effects produced by the several hormones of these two tissues. Earlier, it was noted that the two catechol hormones of the mammalian medulla (adrenaline and noradrenaline) influence carbohydrate metabolism in essentially the same way as does glucagon. But it was also mentioned that the actions of these medullary hormones extend much further than this. The effects of the two differ from each other in detail. Adrenaline in particular seems to be involved in responses to stressful stimuli that evoke pain and emotional reactions. Among its effects are increase in the rate of heart beat, constriction of the blood vessels of the skin, dilation of blood vessels of the muscles, and increase in oxygen consumption. In addition, it evokes subjective feelings of anxiety in human beings. Noradrenaline, by contrast, seems more closely involved in the regulation of the vascular system. It has no effect on oxygen consumption; and it decreases the heart rate, but produces a greater rise in blood pressure, with constriction of the blood vessels of the muscles.

Cannon's argument was that all of these effects could be regarded as a complex, physiologically adaptive response that puts the animal into the best possible condition for resisting stresses, whether these arise from the attack of a predator, for example, from subjection to extreme cold, or from some other circumstance that demands additional activity. Unlike the corticosteroids, however, the catechol hormones are not essential for life. Cannon showed that a cat could survive in the laboratory for as long as three and a half years after its adrenal medulla had been removed, together with the sympathetic component of the autonomic nervous system by which the adrenal medulla is innervated and with which it is closely associated in its functioning. But the significant words are "in the laboratory." An animal in this condition needs careful maintenance, so that it is protected from environmental hazards. Without this protection, it would be unlikely to survive for long.

There is much in Cannon's concept which is probably still valid. It becomes more and more difficult, however, to define at all precisely the physiological adaptations to which the survival of animals under stress are really due. In part, it is because these adaptations are regulated by complex controls in which the nervous and endocrine systems are inextricably linked, and in which the various components of the endocrine system act in the closest cooperation. Earlier, it was emphasized that when one hormone, or one endocrine gland, is studied, the scientist is abstracting from the complex reality of the living organism. It is against this background that one must view another and more recent interpretation of resistance to stress, formulated by Hans Selye in an extensive series of writings.

Selye has argued that animals exposed to harmful conditions manifest a complex response that he calls the Stress Syndrome or General Adaptation Syndrome (G.A.S.). This response, which involves in a generalized way all of the resources of the body, is seen by Selye as the "sum of all non-specific systemic reactions of the body which ensue upon long-continued exposure to stress." He considers the response to fall into three phases. The first phase, which he calls the alarm reaction, involves the immediate mobilization of the body's defensive resources. This mobilization is achieved through general activation of the sympathetic nervous system and an increased secretory output from the cortex and medulla of the adrenal gland, reflected in enlargement of the gland and in histological changes indicative of hormonal discharge. Part of this phase includes the phenomenon known as shock, which is a well-known accompaniment of severe stress in human beings. Continuation of the exposure to stress, always supposing that the animal survives it, leads to the second phase, which is the stage of resistance. The regulatory mechanisms now show some degree of adaptation to the adverse conditions, and it is this that permits prolonged survival. Eventually, however, these adaptive mechanisms may prove insufficient, and the organism passes into the third phase, the stage of exhaustion; this evokes pathological symptoms of various kinds and may eventually lead to death.

If we follow the development of the G.A.S. in time, we can see that it goes through a typical triphasic course. To illustrate this I pointed out . . . that if an animal is continuously exposed to some stressor (say, cold), the adrenal cortex first discharges all its microscopic fat-granules which contain the cortical hormones (alarm reaction), then it becomes laden with an unusually large number of fat-droplets (stage of resistance) and finally it loses them again (stage of exhaustion). As far as we can see, the same triphasic course is followed by most, if not all, of the manifestations of the G.A.S.

The next figure illustrates this graphically, using general resistance to injury as an indicator [*Fig. 4-12*].

In the acute phase of the alarm reaction (A.R.), general resistance, to the particular stressor with which the G.A.S. had been elicited, falls way below normal. Then, as adaptation is acquired, in the stage

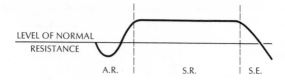

LEVEL OF NORMAL
RESISTANCE

A.R.   S.R.   S.E.

Fig. 4-12. Diagram illustrating the triphasic course of the general adaptation syndrome. (From H. Selye, *The Stress of Life.* New York: McGraw-Hill Book Company, 1956, p. 87. Published in England by Longmans, Green & Company, Ltd.)

of resistance (S.R.), the capacity to resist rises considerably above normal. But eventually, in the stage of exhaustion (S.E.), resistance drops below normal again.

You may well ask, "How does one find out about such things in actual practice?"

We exposed large numbers of rats to various stressors over long periods of time and tested the resistance of sample groups among these animals at repeated intervals. For instance, in one experiment we placed a hundred rats in a refrigerated room where the temperature was near freezing. Thanks to their fur coats, they could stand this quite well, although during the first 48 hours they developed the typical manifestations of the alarm reaction. This was proved by killing ten animals at the end of the second day; all of them had large fat-free adrenals, small thymuses, and stomach ulcers.

At this same time—after 48 hours of exposure—twenty other rats were also removed from the cold-room to test their resistance to low temperatures. They were now placed in a still colder chamber, together with normal rats which up to then had lived at room temperature. It turned out that the rats which had already developed an alarm reaction due to moderate cold were even less than normally resistant to excessive cold.

Five weeks later another sample of rats was taken from the cold-room. By that time they had fully adapted themselves to life at low temperature and were in the stage of resistance of the G.A.S. When these animals were placed in the still more refrigerated chamber, they survived temperatures which nonpretreated animals could never withstand. Evidently their resistance had risen above the normal level.

Yet, after several months of life in the cold, this acquired resistance was lost again, and the stage of exhaustion set in. Then the animals were not even capable of further surviving in the comparatively moderate cold of the refrigerated chamber in which they had spent so much time in a state of perfect well-being, ever since the initiation of the experiment.

The three waves in the curve (down, up, and down again) represent a summary of many such observations, because this type of experiment was repeated with various other stressors (forced muscular work, drugs, infections) and the result was always the same.

Adaptability can be well trained to serve a special purpose, but eventually it runs out; its amount is finite.

This was not what I had expected. I should have thought that once an animal has learned to live in the cold, it could go on resisting low temperatures indefinitely. Why shouldn't it, as long as it received enough food to create the internal heat necessary for the maintenance of a normal body-temperature? Naturally, in order to get used to cold, the organism must learn how to produce an excess of heat by the combustion of food. For additional safety the body must also learn to prevent unnecessary loss of heat. It does this through a generalized constriction of the blood vessels in the skin which interferes with the cooling of the blood on the surface. But once all this has been learned and the animal has become well adjusted to life at low temperatures, one would expect that nothing but lack of food (caloric energy) would stand in the way of continued resistance to cold. Observation shows that this is not the case.

Similar experiments have then revealed that the same loss of acquired adaptation also occurs in animals forced to perform intense muscular exercise, or in those given toxic drugs and other stressors over long periods of time. . . .

. . . The basic mechanisms involved in all types of stress-reactions . . . can be visualized by the following sketch [*Fig. 4-13*]:

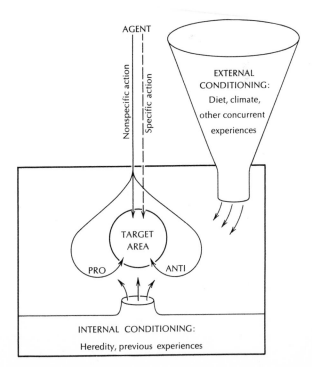

Fig. 4-13. Diagram illustrating the basic mechanisms of the stress response. (From H. Selye, *The Stress of Life.* New York: McGraw-Hill Book Company, 1956, p. 87. Published in England by Longmans, Green & Company, Ltd.)

. . . We note that the agent produces both specific and non-specific actions, through which it influences the whole body (here represented as a square). But this picture also shows that the agent does not act on the whole body evenly; it usually hits some part, the direct target area, more than other regions.

For example, if I accidentally swallow some corrosive fluid, my whole body suffers to some extent, but no part of it will be as much affected as the tissues between my lips and stomach, which came into direct contact with the poison. These represent the target area in this case. Yet, parts far away from this region are also affected; for instance, the adrenals are stimulated to produce an excess of pro-inflammatory and/or anti-inflammatory corticoids; there are nervous and emotional reactions and various biochemical changes which influence metabolism. As a result of all this, virtually every tissue in the body is eventually affected to some extent.

The drawing also reminds us that the whole development of the reaction largely depends on conditioning factors. These can be in-variables which act upon us from within: our hereditary predisposi-tions and previous experiences (internal conditioning), as well as variables which influence our body simultaneously with the agent from without (external conditioning). All these are integral elements of the response during stress; they all contribute something to the picture of the G.A.S.[2]

Not all authorities would agree that the wide-ranging implications of this bold hypothesis of the General Adaptation Syndrome are adequately justified by the data, largely derived from experimental animals, upon which the argument is based. Zoologists who have adopted Selye's views, however, have seen in the third phase a pos-sible explanation of the fluctuations in numbers that are found as a natural phenomenon in populations of wild mammals. Overcrowd-ing, or other adverse circumstances, might, it is thought, evoke a stress syndrome and so lead eventually to heavy mortality and the restoration (for the survivors) of more acceptable conditions. What-ever truth there may be to this, it is certainly of interest to find that those concerned with animals in the field are able to make use of results emerging from the experimental analysis of regulatory mech-anisms. An obvious corollary is that the laboratory experimenter should never forget that his bench material was once part of a living animal related to members of wild populations, even if it was never itself a member of one.

■ THE PITUITARY GLAND AND ITS FUNCTIONAL RELATIONSHIPS

An essential element of Selye's hypothesis, and one that influences all present analysis, is the means by which the adrenal gland is enabled to respond to such varied and ill-defined stimulation. This is an issue that is fundamental to the understanding of endocrine mechanisms throughout the animal kingdom, for the value of all of these mechanisms lies in their capacities to contribute to some element of physiological adaptation; implicit in this, therefore, is the ability of the endocrine glands to respond to changes both in the external and internal environment. In other words, although endocrine organs are regulating agents, they must themselves be subject to regulation. *Quis custodiet ipsos custodes?*

Enough has been said of endocrine action to appreciate that the answer to the above question must vary with the gland concerned. The endocrine secretions of the alimentary tract are released by the presence of food materials and digestive secretions; simultaneously, they contribute to the regulation of the latter. The secretion of insulin is primarily regulated by the level of glucose in the blood that circulates through the islets. In neither of these cases is secretory activity under direct control of the nervous system. Indeed, it is unusual in vertebrates for endocrine secretory cells to be directly innervated. The cells of the adrenal medulla, however, are an important exception to this, for they are directly innervated by fibers of the sympathetic nervous system. The reason for this merits examination, for it results from the exceptional character of the medullary tissue.

It is generally thought that medullary cells have evolved out of certain nerve cells of the sympathetic nervous system. This view is based, in part, upon the fact that noradrenaline is secreted within the sympathetic nervous system as well as in the adrenal medulla. In the nervous system it serves as a so-called chemical transmitter substance. Released at the sympathetic nerve endings by the arrival of nerve impulses, it evokes a response in the target cells that those endings innervate. Such a chemical transmitter substance, acting locally and for only a very brief period of time, is called a neurohumor. It is to be distinguished from the neurohormones discussed earlier; for these, by passing into the blood stream, have their range of action extended both in space and time. Moreover, they are associated with visible and stainable neurosecretion, whereas neurohumors are not.

The argument, then, is that certain sympathetic nerve cells have become modified into the endocrine cells that now form the adrenal medulla. These medullary cells, secreting both noradrenaline and adrenaline, and releasing them as hormones into the blood stream, have, it is supposed, retained their direct synaptic relationship with other cells of the sympathetic nervous system; and it is because of this that the adrenal medullary tissue forms an innervated endocrine gland. Its products are regarded as hormones, not as neurohumors, because they function by circulating in the blood stream; noradrenaline is thus classified under both headings, according to the site of its production and mode of functioning. The medullary hormones are not regarded as neurohormones, because they are not associated with stainable neurosecretion. The cell granules that carry the hormones do, however, develop a characteristic yellow or brown color when the cells are fixed in fluids containing dichromate, chromic acid, or iodate. This is called the chromaffin reaction; and, because of it, the cells are commonly referred to as chromaffin cells.

Accepting, therefore, that the relationship of the adrenal medulla with the nervous system is unique, one still must explain how the secretory activity of the other endocrine organs of vertebrates, including the adrenal cortex, can be adjusted to cope with the information obtained by the nervous system from the environment. The key to understanding this is provided by the pituitary gland, an organ which plays a central role in the physiological regulation of vertebrate life at all levels of evolution.

As far as the hypothalamic polypeptides are concerned, the situation is in one sense a simple one; for the secretory cells are actually specialized cells of the central nervous system. It is difficult to judge whether the discharge of the hormones from their neurosecretory fibers is brought about by nerve impulses in the fibers themselves, or whether they are activated by impulses traveling in ordinary fibers that accompany them; but, at least, they are in direct relationship with the hypothalamus. Indeed, the initial evolution of neurosecretory systems and their widespread distribution in the animal kingdom must surely be a consequence of the way in which they provide so close a link between neural and chemical coordination.

The regulation of the adrenocortical tissue presents a wholly different problem; but again the key lies within the pituitary gland, this time within the adenohypophysis. The pars intermedia of this organ secretes one or more hormones that seem to be of little importance in higher vertebrates but are involved in adaptive regulation of color change in cyclostomes, fish, amphibians, and some reptiles. The pars distalis, which is the immediate concern of this discussion, is distinct from this region and much more complex in its functions. It secretes no less than six hormones. Two of these are growth hormone and prolactin, exerting their own direct effects on various aspects of metabolism; growth hormone was mentioned earlier, and prolactin will be discussed later in this chapter.

The four other hormones are called tropic hormones (*trope,* turn), or sometimes trophic hormones (*trophe,* nourishment), because their actions are turned or directed toward the development and regulation of certain other endocrine glands, which can be regarded as the target glands of the pituitary. Thyrotropic hormone (thyrotropin, thyroid-stimulating hormone, TSH) is related in this way to the thyroid gland; two gonadotropic hormones (follicle-stimulating hormone, or FSH, and interstitial cell-stimulating hormone, or ICSH, alternatively called luteinizing hormone, or LH) are related to the gonads; adrenocorticotropic hormone (ACTH, or corticotropin) is related to the adrenal cortex. Manifestly, one is concerned here with an important principle of vertebrate organization, but it will be convenient in the present context to consider it specifically in relation to the control of the adrenal cortex. The principles thereby exposed are directly applicable to the other tropic hormones.

The dependence of the adrenal cortex upon the adenohypophysis can be well shown in a variety of operative procedures. Hypophysectomy (removal of the pituitary gland) results in atrophy of the adrenocortical tissue, while the normal appearance of the tissue can be subsequently restored by implanting adenohypophyseal tissue, or extracts of it, into the body. That the level of activity of the adrenocortical tissue is also regulated by corticotropin is indicated by experiments in which such extracts are injected into animals with normal adrenal glands; after this treatment, the tissue shows clear histological signs of increased secretory activity. This dependent relationship can be demonstrated also in the lower vertebrates, down to the level of fish, as well as in mammals, so that the principle involved may be considered to be a characteristic of vertebrate physiological organization. Mammalian corticotropin itself has been prepared in a chemically pure form and its amino acid sequence worked out in detail; the molecule proves to be a relatively simple polypeptide, with a straight chain of 39 amino acid residues.

Demonstration of the existence of corticotropin, and of the dependence of the adrenal cortex upon it, does not, however, explain how the output of cortical secretion can be adaptively regulated in relation to the needs of the body and in response to stimuli that the body receives from the environment. Such regulation is, in fact, achieved through a functional relationship between the hypothalamus and the pituitary gland. This relationship brings the adenohypophysis under the control of the central nervous system, while it also contributes to a feedback system linking the pars distalis with the adrenal cortex, the thyroid gland, and the gonads.

An essential element of this hypothalamic relationship in higher vertebrates is the median eminence. This structure contains a capillary network *(Fig. 4-14)*, which is vascularized from the internal carotid artery and which discharges its blood through portal vessels into the adenohypophysis. There is now convincing evidence that this hypophyseal portal system, as it is called, provides the essential functional link between the central nervous system and the pars distalis. Information in the form of nerve impulses, passed through the nervous system into the hypothalamus, is believed to result in the release from that region of secretions that function locally and that nay be regarded as chemical transmitter substances. These, it is supposed, are passed into the median eminence; from there they are carried into the hypophyseal portal vessels and subsequently into the pars distalis, where they evoke appropriate responses in the tropic secretory cells. The capillary system of the median eminence is an adaptation that facilitates the taking up of these chemical transmitters. The earliest vertebrates probably lacked it, for it is not found in lampreys; although, other living cyclostomes (the hagfishes) are said to have something similar but differently arranged. The situation in fish has not yet been adequately investigated, but it is probable that only in the lung fishes (which, significantly, are close relatives of amphibians) is there a beginning of a true hypophyseal portal system. Nevertheless, fish have vascular pathways that probably serve to some extent as substitutes for this system.

Evidence of the involvement of the hypothalamus and the median eminence in adrenocorticotropic responses to stress is derived from two types of experiment: those in which the pituitary has been isolated from the hypothalamus, either by section of its stalk or by trans-

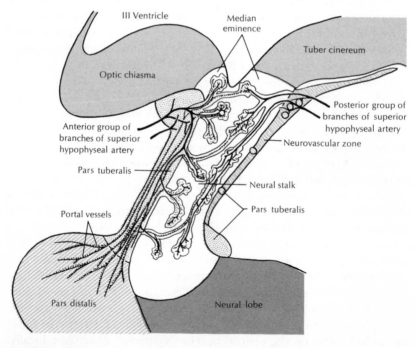

Fig. 4-14. Diagrammatic representation of the hypophyseal portal vessels. (From J. D. Green, *Anatomical Record*, 100 (1948), 273-276; and from C. Fortier, in *Comparative Endocrinology, 1*, U. S. von Euler and H. Heller, ed., New York: Academic Press, 1963, p. 3.)

plantation to other sites in the body; and those in which lesions have been made in the median eminence. The results of these experiments have not always been in full agreement, but it seems reasonably well established that increased release of corticosteroid hormones in response to many types of stressful stimuli does depend upon the full integrity of the hypothalamus and of its functional association, through the hypophyseal portal system, with the pars distalis. This association makes it possible for the pars distalis to be brought under the influence of the higher nervous centers and, accordingly, of the information that is passed to these centers from the various receptors of the body. What is less certain is how far the tropic cells of the pars distalis can function independently in a feedback system without the participation of the hypothalamus. There is no very clear answer to this as far as the secretion of corticotropin is concerned, but more definite evidence has been obtained from studies of the control of the thyroid gland.

Evidence of negative feedback from the thyroid gland through the hypothalamus is obtained when a small mammal is moved from a warm room to a cold one. The stimulus of lowered temperature results in an increased output of thyroid hormones. This can be shown, for example, by the increased release of radioactive iodine from the gland in rabbits which have previously received injections of this isotope *(Fig. 4-15)*. Such a reaction of the thyroid is part of the complex response to cold stress that was referred to by Selye in the passage previously quoted; as discussed in Chapter 6, the increased thyroid secretion brings about a rise in metabolic rate. The response of the gland is a consequence of an increased output of thyrotropin; and it is certain that it is mediated through the hypothalamus, for it is eliminated by lesions in that region, or by transection of the pituitary stalk which separates the pars distalis from the brain.

Another feedback response, however, is seen when thyroxine is injected into a laboratory mammal. In this instance the increase in concentration of circulating thyroxine depresses the output of thyrotropin, and this brings about a reduction in output of thyroid hormones. This happens even when the pituitary has been separated from the hypothalamus, either by sectioning the stalk or by transplanting the gland to another part of the body. In this case, then, the thyrotropin-secreting cells of the pars distalis must be responding directly to changes in the concentration of circulating thyroxine. On present evidence, therefore, it must be concluded that negative feedback between the pars distalis and the thyroid gland can, in general, operate either through the pars distalis, or indirectly through the hypothalamus. The same is probably true of the adrenal cortex and the gonads, although in these instances the feedback to the pituitary seems very often to depend upon the mediation of the hypothalamus.

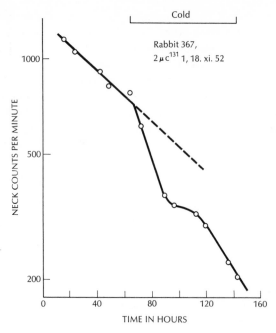

Fig. 4-15.   The effect of cold on the release of ^{131}I from the thyroid gland of the rabbit. The animal had received an injection of 2μc of the isotope which is captured readily by the thyroid gland and incorporated into the thyroid hormones. The radioactivity of the thyroid region of the neck was determined by external counting at the times indicated after the injection. The broken line shows the rate at which the radioactive iodine would have been discharged from the gland had the secretion of the hormones not been accelerated by transference of the animal to a cold room. (From K. Brown-Grant, C. von Euler, G. W. Morris, and S. Leichlin, *Journal of Physiology*, 126 (1954), 21. With permission of the Editorial Board of the *Journal of Physiology*.)

Which particular pathway is involved in given response must in any case be determined by separate investigation; *Figure 4-16* simply illustrates the possibilities of the situation.

One aspect of the relationship between the hypothalamus and the pars distalis has only recently been investigated. Certain hypothalamic neurosecretory fibers appear to end in close relation to the median eminence (*Fig. 4-7C*, p. 139). This makes it likely that at least some of the chemical transmitters may be passed down those fibers as a neurosecretion, and it may be that these transmitter substances are chemically related to the hypothalamic polypeptide neurohormones that are similarly transmitted down other neurosecretory fibers into the neural lobe. Should this view eventually prove to be correct, it would be a logical extension of the interpretation of the hypothalamus as a center for coordinating adaptive regulation. Indeed, it has been suggested that initially the secretory activity of the hypothalamus may have been directed primarily toward regulation of the adenohypophysis, and that its neurosecretory hormones may have arisen as a specialized development of such activity. This would conform well with two aspects of these hormones that will be discussed later: the considerable molecular variation that they show; and the fact that their functions, while extensive and well defined in the higher vertebrates, have so far proved much more difficult to identify in cyclostomes and fish. Because of scientists' relative ignorance of the endocrine physiology of these lower forms, one recognizes both the exciting possibilities of study within this field and the extensive investigation which must be carried out before these various speculations can be regarded as well founded.

The relationship between the adrenocortical tissue and corticotropin is sometimes referred to as the pituitary-adrenal axis. Recognition of this relationship permits a better understanding of Selye's theory of the stress syndrome, for it is supposed that both alarm and resistance are mediated through this axis. There is a difficulty here, however, for the pituitary exerts little, if any, control over the secretion of aldosterone in mammals. This hormone is secreted mainly in the more peripheral part of the cortex, the zona glomerulosa, and this region seems not to be involved in a feedback relationship with the pars distalis. This feedback affects primarily the more central part of the cortex, the zona fasciata, where the glucocorticoids are

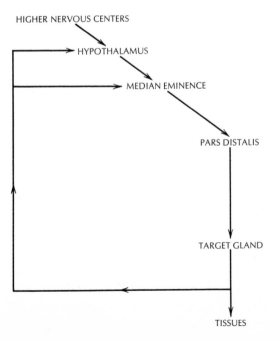

HIGHER NERVOUS CENTERS

HYPOTHALAMUS

MEDIAN EMINENCE

PARS DISTALIS

TARGET GLAND

TISSUES

Fig. 4-16. Diagram to illustrate the probable feedback pathways linking the hypothalamus, the pars distalis of the pituitary gland, and the target glands of its tropic hormones.

chiefly secreted. Stimulation of the pituitary-adrenal axis may thus be expected to increase glucocorticoid output rather than mineralocorticoid, yet in practice it is the mineralocorticoids that produce in experimental animals the pathological changes associated with chronic stress.

These are difficulties that cannot now be pursued further. They are mentioned here to indicate some of the complexities that are revealed when a far-reaching hypothesis is subjected to detailed investigation; it is clearly unwise at this stage to ascribe to the adrenal gland, whether the medullary or cortical component, an exclusive or even dominant role in the regulation of the responses of animals to adversity. So it is that some biologists have been unwilling to accept fully the implications of Selye's concept of the physiology of stress. In any case, even though the adrenal gland may be closely associated with stress responses, it does not follow that it is the primary causal agent in promoting them. On surveying this difficult field it is worth bearing in mind the earlier suggestion that hormones may sometimes have a permissive action; that is, they may allow or facilitate a response without being the agents that actually evoke it. It has also been suggested that hormones may sometimes have had generalized supporting and permissive effects when they were first incorporated into the physiological organization of a group, and that their more precise effects evolved *pari passu* with the development of increasing physiological complexity in higher members of the group.

The homeostasis to which this volume has been paying special attention comes to full flower in the higher vertebrates, as they move from water onto land and adjust to the more stringent and variable conditions that they encounter there. One cannot expect, however, that interpretations derived from studies of higher forms will necessarily be directly transferable to lower ones, and it will be well now to illustrate this by considering some aspects of water and ion metabolism in the lower forms.

■ THE REGULATION OF WATER AND ION METABOLISM IN SOME LOWER VERTEBRATES

The examples of vertebrate hormonal regulation that have been met in earlier chapters have been concerned with functions that are broadly common to all members of the group. The regulation of water and ion metabolism, however, presents an altogether more complex situation, for it must necessarily have been profoundly affected by the transition from aquatic to terrestrial life. Both fish and amphibians may be expected to have patterns of adaptive regulation, each group with its own characteristics, and both groups differing from the fully terrestrial mammals. The situation will be examined chiefly as it appears in the amphibians, for regulation of the body fluids is at present much better understood in these animals than it is in fish. Moreover, a study of amphibians affords good insight into some of the problems that had to be faced by the vertebrates in their exploitation of terrestrial life.

Particularly characteristic of amphibians is the high permeability of their skin, which is linked with its use in respiration. In aquatic conditions, therefore, these animals have a substantial osmotic flow of water into their bodies; this leads to the excretion of a copious urine and to an accompanying loss of a great deal of sodium. As seen earlier, however, the frog's skin has proved to be classical material for the demonstration of the active uptake of sodium. This uptake, which is accompanied by the passive, inward movement of chloride, compensates for the urinary loss of salt. In principle the situation has something in common with that found in *Nereis diversicolor* when it has adjusted to dilute sea water, for amphibians are under similar ionic stress when they are in fresh water.

A further characteristic adaptation of amphibians is their capacity to reduce their loss of sodium by active uptake through the wall of the bladder, so that the ion can be taken up from the stored urine and returned to the blood. Both of these sites of uptake (skin and bladder wall) are under the influence of the corticosteroids, which, it will be realized, have no such action upon the corresponding tissues in mammals. The evidence for their action in amphibians is obtained from various experimental procedures. For example, frogs that have been adrenalectomized show an increased loss of sodium through their skin. So also do animals from which the pars distalis of the pituitary has been removed, for the consequent loss of corticotropin results in a decreased output of corticosteroids from the adrenal cortex. Normal sodium balance can be restored by treating the animals with mammalian corticotropin or by administering aldosterone. This latter hormone can also be shown to increase active transport of sodium through the wall of the bladder.

Equally characteristic of amphibians are adaptations, closely linked with the above, for regulating the water content of the body. In this respect amphibians' needs are particularly exacting when they are on land, for the permeability of their skin leaves them always prone to desiccation. Here the hypothalamic polypeptide secretion is of the greatest importance. The first indication of this came from the discovery by F. Brunn in 1921 that frogs injected with mammalian neurohypophyseal extracts increase considerably in weight as a consequence of the uptake of water, provided, of course, that they are placed in water. Subsequent study of this Brunn effect (as it is called) by many workers has clearly established that it is mediated by a hypothalamic polypeptide hormone, present in the neural lobe, and that it provides a means for the rapid uptake of water, when it becomes available. It is, in part, an antidiuretic response; and to this extent it resembles the action of vasopressin in mammals, for it results in increased uptake of water through the kidney tubules. But two other sites of action are also involved, neither represented in mammals: there is increased uptake of water through the skin, while water passes through the bladder wall from the urine into the blood stream.

A further difference from mammals is an interrelationship of the Brunn response with ionic fluxes. Active uptake of sodium is increased by the water-balance response in the skin, in the bladder, and in the kidney tubules. It will be recalled that in mammals the hypothalamic hormones are concerned only with the movement of water, not with ionic fluxes. Thus the water-balance response has its own distinguishing characteristics, both in its sites and in its modes of action. It is, in fact, a response peculiar to amphibians, related to their own particular needs, and found in no other class of vertebrates. Force is given to this conclusion by another consideration: the very precise way in which the response is adapted within the Class Amphibia to the varying risks of water deprivation encountered by different species. For example, the toad *Bufo* is more fully terrestrial than is the frog *Rana*, and the former shows a stronger water-balance response. *Xenopus*, which is a permanently aquatic toad, differs from both in showing virtually no response at all. Similarly, the permanently aquatic urodele *Necturus* shows a much weaker response than does either *Rana* or *Bufo*. Such relationships are what one expects to find in adaptations that have become established by natural selection acting with different degrees of intensity in different ecological conditions.

The differences between amphibians and mammals are not confined, however, to the gross physiological effects of the polypeptides; it is now known that the hormonal molecules concerned are also different. Evidence that this was probably so was formulated by H. Heller in 1941, when he showed that the amounts of mammalian oxytocin and vasopressin required to evoke the water-balance response was far in excess of the oxytocin-like and vasopressin-like activity actually present in the frog's pituitary.

RESULTS

IS THE "WATER BALANCE" PRINCIPLE IDENTICAL WITH ANY OF THE KNOWN HORMONES OF THE POSTERIOR PITUITARY GLAND? It will be noted (*Figs.* [*4-17, 4-18*]) that the weight of a series of frogs each injected with the extract of one frog pituitary gland increases for over 5 hr., reaching a maximum of over 10% above the initial weight. It was mentioned above that the antidiuretic activity of one frog pituitary gland equals about 3.5 mU. pitressin [Heller, *Journal of Physiology*, 99 (1941), 246]. *Fig. [4-17]* shows that the injection of 10 mU. of pitressin [a commercial preparation rich in vasopressin] per frog has practically no effect on the water balance. An increase of the duration and intensity caused by the extract of a single frog pituitary gland can, therefore, hardly be explained by its content of antidiuretic activity. The dose of a commercial (mammalian) post-pituitary extract which has to be injected to obtain an effect comparable to that of the extract of a single frog pituitary gland, amounts to about 800 mU. *(Fig. [4-18]).*

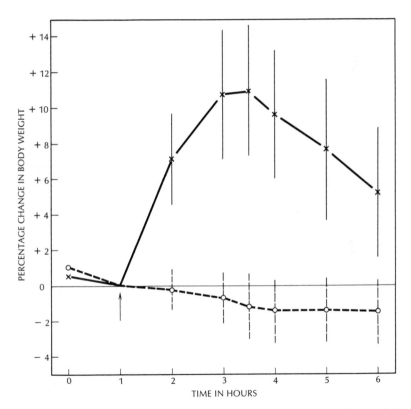

Fig. 4-17. The difference between the effect on the water balance of frogs of the extract of a single frog pituitary gland and of 10 mU pitressin. Note that the maximum antidiuretic activity of a frog pituitary gland was found to equal 5 mU pitressin. X——X mean percentage changes in weight of twenty frogs injected with the extract of one frog pituitary gland each. O——O indicate the same frogs injected with 10 mU pitressin each. The vertical lines indicate the standard error. In this, and in following experiments, the significance of the differences observed was investigated by Fisher's "*t*" test. The following figures were obtained for the present experiment: *t* (for maximum increases of weight) = 2.76, *P* 0.02. (From H. Heller, *Journal of Physiology*, 100 (1941), 127. With permission of the Editorial Board of the *Journal of Physiology*.)

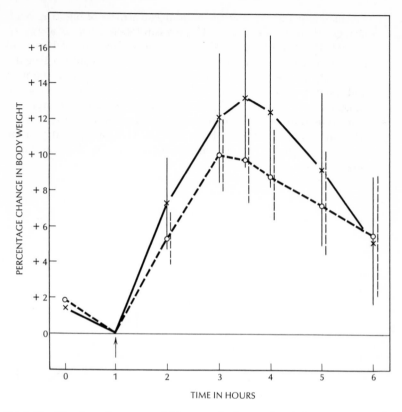

Fig. 4-18. The dose of a commercial (mammalian) posterior pituitary extract required to equal the water-balance activity of an extract of a single frog pituitary gland. X——X mean percentage changes in weight of twenty frogs injected with the extract of one frog pituitary gland each. O——O same frogs injected with 800 mU of B.D.H. posterior pituitary extract each. Injections at the time marked by arrow. The vertical lines indicate the standard error. The values for standard errors indicated by broken lines and belonging to the graph indicated by broken lines were obtained at the same relative times as those shown in full lines but are placed alongside for technical reasons. *t* (for maximum increases of weight) = 0.73, *P* < 0.5. (From H. Heller, *Journal of Physiology*, 100 (1941), 128. With permission of the Editorial Board of the *Journal of Physiology*.)

The objection could be raised that the action of commercial post-pituitary extracts is modified by the more complicated methods used for its preparation. Rat pituitary extracts, prepared in the same manner as the frog pituitary extracts, were therefore assayed for their effect on the frog's water balance. Table [4-5] shows that the extract of one rat pituitary gland, which contains about 1000 mU. of the antidiuretic hormone (Heller, 1941a), causes a smaller increase of the body weight of frogs than the extract of one frog pituitary gland which contains the equivalent of 3.5. It seems therefore justifiable to assume that the principle causing the changes of the body water of frogs (water balance principle) and the post-pituitary antidiuretic hormone are not identical. This conclusion agrees with earlier results [Heller and others], which proved that the vasopressor-antidiuretic fraction of post-pituitary extracts had a considerably weaker action on the water uptake of frogs than the oxytocic fraction.

This suggests the possibility of an identity of the oxytocic hormone with the amphibian water-balance principle. The oxytocic potency of frog pituitary extracts was, therefore, determined. *Fig. [4-19]* establishes it at considerably less than 40 mU. (oxytocic) per one frog pituitary gland. These results suggest strongly that the effect on the water balance of frogs exerted by the extract of frog pituitary glands is not due to their oxytocic activity. The difference between the action of an injection of 40 mU. of pitocin [a commercial preparation rich in oxytocin] per frog and the effect of an injection of the extract of one frog pituitary gland per frog is clearly shown in *Fig. [4-20]*.

The discrepancy between the average amounts of the antidiuretic principle (about 3.5 mU.) and of the oxytocic principle (less than 40 mU.) contained in the pituitary gland of the frog is more apparent than real. The extracts used for the determination of the oxytocic potency were crude and contained small amounts of impurities which had an oxytocic effect. A slight fall of blood pressure was regularly observed when the extract of a frog pituitary gland was injected into the vein of a spinal cat (*Fig. [4-21]*, p. 170). This finding indicates the presence of histamine-like impurities which enhance the oxytocic potency of crude frog pituitary extracts. *Fig. [4-21]* also shows that the pressor effect of the extract of a single frog pituitary gland is negligible. It is

TABLE 4-5

Comparison Between the Effects of Frog and Rat Pituitary Extracts on the Water Balance of Frogs.[a]

Time after Injection (hr.)	Series A* Percentage Changes of Body Weight	Series B* Percentage Changes of Body Weight
1.0	+3.3 ±1.3	+ 7.5 ±2.51
2.0	+4.4 ±1.08	+11.6 ±3.47
2.5	+4.2 ±0.73	+12.6 ±2.19
3.0	+3.6 ±0.94	+12.6 ±2.03
4.0	+2.9 ±1.13	+10.9 ±2.55
5.0	+2.1 ±0.86	+ 8.3 ±2.39
24.0	+0.7 ±2.24	− 0.5 ±1.80

[a] From H. Heller, *Journal of Physiology*, 100 (1941), 129.

* Series A = ten frogs injected with extract of one rat pituitary gland each; Series B = ten frogs injected with extract of one frog pituitary gland each. Weight immediately after injection = 100%. t (for maximum weight increases) = 3.34, $P < 0.01$.

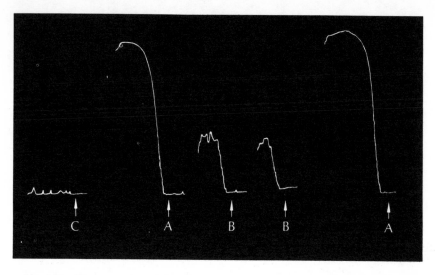

Fig. 4-19. The oxytocic activity of an extract of one frog pituitary gland. Isolated uterus of guinea-pig. Read from right to left. *A, A* = 8 mU posterior pituitary extract B.D.H. *B, B* = 20 volume % of extract of one frog pituitary gland. *C* = control extract of indifferent frog brain. The extract of one frog pituitary gland contains less than 40 mU of the post-pituitary oxytocic principle. (From H. Heller, *Journal of Physiology*, 100 (1941), 131. With permission of the Editorial Board of the *Journal of Physiology*.)

certainly much less than that caused by 40 mU. of post-pituitary mammalian extract, i.e. a twentieth of the amount which has been shown (*Fig.* [*4-18*]) to be just sufficient to reproduce the effect on the water balance of an extract of a single frog pituitary gland.

THE CONTENT OF WATER-BALANCE PRINCIPLE OF THE PITUITARY GLANDS OF VARIOUS VERTEBRATE CLASSES: . . . When comparing the water-balance activity of mammalian and non-mammalian pituitary extracts the objection could be raised that the lower water-balance activity of the mammalian extracts is apparent rather than real because their high content of vasopressor-antidiuretic principle interferes with the estimation of the water-balance activity. It is conceivable, for instance, that the absorption from the lymph sac is impeded by a high concentration of the vasopressor principle. If that were so one would expect "pituitrin" [commercial extract of posterior lobe] to have a smaller effect on the water balance of frogs than the equivalent dose (equivalent as to oxytocic activity) of "pitocin." However, according to Boyd and Brown [*American Journal of Physiology*, 122 (1938), 191] this is not the case. It can also be shown that the water-balance effect of frog pituitary extract is not significantly altered if amounts of a mammalian vasopressor-antidiuretic preparation are added which raise the antidiuretic potency of frog pituitary extracts to the level of mammalian pituitary extracts. An experiment on ten frogs gave the following figures: (*a*) maximum increase in body weight of frogs each injected with 50 mU. of "specially prepared" pitressin = 1.4 ±1.73%. Weight at time of injection = 100%; (*b*) maximum increase in body weight of the same frogs each injected with the extract of one-third of a frog pituitary gland = 7.7 ±3.58%; (*c*) maximum increase in body weight of the same frogs each injected with the extract of one-third of a frog pituitary gland to which 50 mU. of pitressin had been added = 8.0 ±3.65%. The difference between (*b*) and (*c*) is not significant as $t = 0.06$ and $P > 0.9$.

THE SITE OF FORMATION OR STORAGE OF THE WATER-BALANCE PRINCIPLE IN THE PITUITARY GLAND: The experiments so far reported

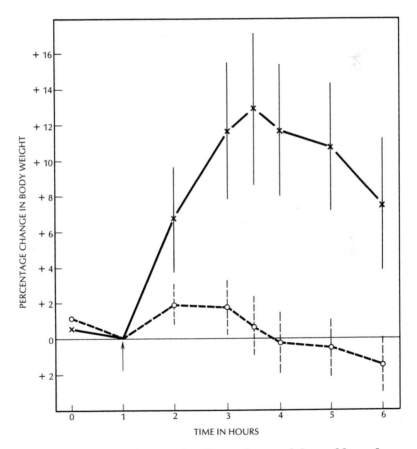

Fig. 4-20. The difference between the effect on the water balance of frogs of an extract of a single frog pituitary gland and of 40 mU pitocin (see Figure 4-17). X———X mean percentage changes in weight of twenty frogs injected with extract of one frog pituitary gland each. O———O same frogs injected with 40 mU pitocin each. Injections at the time marked by arrow. t (for maximum increases of weight) = 2.58, $P < 0.02$. (From H. Heller, *Journal of Physiology*, 100 (1941), 129. With permission of the Editorial Board of the *Journal of Physiology*.)

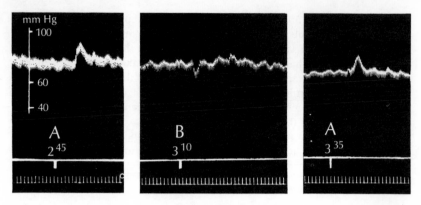

Fig. 4-21. Effect on blood pressure of spinal cat of extract of one frog pituitary gland. *A* = intravenous injection of 40 mU pitressin. *B* = intravenous injection of extract of one frog pituitary gland. Time marker = 10 seconds. The frog pituitary extract contains less than the equivalent of 40 mU of vasopressor principle. Note slight fall of blood pressure after injection of frog pituitary extract indicating presence of histamine-like impurity. (From H. Heller, *Journal of Physiology,* 100 (1941), 131. With permission of the Editorial Board of the *Journal of Physiology.*)

were performed with extracts of the whole pituitary gland. It was therefore impossible to say whether the water-balance principle was a posterior or an anterior pituitary hormone. The action on the water balance of frogs of mammalian posterior pituitary extract suggests the pars nervosa as the site of formation or storage in that class of vertebrates. In addition Biasotti showed in 1923 that mammalian anterior pituitary extract failed to influence the water balance of frogs. I repeated Biasotti's experiments using freshly prepared extracts of cat anterior pituitary lobes and obtained equally negative results. However, these findings do not necessarily apply to the pituitary glands of lower vertebrates. . . . The pars anterior of frog glands was separated from the neuro-intermediate lobe in the following manner. The frog was decapitated and the skull opened from the dorsal surface. Using a dissection microscope, the olfactory lobes were pushed back with a blunt needle. The second and third nerves and the optic chiasma were cut and the brain pushed backwards until the pituitary gland became plainly visible. The anterior lobe was removed with the help of one sharp and one blunt needle, quickly rinsed in a drop of saline and put into a test tube containing 0.25% acetic acid. The remaining pituitary tissue was removed with a pair of fine pincers and the cranial cavity cleaned with a small swab of cotton wool. The swab and the brain tissue proximal to the pituitary gland were added to the posterior lobe fraction. A comparison of *Fig.* [*4-17*] and *Fig.* [*4-22*] shows that extracts of the frog pars nervosa prepared in this manner have quantitatively much the same effect as those of the whole pituitary gland, indicating that little of the active material had been lost in the process of separation. *Fig.* [*4-22*] shows also that extracts of the anterior lobe had no noticeable effect on the water uptake of frogs.

It seems sufficiently clear from these results that in the species of vertebrates investigated the posterior lobe must be regarded as the site of formation or storage of the water-balance principle.[3]

From these and other results, which included data obtained from the pigeon and the cod, Heller concluded that the secretion extracted from the amphibian neurohypophysis must differ from that extracted from the homologous mammalian structure, and that the water-balance principle was not identical with any of the known posterior pituitary hormones. Yet it was not possible then to give greater pre-

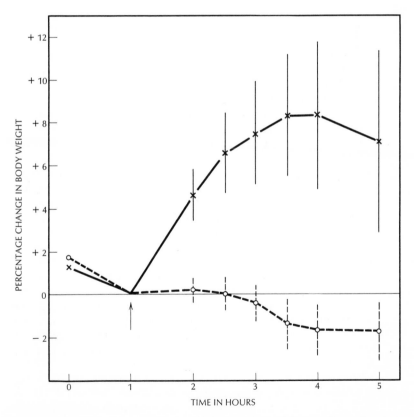

Fig. 4-22. Difference between the water-balance activity of *frog* anterior and posterior pituitary extracts. X——X mean percentage changes in weight of twenty frogs injected with extract of one frog posterior pituitary lobe each. O——O same frogs injected with extract of one anterior pituitary lobe each. Injections at the time marked by arrow. *t* (for maximum increase of weight) = 2.76, $P < 0.02$. Note that anterior lobe extract fails to increase the water uptake of frogs. (From H. Heller, *Journal of Physiology*, 100 (1941), 137. With permission of the Editorial Board of the *Journal of Physiology*.)

cision to this conclusion, for the chemical constitution of the mammalian hormones was still unknown. Indeed, it was not even clear at that time whether or not oxytocin and vasopressin were indeed two separate hormones, or whether they were two component parts of a larger single molecule. Further clarification did not result until 1959, by which time V. du Vigneaud had resolved this last problem by synthesizing the molecules of these two polypeptide hormones. In addition, he was able to synthesize analogues of them, that is, molecules of the same basic structure but with arbitrarily determined differences in amino-acid composition. In the course of these studies he had synthesized the compound that became known as arginine vasotocin (*Fig. 4-9*, p. 144).

In connexion with the programme being carried out in this Department on the relationship of the structures of the posterior pituitary hormones to their biological properties, an analogue was synthesized containing the ring of oxytocin attached to the side-chain of arginine vasopressin; for convenience, this substance was called arginine vasotocin. This highly purified compound was tested for its uterus-contracting activity with the isolated rat uterus and for its pressor activity in the rat. Our best information at the present time is that the arginine vasotocin has approximately twice the rat-uterus contracting activity and about one-fourth the rat-pressor activity of arginine vasopressin.

Although the arginine vasotocin is not as active with regard to pressor activity as arginine vasopressin, the high pressor activity of the vasotocin is noteworthy in indicating the contribution to pressor activity of the basic amino-acid in the side-chain, since oxytocin, which differs from arginine vasotocin in having leucine in place of arginine in the side-chain, has approximately one-tenth the pressor activity of the arginine vasotocin. The results also indicate that the phenylalanine in the ring of arginine vasopressin is of significance to pressor activity, since the vasopressin is more active than vasotocin, which has *iso*leucine in place of the phenylalanine. Furthermore, the fact that arginine vasotocin has twice the oxytocic activity of arginine vasopressin indicates that *iso*leucine in place of phenylalanine raises the oxytocic activity. In other words, replacement of phenylalanine by *iso*leucine has decreased the pressor activity and raised the oxytocic activity.

Because of the interesting pharmacological properties of arginine vasotocin, a sample of the synthetic product was made available to Prof. H. B. van Dyke for more extensive pharmacological investigation.

In view of the strong evidence of the possible occurrence of arginine vasotocin in non-mammalian sources adduced by Sawyer, Munsick and van Dyke . . . and the possible correlation of their work with the results of Pickering and Heller . . . on the occurrence of an active peptide in certain non-mammalian vertebrate neurohypophyses, it was felt that this brief communication on arginine vasotocin would be appropriate.

If subsequent chemical results substantiate the evidence for the occurrence in nature of arginine vasotocin, the synthesis of the arginine vasotocin would represent a remarkable example of the synthesis of a polypeptide hormone before its identification as a natural product.[4]

Heller and B. T. Pickering in the work to which P. G. Katsoyannis and Du Vigneaud referred, had used paper chromatography to separate two polypeptide hormones from pituitary extracts obtained from fish and amphibians. They had eluted these two compounds from the paper and had shown that one had pharmacological properties very similar to those of mammalian oxytocin, while the other differed from mammalian vasopressins in having a very marked frog water-balance activity. They had inferred that teleosts and amphibians might be secreting a polypeptide different from any found in mammals.

Meanwhile, W. H. Sawyer and his colleagues had shown that the pharmacological spectra of neurohypophyseal extracts prepared from the green turtle, the bullfrog, the American toad, the pollack, and the marine lamprey were consistent with the assumption that they contained arginine vasotocin, whose pharmacological spectrum was also well established. In particular, they showed the high level of frog-bladder activity which is characteristic of the compound. Further, they concluded that in all of these animals, excepting the lamprey, there was also an oxytocin-like compound, indicated by the level of action of the extracts on the rat uterus, which was greater than was given by arginine vasotocin alone (Table 4-6).

From all of these results it now seemed likely that arginine vasotocin was a hypothalamic polypeptide of many lower vertebrates, that it was the long-postulated substance that mediated the water-balance response of amphibians, and that, as Du Vigneaud suggested, it had indeed been synthesized before it had been discovered as a hormone. This conclusion has since been amply confirmed, but the facts have proved to be much more complex than could have been envisaged in 1959. It is now clear from the work of a number of laboratories, including those mentioned above and others in France and elsewhere, that a number of polypeptide hormones are secreted in the hypothalamus of vertebrates, and that these compounds show from group to group a degree of molecular variation that, while small in extent, materially affects their properties. The facts of the situation are still being unraveled, and new results are constantly making it necessary to revise earlier hypotheses. As far as present information goes, however, it appears that the vasopressins are

TABLE 4-6

Pharmacological Spectra of Frog and Turtle
Pituitary Extracts and of Arginine Vasotocin.[a]

	Arginine Vasotocin (U/mg)	Frog Neuro-intermediate lobe extract (U/mg)	Turtle Neuro-intermediate lobe extract (U/mg)
Rat vasopressin	64.	0.52	4.8
Rat antidiuresis	74.	0.48	6.0
Rat uterus, no Mg.	37.	0.59	5.4
Rat uterus, with Mg.	71.	0.72	9.9
Rabbit milk ejection	79.	0.81	9.7
Hen oviduct	640.	3.5	45.
Toad water balance	c.60.	c.0.23	—
Frog bladder	10,000.	79.	1060.
Frog antidiuresis	19,000.	190.	—
Frog sodium uptake	4,400.	47.	—
$\dfrac{\text{Rat uteris, no Mg}}{\text{Rat vasopressin}}$	0.59	1.13*	1.12*
$\dfrac{\text{Frog bladder}}{\text{Rat vasopressin}}$	160.	152.	221.

[a] Data selected from W. H. Sawyer, R. A. Munsick, and H. B. van Dyke, *General Comparative Endocrinology*, 1 (1961), 32.

* Ratios marked with asterisk differ significantly ($P < 0.01$) from the corresponding activity ratios for arginine vasotocin.

peculiar to mammals, and that oxytocin is found only in that group and in birds. Other groups have other polypeptides which differ in amino acid substitutions, just as do oxytocin and the two vasopressins.

Only one hypothalamic polypeptide has been identified so far in the cyclostomes, i.e., arginine vasotocin *(Fig. 4-9)*. For the present this may be considered the primitive condition in vertebrates. Arginine vasotocin persists throughout the vertebrates, up to and including the birds, but in mammals it has been replaced by the vasopressins. It will be noted *(Fig. 4-9*, p. 144) that arginine vasopressin could be derived from arginine vasotocin by a single substitution which could conceivably be the result of a single mutation. Since arginine vasopressin has been identified in monotremes and marsupials, it seems likely that the transition occurred during the period when mammals were evolving from reptiles.

All vertebrates above the cyclostomes have at least two hypothalamic polypeptides. Amphibians, in addition to their arginine vasotocin, have mesotocin; this compound, taking the place of the oxytocin of birds and mammals, has now been identified as the oxytocinlike compound mentioned in the studies just quoted. Mesotocin and oxytocin, like vasotocin and arginine vasopressin, differ by only one substitution (*Fig. 4-9*, p. 144). Mesotocin is found also in lung-fish; of all living fish these are the ones that are most closely related to the amphibians, and it is particularly interesting that the endocrine systems of these two groups should share a common feature of molecular organization. The situation in the dominant group of living bony fish (the teleosts and their relatives) differs from this, for R. Acher and his colleagues in France have shown that these animals have in place of mesotocin, another polypeptide called isotocin (or ichthyotocin). This molecule, which is now known to be the oxytocinlike compound described in earlier work, differs from all the others in having a substitution at position 4, a peculiarity in line with the fact that teleosts are, in many features of their organization, a highly specialized side line of vertebrate evolution.

The history of the corticosteroids has been very much simpler than that of the hypothalamic polypeptides. Cortisone, cortisol, and corticosterone, the primary mammalian hormones, have been identified in one or another of the remaining vertebrate groups, and there is no evidence that in the lower forms the corticosteroid hormones differ from those of mammals. So far, however, aldosterone has not been identified in either cyclostomes or fish. This may be a consequence of the difficulty of identifying a hormone that, even in mammals, is present in only very small amounts; but it may mean that this hormone did not become functional until the assumption of terrestrial life and the accompanying increased demands for regulation of the composition of the body fluids. This, again, can be a matter only for speculation, until further evidence is provided.

Assuredly, there are great difficulties in extracting from these facts a unified picture of the regulation of vertebrate water and ion metabolism and the adaptive changes in mechanism that have accompanied their evolutionary history. There is, indeed, little that can usefully be said at this stage about cyclostomes and fish. The design of experiments in this field is, unfortunately, greatly complicated by the sensitivity of fish to handling. The introduction of techniques of remote control have been of value, however; and certain experiments designed along these lines have given some evidence that both hypothalamic polypeptides and corticosteroids do influence the flux of sodium through the gills of the lamprey, the eel, and the trout. That the gills should be a target tissue of these hormones is to be expected, in view of the known importance of these organs in ionic regulation. It is impossible as yet to judge, however, whether these effects are of any physiological significance in the lives of these animals, or whether they are simply pharmacological properties that are manifest under artificial experimental conditions.

It should be remembered that most fish live in a stable environment where there is no shortage of water, and where the ionic composition remains substantially constant. It may be, then, that with the exception of euryhaline species, which migrate between sea and fresh water, hormonal regulation of ionic movements is not ecologically necessary for them. Nevertheless, the pituitary of fish is known to secrete corticotropin, and their adrenocortical tissue is certainly dependent upon the presence of the pituitary gland for its normal functioning. This implies that the corticosteroids must be of importance to them in some way. For the present, one must consider this field of vertebrate physiology as an area demanding a great deal of further research. From this may come unexpected results, as has already been shown in recent studies of the role of prolactin in certain teleosts.

The hormone prolactin, secreted by the adenohypophysis, is essential in the female mammal for full differentiation of the mammary gland tissue and is responsible for the initiation of lactation after the young have been born. In certain birds it is involved in a somewhat analogous function. Doves and pigeons produce in their crops a nutritive product called crop "milk," which is fed to the newly hatched young. The production of this material, which consists of desquamated epithelial cells, is a specific response to the action of prolactin and can, in fact, be used as a biological assay for mammalian prolactin. Further, this hormone is involved in the formation of the richly vascularized patches of skin called incubation patches that develop in many species of birds during the period of incubation. These phenomena show in an interesting way the action of a hormone upon quite different target tissues in two different groups, although there is admittedly some functional uniformity, in that all of the effects are related to reproductive and maternal activities.

What is altogether more surprising is to find that prolactin is involved in ion metabolism in certain teleost fish. It is now known that certain of these animals, including *Fundulus heteroclitus* and *Poecilia latipinna*, cannot survive in fresh water after hypophysectomy. *Poecilia*, however, which can normally live either in fresh water or in the sea, can survive in salt water in the absence of its pituitary. These effects are associated with disturbances in ionic balance. Loss of the pituitary is followed by a fall in blood chloride and sodium, and it is this fall that leads to death. It might be thought, in view of the previous discussion, that this would most likely be a result of a disturbance of adrenal function consequent upon the loss of corticotropin. This, however, is not so, for the hormone actually involved is prolactin. Administration of this hormone, or of whole pituitary extracts in which it is present, will correct the ion balance in the hypophysectomized fish and will maintain them alive for an indefinite period (Table 4-7).

TABLE 4-7

*Plasma Sodium and Potassium Concentration
in Adult Female* Poecilia latipinna.[a]

Treatment	Number of Fish	Sodium (m-equiv./1)	Potassium (m-equiv./1)
1. Intact, 6 weeks in D.S.W.	10	163.3 ±0.45[*]	—
2. Intact, reared in F.W.	9	151.3 ±1.57	—
3. Hypox, 2 weeks in D.S.W.	7	160.3 ±0.82	—
Group A. Fish killed 18-24 hr. after transfer from D.S.W. to F.W.			
4. Intact	9	129.2 ±2.73	—
5. Hypox	5	88.1 ±2.96	—
Group B. Fish operated 3 days after transfer from D.S.W. to F.W., killed after 4 days.			
6. Intact controls at 3 days	8	148.7 ±1.25	9.4 ±0.27
7. Sham hypox, injected CMC	7	144.7 ±0.72	9.5 ±0.30
8. Hypox, injected CMC	10	111.2 ±1.34	9.8 ±0.92
9. Hypox, injected prolactin	10	141.5 ±1.81	9.8 ±0.66

[a] From J. N. Ball and D. M. Ensor, *Journal of Endocrinology*, 32 (1965), 269.
[*] Means ± standard errors.
D.S.W. = dilute sea water (12 parts/1000); F.W. = fresh water; hypox = hypophysectomized; CMC = 1% sodium carboxymethylcellulose in 0.6% NaCl solution (vehicle of prolactin preparation).
"t" test for sodium values: 1 and 2, $P < 0.001$; 1 and 3, $P < 0.01 > 0.001$; 1 and 4, $P < 0.001$; 2 and 4, $P < 0.001$; 4 and 5, $P < 0.001$; 2 and 6, $P = 0.3$; 6 and 7, $P < 0.05 > 0.02$; 7 and 8, $P < 0.001$; 7 and 9, $P < 0.001$; 8 and 9, $P < 0.001$. The differences between the potassium values were not significant.

Prolactin, then, apparently present throughout the vertebrate series from at least the fish upwards, reacts with target cells in a way that is quite unpredictable and that is still difficult to explain. It is obvious that the results of the above experiments further complicate any interpretation of the role of hypothalamic polypeptides and corticosteroids in regulation of water and ion metabolism in the lower vertebrates. As an example of the difficulties that must be explained, at least one fish (the eel) is able to survive in fresh water after hypophysectomy; and this may prove true of other fish also. Moreover, the involvement of prolactin in regulation of ion balance in fish seems to be a genuine physiological phenomenon, which is more than can be said to date of the actions of the polypeptides and corticosteroids.

It is fair to add, however, that there is some indication that prolactin, as well as its target tissues, may have undergone some evolutionary change. It is thought that fish prolactin is unable to produce quite the same stimulation of the pigeon crop as does the mammalian hormone, which suggests that during vertebrate evolution this particular molecule may have undergone structural changes that affect its activity. But this, too, is an aspect of the problem that is only beginning to receive intensive study. Generations of effort have been devoted to the study of physiological regulatory mechanisms in vertebrates. It is well to recognize that despite all of this there are still large areas in which one can do no more than frame broad hypotheses, using these as a basis for the planning of further investigations which in turn are certain to lead to modifications of these hypotheses.

One aspect of general evolutionary interest, however, can be usefully mentioned at this stage. It has been firmly established that the water-balance response of amphibians, despite its partial similarity to the antidiuretic response of mammals, is mediated by a hypothalamic polypeptide that differs from the two polypeptides present in the latter group. As previously suggested, the amino acid substitutions that are the basis of the variation within this set of compounds could each be the consequence of a single mutation. The evolutionary mechanics of the situation would then be simple, in the sense that such a mutation would readily spread in a group if it carried adequate selective advantage. This suggests an attractively simple hypothesis: that molecular evolution in these polypeptides might have taken place in response to the varying adaptive needs of the vertebrates, leading to the production of new hormones at periods of major transitions in the modes of life of these animals.

Unfortunately, the reality is not as simple as one might wish it to be. On the one hand, the distribution of the various polypeptides seems to be in general conformity with the phylogenetic relationships of the main vertebrate classes. On the other hand, it cannot be related easily to the changing adaptive requirements of those groups, for current knowledge provides no clear evidence of a new hypothalamic polypeptide being evolved to meet new adaptive needs. Thus, amphibians have drawn into use for their water-balance response a molecule that was already in existence and that had been available from the beginning of vertebrate history. As for the vasopressins of mammals, they are certainly new hormones that are not present, as far as is known, in lower forms; yet mammals have used these for the antidiuretic response that to some extent parallels a response mediated in amphibians by arginine vasotocin.

Similar complexities exist in the characteristically mammalian requirements for uterine contraction and milk-ejection, both of which depend upon oxytocin. While this substance is also present in birds, its effects in that group are so weak that some investigators have suggested it may be merely a vestigial hormone. Contrary to what might have been predicted, the contractions of the oviduct of birds, which are probably of some value in egg-laying and which superficially recall the uterine contractions of mammals, are not mediated by oxytocin at all but primarily by arginine vasotocin. Evidently, the relationships established between these hormones and the tissues that they regulate are complex and fall into no easily analyzable pattern.

No doubt, the evolution of the endocrine control of physiological regulatory mechanisms, as it is seen operating in vertebrates, has involved some degree of evolution of certain hormones. This has happened with the hypothalamic polypeptides and apparently with prolactin. Primarily, however, there has been a dependence upon evolution of the target tissue. Much of the hormonal equipment of vertebrates was laid down at a very early stage of their evolution and has remained surprisingly constant. The flexibility of endocrine regulation in evolution arises from the possibility of continuous adaptive modification of the target tissues to give responses that are adapted to the needs of particular groups in particular habitats. It may be helpful to think of the functional interrelationship between the messenger molecule and its target as having something in common with the interrelationship between a man-made guided missile and the target which it is designed to hit. For example, in amphibians but not in mammals, this relationship exists between corticosteroids and the skin and bladder; this is also true of the hypothalamic polypeptides. The principle is of wide application, operating throughout the endocrine system and always in relation to the characteristic modes of life of the groups concerned. Admittedly, from this point of view it is difficult to see why the hypothalamic polypeptides and prolactin should have evolved at all. At present, one can only speculate that their variability may be related to the variability of protein molecules, which leads to every species developing its own characteristic protein pattern. But the problem is manifestly one that needs much further study.

1. L. J. Henderson, *The Fitness of the Environment* (Boston: Beacon Press, 1958), pp. 111–112, 113–115, 118, 120–122. Reprinted by permission of the Beacon Press. Copyright © 1913 by The Macmillan Company.
2. Hans Selye, *The Stress of Life* (New York: McGraw-Hill Book Company, 1957), pp. 87–89, 97–98. Published in England by Longmans, Green & Co., Ltd. Reprinted by permission of the publisher.
3. H. Heller, "Differentiation of An (Amphibian) Water Balance Principle from the Antidiuretic Principles of the Posterior Pituitary Gland," *Journal of Physiology*, 100 (1941), 126–131, 133–137.
4. P. G. Katsoannis and V. duVigneaud, "Arginine Vasotocin," *Nature*, 184 (1957), 1465.

CHAPTER 5 ◙ Temperature
and Water

■ ANIMALS AS HEAT EXCHANGERS

It is a matter of common observation that both the activity and the
distribution of animals are influenced by the temperature of their
environment. This stems from the fact that the rates of animal metabolic reactions are, in general, accelerated by a rise of temperature
and depressed by a fall. However, it is the temperature of the body,
not that of the ambient environment, which is the ultimate determining factor; and these two are not necessarily the same. Moreover,
the temperature of the body may vary from point to point. Active
tissues will tend to have a higher temperature than inactive ones,
since the former are releasing more heat. The body surface may have
a temperature different from that of the inner parts, or core. On the
other hand, a well-developed circulatory system will tend to neutralize these differences, since it distributes heat around the body. There
is, therefore, an element of abstraction in the concept of body temperature, a consideration that becomes particularly important in
evaluating the thermal relationships of terrestrial vertebrates. This
consideration, however, can be neglected in a preliminary analysis,
and one can begin the study of this topic by recognizing that body
temperature is determined at any given moment by the balance existing between factors that are partly biological and partly physical. Of

these, the primary biological factor is the production of metabolic heat within the body, for naturally this tends to raise body temperature. The physical factors are those involved in the heat exchange that takes place between the animal and its environment; they comprise radiation, conduction, convection, and evaporation.

The radiation of heat is an electromagnetic phenomenon that is similar in character to the radiation of light. At low temperatures it is not a visible phenomenon, so that it is easy to overlook its importance. At higher temperatures, however, the maximum concentration of energy shifts toward the longer wave lengths of the electromagnetic spectrum, so that radiation now becomes associated with visible light. Exposure to visible solar radiation, therefore, provides animals with an important source of heat; but, since the body itself also radiates, the total effect of radiation will depend upon the balance established between uptake and loss of heat. This, in its turn, depends upon the difference between the temperature of the body and that of the environment. If, for example, the temperature of the body is above the ambient temperature, there will be a net heat loss as far as radiation is concerned. The rate of this loss can be expressed as $K(T_b - T_e)$, where K is a constant, and T_b and T_e are respectively the temperature of the body and the external environment. If, on the contrary, the temperature of the body is below that of the environment, then the opposite relationship is found, giving a net increase of heat.

Similar considerations apply to heat transfer by conduction and convection. Conduction is a form of heat transfer that takes place between two bodies when they are in contact with each other but are not undergoing any visible movement relative to each other. It thus depends solely upon molecular movement. The rate at which conduction takes place is proportional to the temperature gradient (i.e., the fall in temperature per unit length) and to the area across which conduction is occurring. It can be expressed in the formula

$$Q = \frac{kA(T_1 - T_2)}{x},$$

where Q is the rate of heat flow, A the sectional area, $T_1 - T_2$ the temperature difference, and x the thickness or distance through which conduction is taking place. The constant k is the coefficient of thermal conductivity, usually expressed in calories/sq cm/cm/sec/degree centigrade. The value of this coefficient can be of great biological importance. Thus the values for air and water are both low, being respectively 0.00005 and 0.0014. Air, indeed, is an exceptionally bad conductor of heat. In contrast, metals are good conductors, which is the reason they feel cold when warm hands touch them. As an example, the coefficient for copper is 0.93 at 10°C.

Heat transfer by convection involves detectable movements within the substance that is being heated, as compared with the purely molecular movement of conduction; thus it can take place only in gases and liquids. The movement is a consequence of the density of the substance varying with temperature, as in the familiar case of water, where heating of the bottom of a vessel results in water at that point becoming less dense and therefore rising. The importance of this form of heat transfer for animal life is that loss of heat from the surface of the body will heat the ambient medium, whether this be air or water, and will thus set up convection currents. These will then continue to promote the loss of heat, since they bring a continuous supply of the unheated medium to the surface. The rate of heat loss by convection may be taken as proportional to the temperature difference between the body surface and the surrounding medium.

The remaining factor to be brought into the analysis is evaporation, whose importance results from the fact that animals are open systems. This means that parts, at least, of an animal's body surface must be permeable, so that in terrestrial animals water will evaporate at these sites. Such a situation can be disadvantageous, for it can create a risk of dehydration. On the other hand, evaporation is potentially of great adaptive value because of the very high latent heat created during evaporation of water. Loss of water vapor from the body surface thus leads to a considerable loss of heat; and, because of this, evaporation is of the utmost importance in the regulation of body temperature of terrestrial forms. This clearly brings one back to an aspect of adaptive organization which has already been given some consideration: the unique value of the properties of water as a medium for the maintenance of life. It will thus be well to return at this point to Henderson's analysis, both to illuminate the arguments that so far have been developed and to prepare the ground for further discussion.

■ THERMAL PROPERTIES OF WATER

Henderson begins his discussion of the thermal properties of water by referring to its heat capacity, or, as it is usually termed, its specific heat.

> This quantity [of water] has the value of 1,000 for the interval between 0° and 1° centigrade, a number which is due to the choice of water in defining the calorie or fundamental unit of heat. The calorie, small calorie, or gram calorie is that quantity of heat which is required to raise the temperature of one gram of water through 1° centigrade. . . .
>
> The approximate specific heats of a variety of important substances are as follows: —

Water: liquid	1.00	Glass	0.20
solid	0.50	Sugar	0.30
gas	0.3-0.5	Ammonia, liquid	1.23
Lead	0.03	Chloroform	0.24
Iron	0.10	Hydrogen	3.4
Quartz	0.19	Alcohol	0.5-0.7
Salt	0.21	Hexane	0.50
Marble	0.22		

. . . The most obvious effect of the high specific heat of water is the tendency of the ocean and of all lakes and streams to maintain a nearly constant temperature. This phenomenon is of course not due to the high specific heat of water alone, being also dependent upon evaporation, freezing, and a variety of circumstances which automatically mix and stir water. But in the long run the effect of high specific heat is of primary importance. . . .

A second effect of the high specific heat of water is the moderation of both summer and winter temperatures of the earth. It is not easy to estimate the total magnitude of this effect, but the manner in which it comes about is well illustrated by the differences between seaboard and inland climates or between the climate of a large part of the United States, which is a continental climate, and that of Western Europe, which is essentially an insular climate. In the most extreme form such moderation of climate is to be observed on the high seas and upon small islands. There are found the smallest known differences between the mean temperatures of different months of the year and of different hours of the day, and the least tendency to violent changes of temperature. . . . It is unnecessary to discuss the effects upon living organisms of the equable temperature of the ocean and of the moderation of climate, for obviously we are here confronted by a true instance of regulation of the environment.

The high heat capacity of water operates in still another manner to regulate temperature upon the land and at the same time to increase the mobility of the environment of marine organisms. For directly or indirectly it is involved in the formation and duration of ocean currents, especially the movement of water in the depths from the polar to the tropical seas, and it determines the amount of heat carried by such currents. A similar and even more important "function" is the direct promotion of winds, with the resulting distribution of aqueous vapor throughout the atmosphere, a primary factor in the dissemination of water by means of the rainfall. Here the essential thing is the existence of a vast warm reservoir in the tropics and of two similar cold reservoirs at the poles. Under these circumstances the circulation of winds, bearing away water vapor from the tropical oceans, is inevitable, and the process is intensified by the high specific heat of water.

The living organism is directly favored by this same property of its principal constituent, because a given quantity of heat produces as little change as possible in the temperature of its body. Man is an excellent case in point. An adult weighing 75 kilograms (165 pounds) when at rest produces daily about 2400 great calories, which is an amount of heat actually sufficient to raise the temperature of his body more than 32° centigrade. But if the heat capacity of his body corresponded to that of most substances, the same quantity of heat would be sufficient to raise his temperature between 100° and 150°. In these conditions the elimination of heat would become a matter of far greater difficulty, and the accurate regulation of the temperature of the interior of his body, especially during periods of great muscular activity, well-nigh impossible. Extreme constancy of the body temperature is, of course, a matter of vital importance, at least for all highly organized beings, and it is hardly conceivable that it should be otherwise. In the first place marked influence of change of temperature will more than double the rate of chemical change. Secondly all living organisms contain both chemical substances and physico-chemical structures or systems which begin to be altered, and usually irreversibly altered, at a temperature which is very little above that of the human body. It is perhaps imaginable that conditions might be otherwise in beings of a very different kind, but to-day every chemist well knows that if he is to control a chemical process, almost the first desideratum is rigid regulation of the temperature at which the process takes place.

It is therefore incontestable that the unusually high specific heat of water tends automatically and in most marked degree to regulate the temperature of the whole environment, of both air and water, land and sea, and that of the living organism itself. Likewise the same property favors the circulation of water by facilitating the production of winds, besides contributing to the formation of ocean currents. Here is a striking instance of natural fitness, which in like degree is unattainable with any other substance except ammonia.[1]

Henderson dealt no less cogently with the many other thermal properties of water which, as he convincingly showed, contribute in a unique way to the maintenance of life. Water's high latent heats of melting and evaporation and its very high freezing point (perhaps 100°C above the average) prevent excessive falls in the temperatures of lakes and seas. These properties, together with the high specific heat of water, enable the oceans to exert a moderating effect upon terrestrial temperatures. Bodies of water at 0°C can warm up a very large amount of colder air, and yet, because they form relatively little ice, their permanency is not affected. It is worth emphasizing that the latent heat of evaporation of water is by far the highest known. Enormous amounts of heat are therefore taken up into the atmosphere when water vaporizes, particularly in the tropics; and this eventually warms other and cooler localities when the vapor condenses as rain. A comparable moderating effect is felt within the animal body, as will be discussed later in Chapter 6.

Finally, two other thermal properties are of great significance. The thermal conductivity of water, although low compared with metals that are good conductors, is yet very high for a liquid (0.0125, as compared with 0.00048 for alcohol); this favors the equal distribution of heat within the watery tissues of the animal body. Secondly, the behavior of water when it freezes is unique, in that its maximum density is at 4°C instead of at its freezing point (as with other common substances), so that ice forms on the surface. It is because of this that large bodies of water can remain in a liquid state in very cold climates. In the absence of this remarkable property, the distribution of life would be very much more restricted than it actually is.

Henderson concludes:

> Such are the facts which I have been able to discover regarding the fitness of water for the organism. The following properties appear to be extraordinarily, often uniquely, suited to a mechanism which must be complex, durable, and dependent upon a constant metabolism: heat capacity, heat conductivity, expansion on cooling near the freezing point, density of ice, heat of fusion, heat of vaporization, vapor tension, freezing point, solvent power, dielectric constant and ionizing power, and surface tension.
>
> In no case do the advantages which these properties confer seem to be trivial; commonly they are of the greatest moment; and I cannot doubt, even after allowances have been made for the probability of occasional fallacies in the development of an argument which, though simple, is beset with many pitfalls, that they are decisive. Water, of its very nature, as it occurs automatically in the process of cosmic evolution is fit, with fitness no less marvelous and varied than that fitness of the organism which has been won by the process of adaptation in the course of organic evolution.
>
> If doubts remain, let a search be made for any other substance which, however slightly, can claim to rival water as the *milieu* of simple organisms, as the *milieu intérieur* of all living things, or in other of the countless physiological functions which it performs either automatically or as a result of adaptation.
>
> In truth Darwinian fitness is a perfectly reciprocal relationship. In the world of modern science a fit organism inhabits a fit environment.[2]

The concluding remarks of that passage contain a challenge to those who live in an age of space travel and who, therefore, must take seriously the imaginative feats of writers of science fiction. A good case can be made for the supposition that elsewhere in the universe there may be many planets on which the course of chemical evolution has been similar to what is believed to have occurred on this earth. On such planets, life similar to man's may well exist. But what of the possibility that totally different conditions of chemical evolution may have resulted in the establishment of life which is different from life on earth but which is no less well fitted to the peculiar conditions of its own environment? In such worlds there may be other writers, extolling no less vividly than Henderson, the fitness of their own *milieu*.

Forty years ago these questions could not have been taken as seriously as they may legitimately be taken today. Had Henderson been writing now, he might well have explored further the intriguing similarities which exist in many respects between the properties of water and ammonia. The boiling point of liquid ammonia, although subzero, is still high when compared with many other liquids. Its specific heat is greater than that of water, its latent heat of vaporization is second only to that of water, and it has high powers of ionization, although its solvent capacity is inferior to that of water. Of course, a liquid medium is not the only requirement for the establishment of life as scientists understand it. No less essential are chemical systems for the transfer of energy, which on earth are based largely, although not exclusively, upon the capacity of iron to exist in oxidized and reduced forms that are readily interconvertible. Nevertheless, it is interesting to reflect that on Jupiter, within the limits of the earth's own solar system, there are probably large amounts of liquid ammonia under great pressure. As W. T. Williams suggests:

> It is at least chemically conceivable that in those eternally cold seas there may be swimming intelligent animals with an internal chemistry fundamentally very like our own; but if there are we shall never meet them face to face, for neither of us can enter the other's world and live.[3]

■ ESCAPE FROM TYRANNY

Conventional analysis of the thermal relationships of animals makes a distinction between poikilotherms and homoiotherms. Poikilothermal animals are those in which the body temperature varies with that of the external medium (*poikilos*, various), although it does not necessarily coincide with it. Homoiothermal animals are those that are able to maintain a constant body temperature (*homoios*, like) in the face of wide fluctuations in ambient temperature. Homoiothermy is characteristic of birds and mammals, but even the members of these two groups are not necessarily homoiothermal at the beginning of life; moreover, there is much specific variation in the constancy with which temperature is maintained in the adult. A further characteristic of homoiotherms, however, is that they maintain a high body temperature as well as a constant one; they are, therefore, often referred to as warm-blooded. Poikilotherms may also be warm, but this depends upon circumstances; often they are cold in comparison with the temperature of man's body, so that one refers to them as cold-blooded. This, however, is an oversimplification of the situation, which does scant justice to the devices by which the disadvantages of the poikilothermal habit are alleviated.

Poikilotherms face dangers (some of which were touched upon in Henderson's analysis) of both overcooling and overheating. As the temperature of an animal's body falls, metabolic processes become slower, with a consequent diminution of competitive efficiency. Eventually, the animal may become comatose and die, for it seems probable that active life depends upon the maintenance of a certain rate of energy production. One difficulty in securing this energy output may be that different enzyme systems respond differently to changes of temperature. Thus at very low temperatures these systems may get out of phase, with a resulting fatal disturbance of normal metabolism. But even without this difficulty, there is eventually the hazard of freezing to be confronted. The formation of ice crystals may be avoided if organisms are frozen very quickly; they may then be able to survive in what is called a vitrified condition. This happens, for example, if protozoa are transferred quickly to the temperature of liquid air. Such vitrified organisms can recover their normal activity, but recovery depends upon their being rapidly warmed. These conditions are obviously remote from those that animals normally encounter; freezing is likely to be slow and commonly fatal. The reasons for death occurring in these circumstances are not clear, but it is likely that various factors contribute. In part, the effect may be osmotic, for the formation of ice can lead to a rise in the electrolyte concentration in the remaining body fluids. Another factor may be mechanical injury, resulting from the formation of ice crystals within the cells.

The effects of overheating are no less deadly than those of overcooling and, like those of overcooling, are an inevitable consequence of the complex physico-chemical make-up of the animal body. Within certain limits a rise of body temperature will favor increased metabolic activity and may thus be expected to improve the speed and efficiency of response. Above these limits, however, metabolic integration is likely to be impaired by progressive destruction of enzymes, many of which are inactivated at various points within the range of 35–45°C. Even before this point, the increased expenditure of energy reserves at higher temperatures may begin to outdistance the capacity of the animal to replace them. Respiratory difficulties may also develop; for example, hemoglobin has a reduced affinity for oxygen at higher temperatures. Changes in molecular organization will also occur, and lipids may change their physical state, with damaging effects upon the selective permeability of cell membranes. No doubt it is the combination of these complex effects of increasing temperature that has established a figure of around 45°C as the common upper limit of heat tolerance. There are, however, exceptions to this; for example, some animals can live in warm springs, but they clearly depend upon exceptional adaptations and, in so doing, confirm the general rule.

These biological considerations, taken in conjunction with the physical principles already outlined, show again how hazardous is the maintenance of life upon the earth, even when one concedes the peculiar fitness of the environment that Henderson emphasized. Fortunately, however, nature has not readily accepted the full weight of the fetters imposed upon it by the physical conditions to which it is subjected, and it is certain that strong selection pressure must always have favored any device that would have tended to relieve animals from some of the restrictive hostility with which they are surrounded. Indeed, such devices are found throughout the animal kingdom, to an extent that varies with the complexity and adaptive potentialities of particular groups.

By analyzing more closely the dependence of metabolism upon temperature, one perceives examples of the adaptive devices mentioned above. The rate of most metabolic reactions (and, indeed, the rate of chemical reactions in general, regardless of whether they are organic or inorganic in context) are governed by a principle that is expressed in an equation formulated initially on empirical grounds by S. A. Arrhenius:

$$\frac{d}{dT} \ln k = \frac{\mu}{RT^2}.$$

This equation states the relationship between rate and temperature, k being the reaction velocity constant, T the absolute temperature, R the gas constant (1.986 cal/degree/mol) and μ a constant termed the temperature characteristic. The relationship appears as a straight line when the natural logarithms of the velocities are plotted as ordinates against the reciprocals of the absolute temperatures as abscissae, the slope of the line being given by the value μ/R (*Fig. 5-1*). The rate of the reaction will rise with rising temperature, but the rate of increase will not be linear; it will itself be accelerated as the temperature rises.

The value of μ is a characteristic of particular enzymes, regardless of the substrates with which they are interacting. Further, when μ values are calculated for biological reactions, they tend to remain constant over a wide range of temperatures. Because of this, it has been suggested that the value of μ for a particular complex reaction may actually be the temperature characteristic of some limiting step in the reacting system; but this suggestion has not been generally accepted. This is partly because it seems likely that the rates of

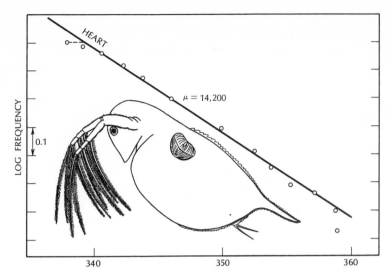

Fig. 5-1. Relationship between temperature and rate of heart beat of *Daphnia*, to illustrate the Arrhenius equation. Abscissae: 1/absolute temperature $\times$ 10^5. Ordinates: log of rate. (From T. C. Barnes, *Textbook of General Physiology* (New York: Blakiston Division, McGraw-Hill Book Company, (1947), p. 391.)

biological reactions are determined by many factors, such as membrane characteristics, which are additional to the enzyme-mediated systems involved in the reaction. Moreover, critics have claimed that the fitting of straight lines to Arrhenius plots is sometimes oversubjective.

It would seem adequate for the present discussion, and certainly simpler and more convenient, to express the relationship between temperature and metabolic rates in terms of a temperature coefficient, the Q_{10} value, derived from the equation

$$Q_{10} = \left(\frac{K_1}{K_2}\right)^{10/(t_1-t_2)},$$

where K_1 and K_2 are velocity constants corresponding to the temperatures t_1 and t_2. The Q_{10} value for a particular reaction is the factor by which the rate of the reaction is increased when the temperature rises by 10°C; for biological reactions it usually lies between two and three. It would be expected to remain constant for a particular reaction over the whole range of temperature in which the organism concerned was viable, if the Arrhenius relationship operated uniformly over that range. In fact, however, it commonly does not remain constant, so that in stating a Q_{10} value it is necessary to state also the range of temperature over which it was determined.

The variability of the Q_{10} temperature coefficient is of great interest

Fig. 5-2. Relationship between temperature and the rate of beat of the isolated heart of the frog in winter. *A.* Data plotted arithmetically. Circles, temperature falling; crosses, temperature rising; squares, temperature falling a second time. *B.* The same data, with the frequency plotted logarithmically. The areas represent the known experimental error. Open areas, temperature falling; black areas, temperature rising; checkered areas, temperature falling a second time. (From J. Barcroft and J. Izquierdo, *Journal of Physiology,* 71 (1930), 147-148. With permission of the Editorial Board of the *Journal of Physiology.*)

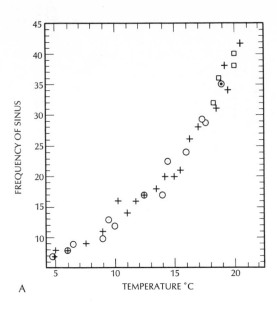

A

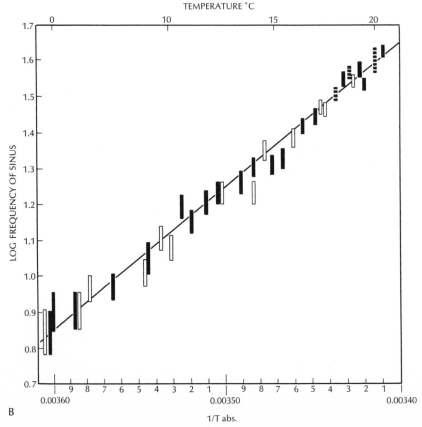

B

because of its adaptive potentiality. An example of it is seen in
J. Barcroft and J. J. Izquierdo's study of the rate of the frog's heart
beat. In this instance the effect of the variability is to depress the rate
of activity below that which would be found if it were increasing
logarithmically with a rise of temperature. In January the pulse rate
of the excised heart increased exponentially with rising temperature
(Fig. 5-2A); and, when plotted against the reciprocal of the absolute
temperature *(Fig. 5-2B),* it showed a logarithmic relationship in conformity with the Arrhenius equation. But this was only up to a temperature of 20°C. Beyond that point the heart ceased to function, as
though, to quote Barcroft, "the machine had jammed." Moreover, in
certain instances the pulse rate fell off at the higher temperature,
sometimes quite suddenly.

The capacity for departing from the simple logarithmic relationship became much more apparent in hearts that were tested in June,
whether these hearts were excised or in the intact animal. To quote
Barcroft again,

> The frequency of the sinus beat gradually fell further and further
> short of that demanded by the logarithmic relation as the tempera-
> ture rose, and indeed approximated to a new relation, namely a
> simpler arithmetical proportion between the temperature and the
> frequency *(Figs. [5-3A; 5-3B]).* In the case of the frog in summer there
> was some gradual influence which became more and more prominent
> as the temperature rose, which influence increasingly depressed the
> velocity of the pulse. What this influence was we did not know. The
> simplest assumption would be that the factors which in the winter
> time operated in spasms at certain given temperatures or not at all,
> in summer came into the field gradually, thus smoothing off the
> curves.

Whatever the explanation of these results, however, Barcroft concluded,

> It is clear that nature has learned so to exploit the biochemical situa-
> tion as to escape from the tyranny of a simple application of the
> Arrhenius equation. She can manipulate living processes in such a
> way as to rule, and not to be ruled by, the obvious chemical situation.
> That is true at least over a wide range of temperatures.[4]

■ ACCLIMATION, ACCLIMATIZATION, AND ADAPTATION

In analyses of the adaptive reactions of animals to their environment,
a distinction is often drawn between two types of response. One of
these is acclimation—modifications individually acquired by an organism as a result of its exposure to experimentally controlled condi-

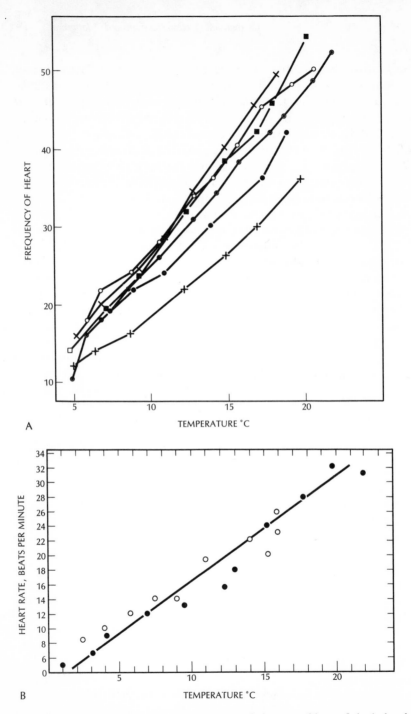

Fig. 5-3. *A*. Relationship between temperature and the rate of beat of the isolated heart of the frog in summer. *B*. The same relationship for the heart of the intact frog in summer. Open circles, temperature falling; black circles, temperature rising. (*A* from J. Barcroft, *The Architecture of Physiological Function*, London, Cambridge University Press, 1938, 49.) *B* from J. Barcroft and J. Izquierdo, *Journal of Physiology*, 71 (1930), 153. With permission of the Editorial Board of the *Journal of Physiology*.)

tions involving only one variable factor. This will be illustrated later, when examples of acclimation to temperature are given. Modifications can also be acquired by organisms as a result of exposure to a range of natural climatic conditions in which there are many variables. This process is called acclimatization.

Acclimation and acclimatization (the latter term is sometimes used to cover both processes) are special cases of adaptation. This phenomenon, which has provided the underlying theme of all earlier chapters, is expressed in many different ways at various levels of organization. At one extreme one finds relatively inflexible adaptive features that are inborn characteristics of a species. These are rigidly determined by coded instructions that have been built into the genotype under the influence of natural selection and have become established during the individual's development. Such characteristics, which are often referred to as genetic adaptations, may be uniform throughout a species; or they may differ from one population of a species to another, in adaptation to differences in the habitats of the populations. In such instances the extent of these differences will depend upon the degree to which the populations are reproductively isolated from each other; for some degree of isolation, with the consequent interruption in the flow of genes through the species, is needed to bring about this adaptive differentiation. In any case, genetic adaptations in the strict sense of the term are those that are laid down during early development and do not, therefore, have to be acquired individually by members of the species during their adult lives.

At the other extreme is a much more flexible pattern of adaptive organization, dependent in general upon complex systems of organs and facilitated by highly evolved neural and endocrine coordination. Here the functioning of an animal is continuously adjusted throughout its life in response to changes in its environment and demands that are made upon its body. To some extent, the distinction between these two types of adaptation is artificial, for the ability of an animal to respond in particular ways must be genetically determined, while the genetic type of adaptation need not be completely inflexible. The distinction, however, does have some validity, for it takes account of the marked variation in flexibility of response that one finds in comparing one group of animals with another. Nevertheless, it should not be pressed too far; in this instance, as is so often the case with biological phenomena, a continuous spectrum of variation leads from one extreme to the other.

Much of the discussion in earlier chapters has been concerned with the more flexible type of adaptive organization which, as the text has indicated, is expressed in many different ways. Sometimes, for example, it may be a prolonged response to a continuous stress, such as the adaptation of man to the hypoxia of great heights; or it may be expressed in the delicate adjustments that maintain homeostasis of mammalian body fluids in continuously changing circumstances. The less flexible genetic adaptations, however, also play an important part in the establishment of adaptive organization, although the extent of their contribution varies from group to group. This variation merits attention, for it has a bearing upon a fundamental aspect of evolutionary biology.

Customarily, one speaks of lower and higher animals, but one does not always pause to consider what is meant by this. It would probably be agreed, however, that part of the basis for the distinction is that lower animals are restricted in their choice of habitats and in their range of activities. Higher animals, by contrast, exploit the resources of the earth with greater freedom; they are found in habitats that impose greater barriers on the maintenance of life and, therefore, are more difficult to colonize. This, incidentally, is one of the respects in which man, as he feels his way into outer space, can truly claim to be the highest form of life. In this analysis there are obvious evolutionary implications, for one visualizes the history of life upon earth as involving a passage from lower to higher forms. The lower forms have a relatively simpler organization, associated with their more restricted adaptive powers; while the higher forms have a more complex organization that corresponds to their greater adaptive freedom.

It will be useful to recall these considerations during the following review of thermal responses. The text will compare the reactions of lower vertebrates, restricted to the relatively constant thermal conditions of aquatic habitats, with those of higher vertebrates that are able to exploit sea, land, and air. By reflecting on this comparison, one will perceive the importance of genetic adaptation in lower forms and the dependence of terrestrial and aerial vertebrates upon the more flexible patterns of response that enable them to flourish in their more exacting habitats. Yet, it must not be forgotten that there are stories in evolution other than those of the vertebrates, and that the course of progress has not always followed the vertebrate pattern. Within the arthropods, for example, there evolved the insects, a group whose superlative success in exploiting a wide range of environments is grounded in large measure upon the rigidity of genetic adaptation.

■ THE DEPENDENCE OF FISH UPON AMBIENT TEMPERATURE

The body temperature of fish follows the temperature of the environment far more closely than does that of the higher, terrestrial vertebrates. There are several reasons for this. First, by virtue of living in water, fish cannot lose water from their body by evaporation; thus they can never have a body temperature below that of their surroundings. On the other hand, it is normally impossible for them to maintain a temperature above that of the water. This is because heat is rapidly removed from the body by conduction and, more particularly, by convection, into the water around them; such loss is aided by the branchial circulation, which is as efficient in heat exchange as it must be in respiratory exchange. In these respects fish are no different from other aquatic poikilotherms; all such animals equilibrate very quickly with the temperature of the water around them.

There are ample data to illustrate this characteristic of poikilotherms. If the teleost *Lebistes* is transferred from water at 17.7°C to water at 13.1°C, the temperature of its muscles is found to have equilibrated with the lower temperature within one minute. So also with amphibians. The body temperature of a frog living in water is unlikely to be as much as 0.1°C higher than that of the water around it. When a frog is transferred from water at 6°C to water at 28°C, equilibration occurs rapidly, achieving an internal temperature of 26.8°C within the first five minutes. Here, of course, branchial circulation is not a factor, but its place is effectively taken by the extensive vascularization of the highly permeable skin.

One can see possibilities of slight departure from the general rule of coincidence between the internal temperature of aquatic poikilotherms and the temperature of the medium. For instance, the size of the body will tend to influence equilibration, so that the internal temperature of a large body may differ slightly from that of the medium. This may be particularly true after a period of very active movement or possibly after the animal has basked at the surface of the water in circumstances in which radiant heat might have been absorbed. Another possibility is that at very low temperatures the respiratory rate may be so reduced that the heat loss from the body is also significantly lowered. Thus it has been shown that the bullhead (*Ameiurus nebulosus*) in ice water may have an internal temperature as much as 0.5°C above that of the medium. However, such differences are so small that they serve to emphasize the general dependence of these animals upon the temperature of the water in which they are living. The restrictive influence of aquatic life upon body temperature has, in any case, a compensating advantage which follows from Henderson's analysis and which will become even more apparent when one considers the contrasted problems of terrestrial forms. This advantage derives from the high specific heat of water which exerts a stabilizing influence upon the temperature of the animals living in it, thereby buffering them both from the extremes and the large fluctuations of temperature that are encountered on land.

The fact remains, however, that fish are vulnerable to fluctuations of temperature which they are unable to avoid, so that one must ask what adaptations help to alleviate this unpromising situation. One factor is that fish have evolved tissues that can function over a wide range of temperatures, or, to put it another way, have a wide thermal tolerance. An extreme case is the goldfish, which can be kept alive over a temperature range of 2.0°C to 38.6°C. Other fish are less flexible in this respect. The Pacific salmon (*Oncorhynchus*), for example, is much more sensitive to higher temperatures and has an upper limit of about 25°C. It is remarkable that complex enzyme systems can continue to work harmoniously over such wide ranges of temperature. However, it does not follow that their efficiency remains unimpaired, and one cannot expect to find fish always living at the upper or lower limits of their thermal tolerance. It would be more efficient for them to live within a more restricted range, in which their tissues could function to the best advantage.

The arctic fish that will be mentioned later in this chapter can hardly be said to satisfy this expectation, but there are other fish in which it is justified. According to C. L. Hubbs, there are many lines of evidence supporting the conclusion that temperature is a factor of prime importance in determining the distribution of marine fish along the Pacific coast of North America. This region is particularly instructive, because at certain points there is an upwelling of cold water from the depths which lowers the surface temperature. Hubbs shows that the consequent temperature differentials are closely reflected in the distribution of certain species. He shows also that this temperature dependence can be used to explain some recorded characteristics of the nineteenth-century fauna.

> The prevalence along the Oregon and Washington coasts of upwelling which lowers the inshore surface temperature, seems to be associated with the absence there of certain fishes, such as the Californian reef klipfishes *Gibbonsia montereyensis* and *G. metzi*, that reappear in British Columbia. . . . The extremely cold water just south of Monterey Bay is correlated with the occurrence there of such northern reef fishes as *Scytalina cerdale, Phytichthys chirus, Artedius harringtoni*, and *Clinocottus embryum*.
>
> Warmer bays have a far more southern fauna than the adjacent open coast. Thus we note the occurrence of a southern pipefish, *Syngnathus arcta*, and the abundance of the least seaperch, *Micrometrus minimus*, and of a southern flatfish, *Hypsopsetta guttulata*, in Elkhorn Slough and Tomales Bay, central California. Morro Bay has a particularly southern fauna, in harmony with the warmth of its waters, caused by the extensive shoals of blackish mud. Here occur the California killifish, *Fundulus parvipinnis*, otherwise seemingly absent north of Santa Barbara, the southern California subspecies of the staghorn sculpin, *Leptocottus armatus*, and the northernmost population of the pipefish *Syngnathus griseo-lineata leptorhyncha*, separated from the main range of this subspecies by another subspecies, *S. g. barbarae*.
>
> The along-shore cooling effects of upwelling in Oregon and Wash-

ington are strikingly evident in the southward extension of the range of many subarctic fishes. Farther offshore, beyond the effects of upwelling, occur fishes of more southern types, such as the mola (*Mola mola*), albacore (*Germo alalunga*), bluefin tuna (*Thunnus thynnus*), and more southern types of sharks.

. . . The fish fauna of San Diego, as sampled from 1853 to 1860, particularly by the Pacific Railroad Survey from 1853 to 1857, was definitely more tropical than that of any subsequent decade. Of the 30-odd species reported, six (about 20%) do not now occur so far north or have been so rare recently that one certainly would not expect any to be caught at present by such incomplete and superficial collecting as that of the 1850's and 1860's. . . .

The air-temperature data for San Diego strongly suggest long-term climatic changes that correlate nicely with the observed faunal changes. The mean temperature seems to have been high during the early years of record, beginning in 1849-50 and continuing through the 1850 and most of the 1860 decades; that is, during the period when the fish faunas at San Diego and at Monterey were distinctly more southern than during any of the subsequent decades. From just before 1870 the general indicated trend was toward cooler weather until about 1910, after which there seems to have been a moderate reversion toward warmer conditions. In possible correlation, there is evidence — rather slight to be sure — that some subtropical fishes are becoming established in the San Diego area.[5]

The conclusion that the distribution of marine fish is influenced by sea temperatures carries the implication that the animals must have very delicate powers of temperature discrimination. Indeed, this has been clearly shown by H. O. Bull, who succeeded in establishing conditioned thermal responses in fish. The principle of his experiments was to place the fish in long tanks that were inclined at an angle. Water entered at the upper (higher) end and drained down to the lower end, where there was adequate depth of water for the fish to survive. When food was placed at the upper end of the tank, the fish moved toward it; but, in order to reach it, they had to splash their way where there was no water to cover them. The response was a difficult one to execute, and only the very strong incentive of the presence of food would have made them undertake it. By slightly increasing the temperature of the entering water, it proved possible to train the fish to associate the presence of food with a rise of temperature, until eventually they would give this exacting food-seeking response to temperature alone, in the complete absence of food. Thus a conditioned response of classical type had been established. In this way Bull was able to show that the cod (*Gadus callarias*), for example, could detect a rise of temperature of as little as 0.05°C. That is to say, this very small increase in temperature of the inflowing water would evoke by itself the food-seeking reaction.

Bull's results have since been confirmed by J. E. Bardach and R. G. Bjorklund, using a somewhat different procedure. In their experiments the conditioning stimulus was the very slow warming or cooling of an aquarium in which the fish were maintained. The rate of temperature change was 0.1°C per minute, food being placed in the tank after 20 minutes, when the temperature would have changed by 2°C. Remarkably enough, once the fish had been trained, they began to show food-seeking behavior within one-half to one minute after the beginning of the temperature change. This means that they were able to detect a change of ±0.05 to 0.1°C, spread over a period of one-half to one minute. Surely, it would be astonishing if man could train himself to detect a similar order of change as he lies in the bath!

It is still uncertain which particular receptors of fish are responsible for this thermal sensitivity. One belief that the ampullae of Lorenzini of dogfish are temperature receptors no longer has adequate experimental support; nor, indeed, is there any evidence that the normal behavior of selachians is controlled so delicately by the temperature of their environment. Even in teleost fish, the ecological significance of the findings of Bull and of Bardach and Bjorklund are not easy to estimate. The difficulty is that many species, when tested in the laboratory, prove to be relatively insensitive to the temperature of their environment; and, if they are offered a choice of temperatures, they do not necessarily choose a sharply defined one. Probably, as J. R. Brett suggests, the undoubted ability of these animals to perceive fine temperature differences may only be effectively exercised when it is evoked by particular internal conditions, for example, when they are engaged in migration or in some other aspect of reproductive behavior. It is possible, too, that their thermal perception becomes important when they are in danger of entering zones of unfavorable temperature. The behavior of these animals may thus be the result of a wide range of thermal tolerance in their tissues, combined with a precision of perception and response, when this precision becomes momentarily advantageous; on this basis, each species could achieve a characteristic total behavior pattern.

■ THE ADAPTATIONS OF FISH TO AMBIENT TEMPERATURE

The facts so far reviewed tend to emphasize the restrictive influence of ambient temperature upon the lives of fish. But fish have also developed adaptations that provide some degree of escape from this tyranny. This becomes apparent when comparison is made of natural populations living at different temperatures. Investigations of such populations starts with a commonplace observation, one that applies to invertebrates as well as to fish: poikilothermal species living in cold conditions (as, for example, in Arctic waters) commonly seem to be as active as related species living in warmer climates (as, for example, in the Mediterranean). This is not what one would expect on a strict operation of the Arrhenius relationship; rather, one would predict a depression of metabolic rate at the lower temperatures and hence reduced activity. However, if this did occur, the animals concerned would be experiencing some of the disadvantages of overheating or overcooling that were outlined earlier; it would be difficult, indeed, for them to maintain optimal activity. What has actually happened is that in many species (although this is not a universal rule) some genetic adaptation has evolved that ensures the maintenance of optimal activity in the particular thermal conditions to which the population or species is adapted.

This adaptation to environment can be simply illustrated by some examples taken from the extensive studies of Munro Fox. Fox compared various parameters of activity in different species of marine invertebrates taken from different latitudes, each species being adapted for life in water of a particular temperature range. The prawn *Pandalus borealis*, for example, is an arctic form; when collected in the neighborhood of Kristineberg, Sweden, it dies if the aquarium temperature rises above 11°C. Fox compared this species with a closely related one, *P. montagui*, taken from the English Channel at Plymouth, where the normal maximum sea temperature is 14–15°C. The respiratory rates of these two species at different temperatures, as shown in the rates of movement of their respiratory appendages, are shown in *Fig. 5-4*. It will be seen that the respiratory rate of *P. borealis* at 7.5°C, within its normal temperature range, is the same as that of *P. montagui* at 12°C, again within its normal range. In some way, then, each is adapted to the temperature at which it normally lives; their respiratory activities are similar, regardless of temperature, and do not fall within a simple Arrhenius relationship.

Previously, it was pointed out that such genetic adaptation is not an invariable rule. An example of its absence is seen when a similar comparison is made of the rates of ciliary current on the gills of *Chlamys septemradiata*, from Kristineberg, and *C. varia*, from Plymouth. The ciliary current is found to be more rapid in the Plymouth species *(Fig. 5-5)*. On the other hand, the type of genetic adaptation seen in *Pandalus* is not restricted to pairs of different species. As suggested earlier in general terms, it may occur also within a single species, when populations are living in widely different habitats. *Pandalus montagui* provides an illustration of this, for it is found both at Kristineberg and at Plymouth. *Figure 5-4* shows that the rate of beat of the respiratory appendages is the same in both regions, although the water is colder in the Swedish habitat. Adaptation within the species to two different habitats is shown by the rate at Plymouth at 16°C being the same as the rate at Kristineberg at 6°C. Through this adaptation the species evades the disadvantageous consequences

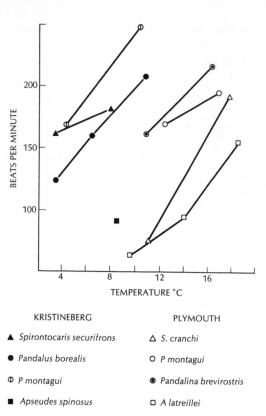

Fig. 5-4. Rates of movement of respiratory appendages of Crustacea at various temperatures. (From Munro Fox, *Proceedings of the Zoological Society of London*, 2 (1936), 952.)

KRISTINEBERG	PLYMOUTH
▲ *Spirontocaris securifrons*	△ *S. cranchi*
● *Pandalus borealis*	○ *P montagui*
⦶ *P montagui*	◉ *Pandalina brevirostris*
■ *Apseudes spinosus*	□ *A latreillei*

that would ensue if its rate of respiratory activity were rigidly controlled by the Arrhenius relationship.

This type of adaptation is certainly widespread in aquatic poikilotherms. One other example is the common jellyfish *Aurelia aurita*, which, like other medusae, swims by pulsations of its bell. Individuals taken from Nova Scotian waters, where the average temperature at the surface of the sea is about 14°C, pulsate actively over a range of 2-18°C and cease pulsating at a lower limit of −1°C and an upper limit of 29°C. In Florida waters, by contrast, 29°C is the normal mean surface temperature in summer, and this is found to be the optimum temperature for pulsation of individuals taken from those waters. In the latter individuals pulsation stops at a lower limit of 12°C and an upper limit of 36°C.

Substantial evidence for the existence of similar genetic adaptations in fish is found in the work of P. F. Scholander and his colleagues, who have analyzed also the ecological implications of their results. They compared the oxygen consumption at different temperatures of a series of arctic and tropical poikilotherms, including invertebrates as well as fish. Some of their results, obtained from fish kept for several hours in respiration chambers at controlled temperatures, are shown in *Figs. 5-6A, 5-6B*. It was found that the points relating oxygen consumption to temperature in the arctic fish were always displaced toward the lower temperatures (which lie to the left of the figures) in contrast to the tropical forms. Moreover, the arctic fish survived in ice-cold water and died at temperatures ranging from 10 to 20°C, whereas the tropical fish died at temperatures below 15 to 20°C but survived up to at least 35°C. These results indicate an inborn metabolic adaptation, the extent of which can be gauged from the broken line in *Fig. 5-7* (p. 205). This line shows what the curve for tropical fish would be if it were extrapolated to 0°C. It appears that if tropical forms were able to survive at this temperature, their metabolic rate would be thirty to forty times below the corresponding rate at 30°C. In contrast to this, the actual metabolic rate of arctic forms at 0°C, which is the normal temperature of their habitat, is only three to four times lower than that of tropical forms at 30°C. Thus there is a considerable metabolic adaptation in the arctic forms relative to the tropical ones, resulting in the metabolic rate of the former being maintained at a high level at low temperatures. Nevertheless, this adaptation must be judged incomplete, for the metabolic rate of arctic forms is still lower at any given temperature than is that of tropical forms of comparable weight at the same temperatures (*Fig. 5-7*).

Thus the data obtained from these metabolic studies do not wholly

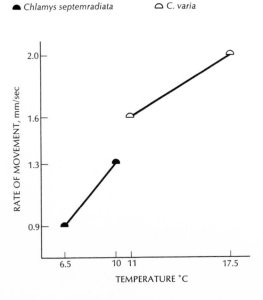

KRISTINEBERG   PLYMOUTH

● *Chlamys septemradiata*   ○ *C. varia*

RATE OF MOVEMENT, mm/sec

2.0
1.6
1.3
0.9

6.5   10 11   17.5

TEMPERATURE °C

Fig. 5-5. Rate of ciliary movement in *Chlamys septemradiata* and *C. varia* at various temperatures. (From Munro Fox, *Proceedings of the Zoological Society of London*, 2 (1936), 951.)

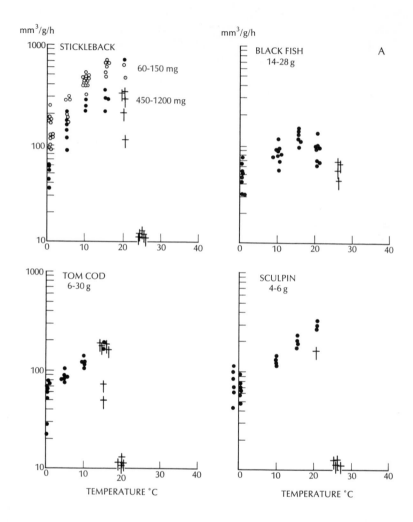

Fig. 5-6. Oxygen consumption at graded temperatures in arctic fishes (*A*) and tropical fishes (*B*). (From P. F. Scholander, W. Flagg, V. Walters, and L. Irving, *Physiological Zoology*, 26 (1953), 77. Published by the University of Chicago Press.)

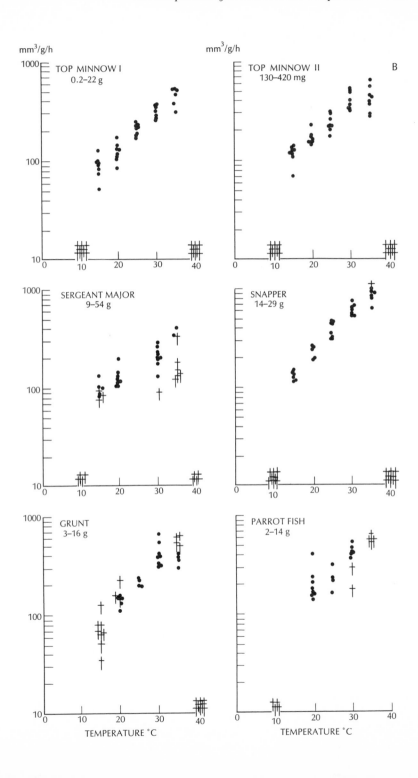

account for the ability of arctic forms to maintain a high level of activity at low temperatures. Scholander and his colleagues suggest, as a possible contributory factor, the ability of arctic forms, once they become active, to achieve especially high levels of metabolism relative to the level of their resting metabolism, which, of course, is the one measured in these experiments. This may well be so, but scientists still lack the information that would enable them to explain how such a high level of activity metabolism is reached and maintained.

Other examples of the success of animals in moderating the tyranny of thermal factors are found in the ability of certain species to resist conditions one would normally expect to result in freezing. This phenomenon is well known in insects, some of which can undergo substantial supercooling, a condition in which the temperature of fluids falls below their freezing point without ice crystals appearing. An extreme example of this is *Bracon cephi*, an insect parasite of the wheat stem sawfly, *Cephus cinctus*. Larvae of the parasite can live throughout the winter in wheat stems, where they are exposed above the surface of the snow to the full rigor of the Canadian climate. By late summer, when they spin their cocoons, they can already supercool to about −30°C; thereafter, the supercooling point falls, until by late November they are able to survive any but the most extreme of cold conditions.

Ordinary water, even under exceptionally favorable circumstances, cannot be supercooled below −41°C; but the presence of solutes lowers this limit by lowering the melting point. It is known that *Bracon* can supercool to the remarkably low temperature of −42°C, which clearly implies that some solute must be involved. G. Salt has shown that this solute is, in fact, glycerol, which accumulates in the hemolymph during fall and early winter to a concentration that may reach 5 molal. This lowers the melting point, which has been known to fall to as low as −17.5°C; thus the actual amount of supercooling is less than 40°C. In effect, then, the glycerol is acting as an antifreeze, which means that insects are foreshadowing man's use of such substances in automobile cooling systems. It is thought, however, that a further advantage of glycerol for the insect is that it protects the tissues from damage, even if freezing does occur, by ensuring that the concentration of electrolytes does not so readily reach toxic conditions. It may also be that the high viscosity of glycerol slows down the rate of formation of ice crystals and also modifies their pattern if they do form. In spring, the glycerol disappears. The value of its presence in winter is then readily demonstrable, for in spring the larvae are unable to survive freezing, nor can they do so in the early fall before glycerol has appeared.

The significance of free glycerol in *Bracon* was first demonstrated in 1958. Some years previously, however, it had been discovered

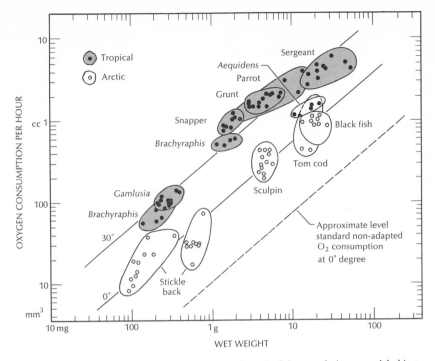

Fig. 5-7. Oxygen consumption in tropical and arctic fishes at their normal habitat temperatures. The tropical forms extrapolated to 0° would fall along the dotted line, some thirty to forty times below the rates at 30°. The arctic forms show a very marked relative adaptation to cold. (From P. F. Scholander, W. Flagg, V. Walters, and L. Irving, *Physiological Zoology*, 26 (1953), 72. Published by the University of Chicago Press.)

accidentally that this substance could improve the ability of cells to survive rapid freezing; this finding was quickly turned to practical use in the development of techniques of artificial insemination. A turning point was a chance observation by C. Polge, A. U. Smith, and A. S. Parkes, who in 1949 found that the recovery of sperm from low temperature storage was greatly enhanced if the semen was equilibrated with glycerol before freezing was begun.

> . . . Dramatic results were obtained with fowl spermatozoa. If fowl semen is diluted with equal parts of Ringer's solution and vitrified at −79°C for 20 min., and then rapidly thawed, no significant revival of spermatozoa is observed. On the other hand, if the dilution is carried out with Ringer's solution containing 40 per cent glycerol, the spermatozoa resume full motility on thawing. So far as retention of motility is concerned, the specimen is indistinguishable from its unvitrified control; it shows even the wave motion characteristic of

fowl semen. Decreasing the final concentration of glycerol below 10 per cent decreases the protection against vitrification. Increasing it above 20 per cent results in progressive immobilization of the spermatozoa, which cannot altogether be reversed by further dilution with Ringer's solution; but with these higher concentrations, no additional loss of motility is caused by vitrification. Specimens of spermatozoa have been found to resume motility completely after long periods (up to ten weeks) of vitrification. Other experiments showed that both propylene glycol and ethylene glycol were more toxic than glycerol, and in relation to their toxicity less protective against vitrification.

The fact that spermatozoa resumed full motility after vitrification under the conditions described above made it possible to investigate the effects of freeze-drying. 1 c.c. of fowl semen was diluted with 1 c.c. of 20 per cent glycerol in Ringer's solution, and vitrified as a thin layer in a 100-c.c. distilling flask at −79°C. The temperature was then allowed to rise to −25°C and the flask connected to a high-vacuum distillation system of which the condenser unit contained liquid air. After 3 hr., when the distillation was stopped, the semen had the appearance of being dry, and 1.7 c.c. of water was thawed from the condenser. While still cold, the dehydrated semen was reconstituted with 1.8 c.c. of water and warmed to 40°C. On microscopical examination with a 4-mm. objective, active spermatozoa were seen in each field. Further experiments on these lines showed that recovery was better when 30 per cent glycerol in Ringer's solution was used, that the whole of the glycerol remained with the dehydrated semen, from which about 90 per cent of the water was removed by the distillation, and that spermatozoa could not be revived if the preparation was left at room temperature for 2 hr., presumably because of the toxic effect of concentrated glycerol. In each of eight consecutive experiments, motile spermatozoa were observed in the reconstituted semen, the best recovery being about 50 per cent of motile spermatozoa. No information is yet available as to the fertilizing power of spermatozoa thus resuscitated.

These experiments suggest that a high proportion of the water can be withdrawn from fowl semen at low temperatures without killing all the spermatozoa. To what extent this result depends on the retention of glycerol or on the unequal distribution of residual water is not yet clear. . . .[6]

It is now well established that sperm vitrified and stored at −79°C or −196°C can show good recovery on warming, provided that glycerol has been used. For example, bull sperm equilibrated with 10-15 per cent glycerol can be stored for at least 6 years and, when thawed, will yield a fertilizing capacity fully equal to that of normal sperm. This piece of biological technology is of obvious value in livestock rearing and is making the bull a less conspicuous feature of the country scene. Not all sperm, however, are as resistant. Rabbit sperm treated in this way will survive but with only a poor fertilizing capacity; frozen human sperm, however, have yielded pregnancies in women.

One other example of freezing tolerance, as demonstrated in fish, must serve to complete this survey of adaptive responses to thermal stress. Henderson, in his analysis, emphasized the importance of water having its maximum density at 4°C. This results, in general, in ice forming at the surface of standing water, so that fish can live unfrozen below it. Yet this does not wholly resolve the problem of the maintenance of the life of fish in arctic waters. The difficulty is that the osmotic pressure of the blood of teleosts is lower than that of the sea (Chapter 4), which means that the freezing point of the blood must be above that of sea water. The implications of such facts for arctic fish can best be examined in the analysis by P. F. Scholander and his colleagues.

It is generally recognized that the freezing point of the blood of most teleost fishes is around −0.5 and −0.8°C. . . . It is also known that Eskimos in many places catch fish through the sea ice, sometimes in the middle of the winter when the water temperature is −1.7° or colder. Hydrographic work during the summer by Iselin and Nutt established that the water at the bottom of several fjords in northern Labrador maintains a temperature of −1.7° to −1.8°C.; i.e., right at the freezing point of the fjord water. By dredging the bottom with a trawl, R. H. Backus brought to light a considerable fish fauna living at these extreme temperatures.

The present investigation originated with a simple question directed to the senior author by Dr. R. H. Backus: "When arctic fishes swim about in ice water at −1.7° to −1.8°, why don't they freeze? Do they have twice as high an osmotic concentration as ordinary fishes, or what is the story?" Since the problem appeared attractively simple, it was decided to make a quick dash to Nain in northern Labrador in April 1953, and return with the answer, which was easy to guess anyway. A wait of three weeks, while rain rotted the ice along the Labrador coast and made airplane landings impossible, diverted the expedition from Nain to the U.S. Air Force Base at Frobisher Bay in Baffin land. With the aid of Eskimos and dogteams two of the authors (Scholander and Hammel) managed to catch three tiny sculpins in the course of two weeks and at the cost of chopping a dozen holes through four foot ice. The largest fish (about 20 gm) yielded half a cubic centimeter of blood, the medium-sized fish was eaten by a dog, and the little one (about 5 gm) yielded a tiny drop of eye chamber fluid. Freezing point determinations made in a tent 20 miles from the base showed that these fish avoid freezing simply by becoming isotonic with the sea water.

These very clear but scant data could not go unchecked, so it was decided to obtain further data from the bottom of Hebron Fjord in northern Labrador, where the temperature stays near −1.7° all year round. This led to a summer expedition in 1954 on the Blue Dolphin, under command of D. C. Nutt. To our bewilderment it was found that all the bottom fishes had a plasma freezing point of only −0.9° to −1.0°, and hence were permanently supercooled by almost one degree. Fishes caught in the warm surface water had very nearly the same values, and froze instantly in a vat of freezing sea water at −1.7°. When they were lowered in a net to exactly the same temperature at the bottom of the fjord they did not freeze. Conversely, when the bottom fishes, who lived all their lives at −1.7°, were put in freezing sea water of this temperature on the surface they froze. After all the thermometers had been rechecked, these conflicting facts had to be reconciled.

A chance observation on supercooled *Fundulus* at the laboratory in Woods Hole offered a solution to the mystery of the arctic fishes, and prompted a third expedition to check on the Frobisher Bay data. This took two of the authors (Scholander and Kanwisher) back to Hebron Fjord in March 1955 where fishes were readily obtained through the ice. At last, then, with two winter expeditions and one summer expedition behind us, we were able to answer this simple question of why the arctic fishes don't freeze while swimming in water of −1.7° to −1.8°.[7]

The study of these workers was based on the determination of the freezing point of the blood, taken as the temperature at which a small ice crystal is in equilibrium with the unfrozen blood. This was determined by direct observation, under magnification, of the freezing, growth, and melting of an ice crystal under conditions of regulated temperature change. A study of several species of deep-water fish showed that the freezing point of their plasma ranged from −0.90° to −1.0°C, whereas the water in which they were living at the bottom of the fjord was at −1.73°C. It follows that these fish, like the sculpins examined earlier, were supercooled by almost one degree centigrade, in line with the previously noted fact that the body temperature of fish agrees with the temperature of their ambient water. Indeed, these investigators showed that even with large cod and sculpin the agreement was within 0.1°C. The supercooled state, however, is an unstable one, and laboratory experiments showed that contact between the supercooled fish and ice rapidly seeded the formation of ice crystals within the animals' bodies. Thus the ability of these particular fish to survive in a supercooled condition depends on an essentially behavioral adaptation; they are protected from seeding, because they live well below the ice level:

> Sea water can readily be supercooled to −3° in a beaker suspended in a thermoregulated bath. It may be stirred gently by air bubbling. Several species of fish taken in cold water at Woods Hole in the winter (*Fundulus*, cunner, eel, toadfish, tautog) were found to survive

for some time in such water. Cunner and *Fundulus* were kept in −3° water for 12 hours. They were torpid, but breathed slowly, and survived apparently without any harmful effects.

If the water containing the fish is supercooled to −2° or −3°, while gently stirred by air bubbling, and is then seeded with a few ice crystals, the water fills up with a whole flurry of ice crystals immediately. The practically motionless fish goes into a few violent convulsions, whitens in patches, and freezes stiff *(Fig. [5-8A])*. In other words, direct ice contact seeds the supercooled fish right through the integument. This happened in all of the five species enumerated above, and also in frogs.

If a fish frozen in this manner is plunged into sea water of room temperature, it will initially float due to the ice in its body, but will soon settle to the bottom when the ice thaws. If such a partly thawed fish, which has ice only in its core *(Fig. [5-8C])*, is placed in a beaker of supercooled water, the water will shortly thereafter freeze, showing that the ice formation will also be propagated across the integument from inside outward.

Fundulus, toadfish, and eel were supercooled in water of −1.5 to −1.7°; i.e., in sea water warmer than its freezing point. If these fishes

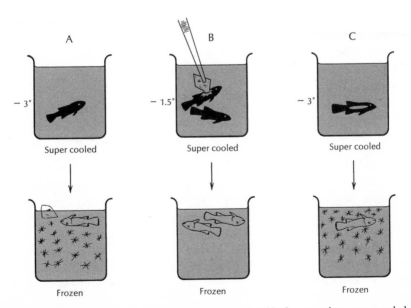

Fig. 5-8. Ice-seeding experiments on *Fundulus*. *A.* Fish freezes when supercooled water is seeded. *B.* Supercooled fish freezes when touched with ice in water above freezing point. One fish may by contact seed another. *C.* Thawed fish with ice core freezes, and seeds supercooled water. (From P. F. Scholander, L. Von Dam, J. W. Karwisher, H. T. Hammel, and M. S. Gordon, *Journal of Cellular and Comparative Physiology,* 49 (1957), 15.)

were touched with an ice cube *(Fig. [5-8B])*, they would go into convulsions, stiffen, and gradually whiten in freezing. Indeed, if only one fish were seeded and frozen, soon the other would freeze also by contact with the first, although the water could not freeze.

From the ice seeding experiments in live fishes it was clear that ice formation would pass right through the integument. This was studied further on pieces of skin of the eel, tautog, toadfish, and frog. The skin was stretched across one orifice of a piece of tubing, which was then filled with isotonic saline, and the whole assembly was placed in supercooled sea water. Seeding on either side of the skin would propagate through and seed the other side.

It was found that ice would propagate through a Corning glass filter, UF with 1-2μ pores, but not through dialyzing cellophane at a supercooling temperature of $-3°$. In respect to ice propagation, therefore, fish and frog integuments seem to be relatively open structures. Considering that they maintain considerable osmotic gradients, it appears that the ice actually spears its way through the tissue. This is suggested by the following observation. If a fish is placed in freezing sea water with its gills exposed these will freeze white rapidly. If the fish is thawed and then put back in the cold water, the gills will not freeze again, probably because the ice crystals have pierced and damaged the osmotic barriers.

The authors conclude that

> Our supercooled bottom fishes represent, we believe, the second instance known in nature where evolution has pushed life into a region of permanent physical metastability. The other case is in plants. It is generally believed that the sap in tall trees is under tension, with pressures sometimes as low as -20 atmospheres or less. The sap is therefore in a metastable and potentially almost explosive state. A return to the stable physical state would in either of these cases be fatal, but it does not occur because of the absence of proper nuclei to trigger the catastrophe.[8]

The above conclusions apply only to deep-water arctic fish. They do not account for the ability of shallow-water fishes to swim close under the ice in winter, for on the above evidence they would be expected to freeze as a result of being seeded. The answer to this problem became apparent when the freezing point of the blood of these fish was measured; this revealed that the blood underwent a marked seasonal change, its winter freezing point being lower than the summer one.

> ... The answer was already indicated by our two little sculpins caught through the ice in Baffin land in the winter of 1953. Their plasma freezing point was $-1.5°$ to $-1.6°$, i.e., very nearly the same as the sea water, and hence they could not be seeded by ice. This called for

further study, and in March, 1955, we (Scholander and Kanwisher) returned to Hebron Fjord. Our Eskimo friends patiently jigged fjord cod and sculpins through holes cut in four foot ice along the shore in from 2 to 8 meters' depth of water. The fish were immediately taken into a heated tent next to the fishing hole, so that blood could be taken by heart puncture. Outside, the blood froze in the needle immediately.

The results showed that with the sea water at its freezing point of −1.73°, the plasma freezing point in the cod averaged −1.47°, and in the sculpin −1.50°, as against the summer value of −0.80° for both species *(Fig. [5-9])*. The shallow-water winter fishes had therefore almost doubled their osmolarity, but some were nevertheless as much as 0.2–0.4° supercooled. Several specimens were therefore transferred directly into a large freezing trough which contained floating pieces of ice in sea water. In this, most of the fishes died, undoubtedly by contact freezing. Two codfish were placed in a flour sack together with a piece of clear ice, and were suspended in the fjord. After a day one fish died, very probably from freezing. The other stayed alive, and was taken out of the bag, still living, after three days. It had then a freezing point of −1.52° and a markedly elevated chloride concentration.

We see, therefore, that considerable adjustments take place in those fishes which risk seeding by contact with ice. From the experiments where sculpins and cod were transferred in the summer to the deep water of −1.73°, it seems clear that the adjustments are conditioned by the change in temperature, rather than by the presence of ice. Whether or not seasonal changes take place in the fishes at the bottom, which live under perfectly constant temperature conditions is not known, but it seems improbable.[9]

In effect, then, these shallow-water arctic fish add an antifreeze to their blood in the winter. In this respect they resemble the insects discussed earlier; indeed, the exploitation of this principle in insects and fish is a remarkable example of the independent evolution of an adaptation that strikingly anticipates a device of man's technology. However, the nature of the teleostean antifreeze is unknown. It is not glycerol, nor can it consist of chlorides. Of the total freezing point depression in these winter fish, amounting to −1.73°, 0.7° is still unaccounted for by chemical analysis.

■ THE ACCLIMATION OF FISH TO AMBIENT TEMPERATURE

This section will consider some examples of acclimation, which was defined earlier as the individual acquisition of a response, as contrasted with the primarily genetic adaptations discussed so far. As long ago as 1916, A. Krogh had argued that the known ability of certain fish to live over a wide range of temperature suggested that they might be able to adjust their level of metabolism to the surround-

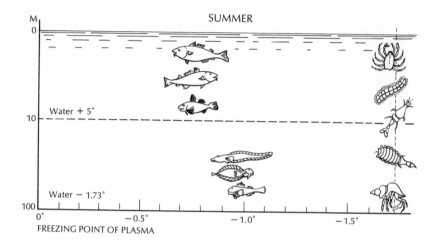

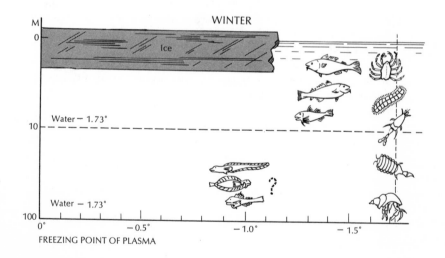

Fig. 5-9. Freezing point of plasma in shallow water fishes (fjord cod and sculpin) and in deep water fishes (*Lycodes, Liparis, Gymnacanthus*). Position of fishes on abscissa indicates the freezing point of their plasma in summer and winter. (From P. F. Scholander, L. Von Dam, J. W. Karwisher, H. T. Hammel, and M. S. Gordon, *Journal of Cellular and Comparative Physiology*, 49 (1957), 18.)

ing temperature. One demonstration that they certainly can do this was provided by an investigation carried out by N. A. Wells. He used for this purpose *Gillichthys mirabilis,* which is an exceptionally hardy teleost. It remains healthy over a range of temperature from 8°C to 35°C, it can live in fresh water or salt water, and it can even survive for some hours out of water.

In one of Wells' experiments *(Fig. 5-10),* two groups of fish, each containing nine individuals, were selected; one group (A_1) was maintained in running sea water for 17 days at about 33°C, while the other group (A_2) was maintained for the same period at about 11°C. Both groups were then brought to the same temperature of 22°C, and the oxygen consumption of the fish was measured over a period of 50 hours. In a second experiment two more groups of fish were selected, with 16 in each group. One group (B_1) was kept for 20 days at 29.6–31.6°C, while the other (B_2) was kept for the same period at 10-12°C. Again, their oxygen consumption was measured after they had been brought to the same temperature; but in this instance the temperature selected was 20°C, since the warm-adapted fish (B_1) had been kept at a lower temperature in this experiment than in the previous one. The results are shown in *Fig. 5-10,* in which the ordinates represent the oxygen uptake in gm per hr, while the abscissae show time in hours from the moment when the fish were placed in the respiratory chambers for the determination of their oxygen consumption.

It is immediately evident that the oxygen uptake of the warm-adapted fish is lower than that of the cold-adapted ones, when measured at the common intermediate temperature; for in every case the values for the warm-adapted fish fall below those simultaneously determined for the cold-adapted ones. The figure suggests the possibility that at 20°C, after warm-adaptation at a lower temperature than that of the first experiment, the difference between the warm-adapted and cold-adapted fish is disappearing. But it is clear that *Gillichthys* can adjust its oxygen metabolism to the temperature of its environment. So also can *Fundulus,* with which Wells obtained similar results.

This is one illustration of what is meant by acclimation. Another is found in the ability of fishes to extend their range of temperature tolerance, as expressed in their upper and lower lethal temperatures. These can be defined as the temperatures that can be tolerated by 50 per cent of a randomly selected group of individuals for a predetermined interval of time. Given adequately controlled laboratory conditions, lethal temperatures can be determined with great precision, in some instances to within ±0.2°C. Thus it is possible to compare the temperature tolerance of one species with another and to study changes in tolerance resulting from acclimation to particular levels of temperature.

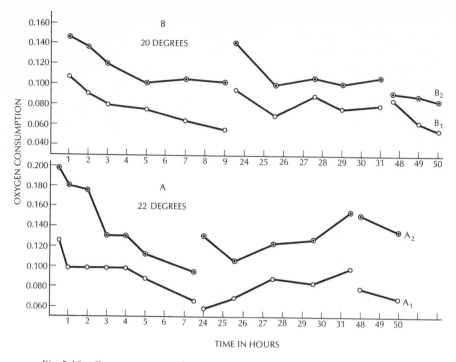

Fig. 5-10. Oxygen consumption at a common temperature of fishes (*Gillichthys mirabilis*) acclimatized to different temperatures. Ordinates: oxygen uptake in g per hr at a temperature of 22°C in *A* and 20°C in *B*. Abscissae: time in hr from the moment of transfer of the fishes to the respiratory chambers. The upper curves in both *A* and *B* are the values obtained from the fishes of cold-water history; the lower curves are the values obtained from those of warm-water history. See text for further explanation. (From N. A. Wells, *Biological Bulletin*, 69 (1935), 363. By permission of the *Biological Bulletin*.)

An example of such a comparison is shown in *Fig. 5-11,* which illustrates the lethal temperature relations of the chum salmon, *Oncorhynchus keta*, and the bullhead, *Ameiurus nebulosus*. The upper line for each fish shows its upper lethal limit, the lower one its lower lethal limit. The area enclosed by each trapezium can then be regarded as the zone of tolerance for that species. It is evident that the bullhead is the more tolerant of the two, and that its upper lethal limit is much more readily extended by acclimation than is that of the chum salmon. Indeed, the Salmonidae, with upper lethal limits of about 25°C, are among the least tolerant of teleosts.

These characteristics are of undoubted ecological significance. The bullhead lives in shallow reed beds, where it encounters high summer temperatures that rise rapidly in the spring. Its high thermal tolerance, together with its marked power of acclimation, which enables it to extend its upper thermal limit by 10°C, allows it to survive these conditions. By contrast, the chum salmon divides its life between cold running waters and the seas. In this connection it is significant that it is less resistant to low temperatures than is another salmonid, the char (*Salvelinus fontinalis*). The difference is relatable to difference in mode of life; for the char is a nonmigratory form that lives in lakes and streams, where temperature fluctuations, and hence the hazards of cold, are greater than in the sea.

The physiological basis for acclimation is not yet understood. One difficulty relating to thermal tolerance is that the cause of the death of fish at high temperatures is not precisely known. There is some evidence that the nervous system is particularly sensitive to thermal stress; but, in general, it seems that acclimation must be promoted in some way by changes in the balance of enzyme-controlled reactions. Previously, it was mentioned that cell enzymes differ in their reactions to the influence of temperature; and it is possible that a change of temperature could, through this differential action, promote subtle changes in the metabolic pathways of the cell. Naturally, however, such changes would have to be coordinated in some way, if their consequences were to be adaptively valuable. This is one reason why a distinction between acclimation and adaptation is not always easy to make.

With regard to a possible coordinating mechanism, one might well expect the endocrine system to be involved, inasmuch as coordination throughout the tissues presumably is demanded. There is little positive evidence for this involvement at the moment, but the thought

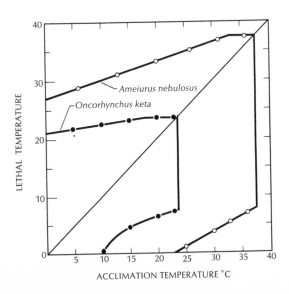

Fig. 5-11. Lethal temperature relations in two species of fish, the bullhead, *Ameiurus nebulosus*, and the chum salmon, *Oncorhynchus keta*. The area enclosed by each trapezium is the zone of tolerance. (From J. R. Brett, *Quarterly Review of Biology*, 31 (1956), 76.)

is at least in line with current concepts of the actions of hormones, which are seen as agents capable of modifying the action, or rate of production, of specific components of the enzyme systems of cells. It is expected that man's understanding of this aspect of physiological adaptation will extend rapidly during the coming years, a fact which makes it increasingly important to appreciate what delicate thermal responses await analysis in poikilothermal animals.

1. L. J. Henderson, *The Fitness of the Environment* (Boston: Beacon Press, 1958), pp. 80–81, 86–91. Copyright © 1913 by The Macmillan Company. Reprinted by permission of Beacon Press.
2. *Ibid.*, pp. 131–132.
3. W. T. Williams, "Problems of Alien Biology," *The Advancement of Science*, 22 (1965), 199.
4. J. Barcroft, *Features in the Architecture of Physiological Function* (London: Cambridge University Press, 1938), pp. 48, 40.
5. C. L. Hubbs, "Changes in the Fish Fauna of Western North America Correlated with Changes in Ocean Temperature," *Journal of Marine Research*, 7 (1948), 461, 464, 472–473.
6. C. Polge, A. U. Smith, and A. S. Parkes, "Revival of Spermatozoa after Vitrification and Dehydration at Low Temperatures," *Nature*, 164 (1949), 666.
7. P. F. Scholander, *et al.*, "Supercooling and Osmoregulation in Arctic Fish." Reprinted from the *Journal of Cellular and Comparative Physiology*, Vol. 49, No. 1, February 1957, pp. 5–7.
8. *Ibid.*, pp. 14–16, 21.
9. *Ibid.*, pp. 16–17.

CHAPTER 6 ■ Temperature and
Terrestrial Life

■ THERMAL RELATIONSHIPS OF AMPHIBIA

It is clear from Henderson's analysis (Chap. 5) that the emergence
of vertebrates on land was bound to present the group with more
exacting thermal problems than it had previously encountered. The
species involved were now liable to undergo much more extreme
conditions. The hottest seas range little higher than about 30°C,
while the coldest antarctic waters have a temperature no lower than
about −1.5°C. Moreover, within any one area, the range of sea temperature is comparatively small; surface temperatures rarely vary by
more than 10°C during the year, or by more than 1°C during 24
hours. In contrast to these figures, surface temperatures over the
land can range as a whole from −40°C to +65.5°C, and even this range
can be exceeded in extreme conditions. In hot deserts a surface temperature of 84°C may be reached at midday, although it is followed
by rapid cooling after sunset. However, the buffering effect of water
is not wholly lost on land. Conditions in the hot and damp tropics can
be remarkably constant, the damp atmosphere and lack of air movement restricting temperature fluctuations to as little as 1°C per day.
Thus the vertebrates, whatever the hazards they encountered, were
presented also with immense opportunities for adapting to widely
different thermal conditions; and their history on land shows how
well these opportunities have been utilized.

In thermoregulation, as in other aspects of physiological adaptation, the Amphibia are imperfectly equipped to cope with the full

rigor of terrestrial life. Since they have achieved at least a modest exploitation of the desert, one should not undervalue their capacities. What these animals do show very clearly, however, is the important contribution that evaporation can make to thermal regulation. This point emerged in a study conducted by K. Mellanby on the body temperature of the frog; in this work, Mellanby used a specially constructed thermometer that gave readings accurate to 0.1°C. Being of low thermal capacity and designed to be inserted into the animal's rectum, the instrument equilibrated rapidly with the internal temperature. This study brought out the point noted earlier: as long as the frog is in water, its body temperature, like that of a fish, is almost identical with that of the surrounding medium; in unsaturated air, however, the situation is very different, for the high level of permeability of the skin results in considerable evaporation and hence in a substantial lowering of body temperature. The extent of this lowering depends upon the prevailing atmospheric conditions; it will be reduced by increasing humidity but increased by air movement. In conditions favorable for evaporation, however, the cooling effect is so marked that the temperature of the body falls to the reading of the wet bulb thermometer. In this instrument the bulb is cooled by evaporation of water from its surface. Its reading is thus the lowest temperature that it is physically possible to reach by evaporation in the environmental conditions occurring at the time. As Mellanby observes, the animal could scarcely be much colder.

The relationship of the frog to its ambient environment is illustrated graphically in *Fig. 6-1*, which shows the responses of one particular frog to a range of atmospheric conditions. In slowly moving air (air speed 0.3 m per second), evaporation, as indicated by loss in weight, was moderately rapid. It was doubled when the air speed was increased to 1.9 m per second, but in still air it was very much less. The effect of these differing rates of evaporation upon the body temperature is clearly shown. Even at the slower rate of air movement, the temperature falls to within less than a degree of the wet bulb reading; while at the faster speed the animal's temperature registered exactly the same as the wet bulb instrument. In still air, on the other hand, it became nearly 3°C warmer than the air. Conduction is likely to have little effect in the conditions of such an experiment, so that the body temperature is essentially determined by the relation between heat lost by evaporation and heat gained by metabolism. Rapid cooling is helped by the low heat production of poikilothermal vertebrates, a point that will be further explored when homoiothermy is discussed later in this chapter. It can be calculated that a 20 g frog maintained at 20°C will produce only about six calories per hour, whereas during this same period evaporation will remove nearly 2000 calories from its body.

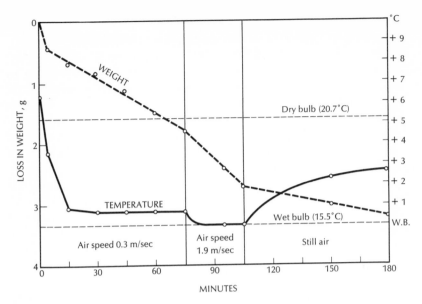

Fig. 6-1. The internal temperature and loss in weight of a frog exposed to different air velocities. (From K. Mellanby, *Journal of Experimental Biology*, 18 (1942), 59.)

There is, of course, an element of biological unreality in such calculations. It will be seen in a later discussion of reptiles how misleading it can be to judge the behavior of an animal in its natural habitat by its performance under controlled and unnatural conditions in the laboratory. Mellanby found that when a small frog, weighing 12.2 g, was placed in an air current of 0.3 m per second, it was dead from loss of water in about two and one-half hours. Thus, as already seen in another context, frogs must necessarily live in damp and sheltered habitats. But this, of course, is exactly what they choose to do, and in these habitats the permeability of their skin presumably helps them to maintain a more equable body temperature than would otherwise be possible. Their capacity to select suitable microhabitats is vital for their survival on land, and it is this capacity that has enabled certain amphibians to establish themselves in the desert. They do this, as P. J. Bentley remarks, "by using their heads"; they burrow into the substratum and find acceptable conditions of temperature and humidity that would certainly not be available at the surface. Nevertheless, the body temperature of amphibians on land is in large measure dependent on the ambient temperature.

In discussing how fish confront this problem of ambient temperature, it was shown that the restrictive action of the environment is to some extent ameliorated by genetic adaptations; these make it possible for different species to achieve levels of activity that are somewhat independent of the normal ambient temperature. It is not surprising, therefore, to find evidence of comparable adaptations in amphibians, especially since Barcroft's studies of the heart beat in frogs showed that this particular organ is able to escape from the rigid application of the Arrhenius relationship.

Convincing evidence of temperature adaptations has come from J. A. Moore's studies of amphibian embryological characteristics, such as the temperature tolerance of the embryo and the rate of its development. These examples of genetic adaptation are attractive to study, because they are readily observable and because the data can be expressed quantitatively. Their value to the species is clear, as spawning and larval development in amphibians must be completed within a limited time period rigidly determined by the range of temperature to which a particular species is subjected. Moore's investigations dealt first with comparisons of amphibian species that are restricted in their geographical distribution and differed, therefore, with respect to the temperature conditions to which they were normally exposed. Subsequently, he extended his analysis to the American meadow frog, *Rana pipiens*, which is remarkable for its very wide geographical range; consequently, the species is exposed to very different temperatures in various parts of this range. Moreover, populations are sufficiently isolated to permit the establishment of intraspecific genetic differentiation of the type mentioned in Chapter 5.

First, northern and southern species were compared to find those characters that showed a correlation with distribution and therefore probably represented adaptations to temperature. . . . This investigation revealed that a number of embryonic characters such as temperature tolerance, rate of development, temperature coefficient of development, type of egg mass, and size of egg were closely correlated with geographic distribution. The nature of the differences between northern and southern species can be brought out in a comparison of *Rana sylvatica* and *Rana catesbeiana* (Table [6-1]). The former may be thought of as the most northern and the latter as the most southern of the frogs found in the New York region. There is little doubt that these embryonic features that distinguish the two species have an adaptive significance. After this preliminary study on different species a single species was investigated. The data to be presented in this paper are concerned with the geographic variation of the above mentioned embryonic characters in *Rana pipiens*.

Rana pipiens has the greatest distribution of any American frog. It occupies most of our continent from northern Canada to Panama. There is considerable variation in the appearance of the individuals from different geographic regions. This has led some investigators to split *Rana pipiens* into a number of subspecies or even into different species. The lack of any generally accepted opinion on the "*pipiens* problem" led to a re-examination of its taxonomy [by Moore]. After studying much material from eastern North America it became apparent that the characters generally employed in dividing the populations into different species or subspecies were not reliable. It was thought best to regard all eastern American meadow frogs as belonging to one species which cannot be divided into a convenient number of readily defined subspecies, unless a tremendous number of races are regarded as valid subspecies.[1]

For the study of temperature tolerance and rate of development, the embryos were examined at intervals and their degree of development expressed in terms of standard stages. Embryos were said to be in a given stage when 50 per cent of them showed the standard features of that stage. Temperature tolerance was expressed as the percentage of normal development at a particular temperature; if 50 per cent or more of the embryos in a particular group at a particular temperature were normal, that temperature was considered to be within the normal range for the species.

Moore found that the upper limiting temperature and the rate of development of the embryos of frogs obtained from certain regions of Vermont, Wisconsin, and New Jersey were substantially identical in all populations studied; similarly, the lower limiting temperature was relatively constant for these embryos. In Louisiana frogs, how-

TABLE 6-1

Comparison of Embryonic Features of Rana sylvatica *and* Rana catesbeiana[a]

	Rana sylvatica	*Rana catesbeiana*
Northern limit	67°30′ N	47° N
Lower limiting embryonic temperature	2.5°C	15°C
Upper limiting embryonic temperature	24°C	32°C
Interval between first cleavage and gill circulation at 20°C	72 hr	134 hr
Temperature coefficient of development	1.98	2.88
Type of egg mass	compact and submerged	loose surface film
Egg diameter	1.9 mm	1.3 mm

[a] From J. A. Moore, *Evolution*, 3 (1949), 2.

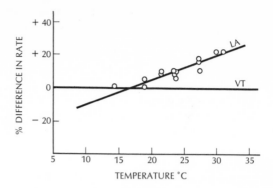

Fig. 6-2. Comparison of rate of development of Louisiana and northern embryos (Vermont and New Jersey). The interval studied was the time between Stages 3 and 20. Values for the northern embryos, labelled as *VT*, are taken as 0. Data from five Louisiana females (LA) are expressed as per cent retardation or acceleration. (From J. A. Moore, *Evolution*, 3 (1949), 10.)

ever, these characteristics were significantly different, to an extent implying adaptation to the much warmer habitat.

>   Observations have been made on embryos from eight Louisiana females. In two cases parallel experiments were made using Vermont embryos. In another case embryos from New Jersey and Ocala, Florida, were available for comparison. In the remaining five experiments only Louisiana embryos were studied.
>   In the first experiment begun November 5, 1942 comparing Louisiana and Vermont embryos, observations were made at 6.4 ±0.4°, 21.9°, 24.0°, 27.7°, 30.2°, 31.6°, and 33.6°. . . . Both groups showed more than 50 per cent normal development at 6.4 ±0.4° but at the higher temperatures there was a marked difference between the Louisiana and Vermont embryos. The former are clearly adapted to higher temperatures . . . [but] no difference could be detected between Louisiana and northern embryos in their resistance to low temperature. . . .
>   The data comparing the rate of development of Louisiana and northern (Vermont and New Jersey) embryos have been summarized in *Fig.* [6-2]. This graph was constructed as follows. The rate of development of Vermont or New Jersey embryos is taken as 0. The degree of acceleration or retardation observed in the Louisiana embryos is then plotted. There is a paucity of data below 20° but the general trend can be ascertained. At the higher temperatures the Louisiana embryos develop about 20 per cent more rapidly than the northern embryos. As the temperature is decreased the difference in rate becomes less. If the curve describing these data represents the average condition we would expect the rate of the two types of Vermont embryos to be more rapid at lower temperatures. This assump-

tion cannot be corroborated by the data presented since so few observations were made below 20°. However, other southern embryos, for which data will be presented, do have the type of development shown by the line of the graph so it is probable that the conclusion is essentially correct.

It is clear that Louisiana embryos are adapted differently to temperature than are the northern races already described.

In his discussion of these and other data, Moore concludes that

Rana pipiens has apparently produced a wealth of genotypes that are adapted to nearly every general region of the North American continent.

It is not surprising to find geographic variation in physiological characteristics such as temperature tolerance and rate of development. In fact, one would expect it to occur more frequently in physiological than in morphological characters. (The reason for this assumption is the fact that every morphological character is the result of physiological processes and in addition there are many physiological processes with no morphological expression.) However, data on geographic variation consist almost entirely of the morphological sort. This is due to the ease of measuring structure as compared with the usual difficulty in measuring physiological processes. It is disturbing to find that the data on geographic variation, which play such an important part in discussions of evolution, are usually based on characters having no discernible adaptive significance.

In the New York region *Rana pipiens* supplies a northern environment for its embryos by spawning early in the spring. . . . Farther south the marked correlation between temperature and breeding time vanishes. Wright believes the population in the southern Georgia area breeds every month in the year. The same appears to be true of Florida. The adaptive changes that have occurred in these southern populations have freed them from the necessity of providing a "northern environment" for their embryos. It is probable that rainfall has replaced temperature as the primary stimulus to breeding in the southern populations.[2]

■ THERMOREGULATION IN REPTILES

Reptiles are in many respects better fitted for terrestrial life than are amphibians, but the nature of this fitness has commonly been misunderstood. For example, much emphasis has been placed upon the supposed impermeability of the reptilian skin, with the implied corollary that heat loss by evaporation must depend solely upon respiratory exchange through the lungs. Bentley and K. Schmidt-Nielsen, however, have shown that the skin is in fact not completely impermeable; evaporation takes place through it to an extent that is inversely correlated with the aridity of the habitat. Thus the crocodile loses water by evaporation at a rate of about one half to one third that found in amphibians, whereas evaporation in the desert lizard *Sauromalus obesus* amounts to about only 5 per cent of the crocodile's. In both of these forms, and in all other reptilian species examined by Bentley and Schmidt-Nielsen, evaporation through the skin provides two thirds or more of the total evaporation.

These facts are important to bear in mind. Admittedly, the permeability of reptilian skin, and particularly that of terrestrial species, is very much less than that of amphibian skin, with the result that reptiles are much freer agents in their terrestrial movements and distribution. Nevertheless, their capacity for evaporation through the body surface, as well as through the lungs, is a valuable factor in the control of body temperature, and one that lends itself to modulation by suitable patterns of behavior.

Reptiles are often discussed as the classical expression of poikilothermy. A common view of their thermal relationships, as compared with those of mammals, is shown in *Fig. 6-3,* which is taken from a study by C. J. Martin. He showed that a variety of mammalian species, exposed under controlled laboratory conditions to a wide range of ambient temperature, were well able to maintain a constant body temperature, although the degree of constancy varied. A lizard in similar circumstances was unable to do this; instead, its temperature varied in close correlation with that of the air around it, which is what is generally understood to be the essence of poikilothermy.

Martin's data accurately represented the behavior of the animals

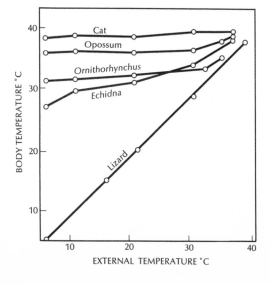

Fig. 6-3. Body temperature of various mammals and a lizard after keeping for two hours in an environment of 5°C to 35°C. (From C. J. Martin, *Lancet,* ii (1930), 565.)

concerned, given the conditions that he had established for them. As A. C. Burton and O. G. Edholm have remarked, and equally correctly, "All that one has to do to reduce the dangerous alligator to a helpless state is to leave him in the ice-box for a few hours." But laboratory equipment and ice-boxes are not the natural habitats of reptiles, and because of this it is dangerous to estimate the normal behavior of these animals by extrapolating from laboratory data. Burton and Edholm continue:

> We are told that the world was at one time populated by poikilother-
> mic animals of fantastic size and strength, and presumably speed.
> Yet their life must have been at the mercy of the climate. On a cold
> day the battle of existence slowed to relative inactivity. Before the
> development of the special group of animals called homeotherms,
> possessing the power, within limits, to be emancipated from thermal
> slavery, the temperature must have played a much less important rôle
> in the story of evolution. The outcome could be little affected when
> both pursuer and pursued were slowed by a fall of temperature.[3]

It will be of interest to test these thoughts against the observed thermal relationships of modern reptiles, observed in the field and in conditions in which their normal behavior patterns are allowed full play.

This aspect of reptilian physiology has been extensively studied by C. M. Bogert. Realizing the difficulties of simulating normal environmental conditions in the laboratory, he and R. B. Cowles set up open cages in the field. But even this procedure has its limitations, so that later Bogert devised a technique for shooting lizards in their natural habitat and recording their rectal temperature within 30 seconds of death. He selected for particular study two common forms, *Sceloporus,* the scaly lizard, and *Cnemidophorus,* the whiptail or race runner. Each of these has a species found in Arizona and a different one found in Florida. In the Arizona locality selected for the work, the mean summer temperature is 4.7°C higher than the Florida locality and the winter temperature 7.3° lower. Rainfall is five times greater in Florida. It was thus possible not only to compare the two genera, but to compare also within each genus the behavior of two species that were adapted for substantially different habitats.

A summary of data obtained from these studies is shown in Table 6-2 and *Fig. 6-4.* In considering them it is important to bear in mind that reptiles, like other vertebrate poikilotherms, have a metabolic rate much lower than that of birds and mammals. The high body temperature of the latter two groups is engendered by "fire in their belly" (p. 1), for which reason Bogert refers to them as endothermic. Reptiles, by contrast, derive their body heat largely from external sources, so that they, like other poikilotherms, may be termed ecto-

Table 6-2

Summary of Data for Body Temperatures of Lizards
and of Air and Substratum Temperatures in °C.
Recorded in Florida and Arizona[a]*

	Sceloporus		Cnemidophorus	
	S. magister (Arizona)	S. woodi (Florida)	C. tessellatus (Arizona)	C. sexlineatus (Florida)
Number	10	42	33	12
Mean, body temp.	34.9 ±.56 (32.0-37.0)	36.2 ±.25 (32.0-39.2)	41.3 ±.24 (37.4-43.5)	41.0 ±.47 (38.5-43.0)
Coefficient of variation	5.09	4.53	3.30	3.93
Mean, body temp. ♂♂	33.5 ±.88 (32.0-34.8)	36.3 ±.42 (32.5-38.8)	40.8 ±.45 (37.4-42.6)	40.9 ±.36 (39.5-42.0)
Mean, body temp. ♀♀	36.1 ±.43 (34.0-37.0)	36.0 ±.35 (32.0-39.2)	41.5 ±.79 (39.3-43.5)	41.1 ±.66 (38.5-43.0)
Mean, body temps. May-June	–	35.9 ±.40 (32.0-39.2)	–	40.5 ±.70 (38.5-42.5)
Mean, body temps. Aug.-Sept.	–	36.5 ±.32 (32.5-38.8)	–	41.3 ±.33 (40.5-43.0)
Mean, air temp. records	32.5 ±.78 (29.3-38.5)	–	33.6 ±.43 (29.2-39.2)	–
Coefficient of variation	7.61	–	7.32	–
Mean, substratum temp. records	32.61 ±.13 (29.6-40.5)	–	41.3 ±1.07 (32.5-58.9)	–
Coefficient of variation	10.36	–	14.86	–

[a] From C. M. Bogert, *Evolution*, 3 (1949), 198.

* Extremes are given below the mean and its standard error. Substratum temperatures were recorded as nearly as possible at the spot where lizards shot were first seen. Air temperatures were recorded 5 cm above the spot, or to one side when lizards were on walls or trees.

thermic. It might be expected from this fundamental difference that the body temperature of reptiles would be very unstable. Yet, one conclusion that emerges from Bogert's observations is that lizards, when in a state of normal activity, actually maintain their body within a surprisingly narrow range of high temperature.

There appears to be a characteristic mean body temperature for each species, conveniently termed its preferred temperature, and fluctuations from this mean value rarely exceed 3°C. Bogert found various reasons for concluding that this temperature must be adaptively regulated. For one thing, there are no significant differences between the sexes or between juveniles and adults. Moreover, there are no significant seasonal differences in the Florida data, even though the ambient spring temperatures are lower than those of late summer. But the most striking evidence of a genetically determined

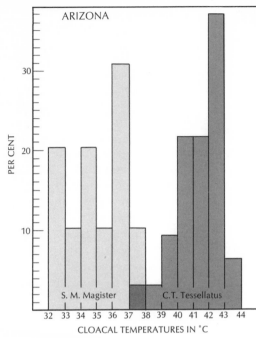

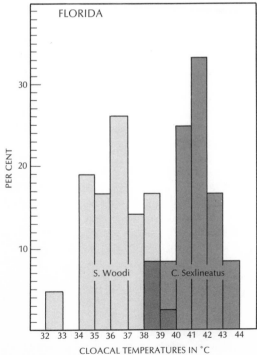

Fig. 6-4. Histograms showing the distributions of body temperatures under field conditions of four species of lizards belonging to two genera *Sceloporus* and *Cnemidophorus* (data from Table 6-2). Cloacal temperatures plotted between limits indicated in °C on the abscissa; percentages of the total sample for each species are shown on the ordinate. (From C. M. Bogert, *Evolution*, 3 (1949), 200.)

adaptation is the close agreement in the preferred body temperature of the two species of each genus, despite the difference in the environments in which they live. To put the matter in another way, *Sceloporus woodi* and *Cnemidophorus sexlineatus* live side by side in Florida, yet the preferred body temperatures of these two species are significantly different; that of *S. woodi* lies close to that of the Arizonan *S. magister*, while that of *C. sexlineatus* lies close to that of the Arizonan *C. tessellatus*.

At the time when Bogert reported these results, it was not certain how these ectothermic animals managed to achieve such elevated and constant body temperatures. He concluded, however, that they probably basked in the morning sun, until radiation and conduction had raised their body temperature to a threshold that permitted normal activity. If this activity then led to any undue rise of temperature, they could dissipate the excess heat by retiring temporarily to sheltered or cooler spots. Thus they would be able to maintain a relatively constant body temperature, until the cool of the evening reduced their heat intake to a level at which this was no longer possible.

The assumption, then, was that these animals were far from poikilothermic during their daytime activity. On the contrary, it appeared that they maintained their preferred body temperature by behavioral reactions that were elegantly adapted to exploit the thermal possibilities of their habitat. This view has been abundantly confirmed by later observations, some of which can best be reported in Bogert's own words.

One convincing example of the use of behavioral adaptation to reach the preferred body temperature is given by the earless lizard of the southwestern United States,

> which is almost never found abroad with its body temperature below 96 degrees. We exposed its secret only by observing what it did in a laboratory cage provided with sources of radiant heat [*Fig. 6-5*]. From its overnight retreat, submerged in the sand, the earless lizard first thrusts its inconspicuous head above the surface; there it waits until the blood coursing through a large sinus in its head has absorbed enough heat from the sunlight to raise the temperature of its entire body. When its temperature is well above the threshold for efficient activity, this wary reptile emerges from the sand, preheated and ready to take off at top speed.

The precision and subtlety of the adaptive thermal responses of these animals is nowhere better illustrated than in the influence of size of body.

> In the desert-dwelling whip-tailed lizard (*Cnemidophorus tigris*) we found that juveniles of the species, weighing two or three grams, keep their bodies at mean temperatures identical with those of adults

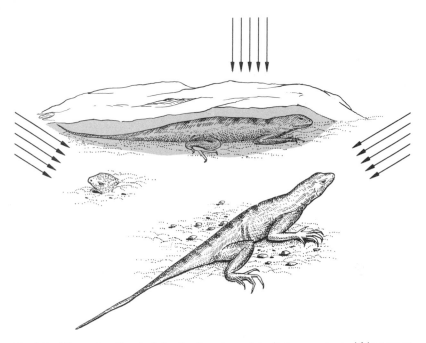

Fig. 6-5. The earless lizard of the Southwest regulates its temperature within narrow limits by means of its behavior. The morning sun (arrows at left) warms the blood in the animal's head while the rest of it remains hidden in the sand until it is warm enough to be active. At noon (*top*) the lizard seeks shelter from the hot sun, but later it emerges and lies parallel to the sun's rays (*bottom*). (From C. M. Bogert, *Scientific American*, 200 (1959), 115.)

weighing up to 16 grams. However, we found a difference between adults and juveniles when we recorded the daily variation of their temperatures. The smaller lizards restrict their temperature fluctuations to a narrow zone of five or six degrees, while the activity zones in adults range over 10 or 11 degrees, from 99 to 110 degrees (37.2 to 43.3 degrees C.). The juveniles may be more responsive to heat and so may adjust their exposure more sensitively, or their body temperature may adjust more quickly by virtue of their smaller bulk.

Other things being equal, the temperature of a smaller lizard should rise or fall faster because it has more surface in proportion to its mass. In the first rough experiment we performed to test the validity of this generalization from the physics of inanimate objects, however, we discovered how important "other things" can be if they are not equal. Our subjects were adult specimens of two species of spiny lizard. The larger of the two was a green spiny lizard (*Sceloporus formosus*), a species restricted to open areas in moist forests of broad-leaved trees at elevations above 5,000 feet in central Honduras; its green skin is marked with black pigment sparsely distributed in a reticulated pattern of lines and smaller blotches. The other was a much smaller, slate-colored spiny lizard (*Sceloporus variabilis*) that lives at elevations up to 3,000 feet in the arid valleys below the cloud forests on the mountain summits. In their very different environments the two species keep nearly the same average body temperature.

Though our two specimens had roughly the same bodily proportions, the greenish one, weighing 27.8 grams, had four times the bulk of the other, which weighed only 6.9 grams. The temperature of both lizards was 77 degrees (25 degrees C.) when they were placed in full sunlight with the air temperature at about 90 degrees. Temperatures were recorded at intervals of three minutes. During the first nine minutes the body temperature of the larger lizard lagged less than a degree behind that of the smaller lizard. But after 12 minutes the temperature of the larger lizard rose slightly above that of the smaller. At the conclusion of the experiment, after 18 minutes, the temperature of the larger lizard was 109 degrees (43 degrees C.), and that of the smaller was 108.7 degrees (42.6 degrees C.). If the two lizards had absorbed heat at rates predicated solely on their weight, the heavier should have required approximately 10 more minutes to reach the temperature attained by the smaller animal in 18 minutes. Though inexact, the results of our simple experiment suggest that the cloud-forest lizard is better equipped, figuratively, "to make hay while the sun shines." Because the pigments in its skin can absorb heat so rapidly, it can attain its threshold temperature quickly enough and often enough during the year to permit it to forage and fuel itself.

We suspected that the outcome of this experiment may have been influenced by changes in the pigmentation of one or the other reptiles in the course of the experiment. To find out how important such changes are in regulating the absorption of heat we performed an experiment with individuals of different weights but belonging to the same species. This time we used regal horned lizards (*Phrynosoma solare*) weighing respectively 12.4, 29.4 and 85.5 grams. The experiment was conducted in August on a clear day, with no wind, in the foothills of the Chiricahua Mountains in Arizona. The body temperature of each lizard was 80 degrees (27 degrees C.) at the start of the experiment; within 15 minutes their temperatures simultaneously reached 109 degrees (43 degrees C.), with the curves on the recording instrument indicating that they had risen at a virtually identical rate. About halfway through the experiment the temperature of the smallest lizard ran a degree ahead of the others, but shifted back to the curves being plotted for the other two, as though some mechanism were regulating the rate of heat absorption. This proved to be the case. Although the three lizards were not conspicuously different in color at the beginning of the experiment, we could discern distinct differences at the conclusion. The largest lizard was the darkest of the three, and the smallest lizard the palest [*Fig. 6-6*].

While their broadly flattened bodies are adapted for the rapid absorption of heat, it is apparent that horned lizards are equally well equipped by pigmentation to regulate the rate at which they absorb heat. The black-pigmented cells, or melanophores, of their skin expand laterally when the animal is cold, thus darkening the body and increasing the rate at which it absorbs radiant energy. When the body is warm the same cells contract, thereby exposing light pigments in adjacent cells that reflect infra-red radiation. To match such efficiency we would need a mechanism that automatically exchanged our dark winter clothing for white linens with the advent of hot weather.[4]

The behavioral control of body temperature in reptiles must demand a considerable degree of sensitivity to changes in the internal temperature of the body and a central mechanism capable of integrating a diversity of responses when this temperature departs too

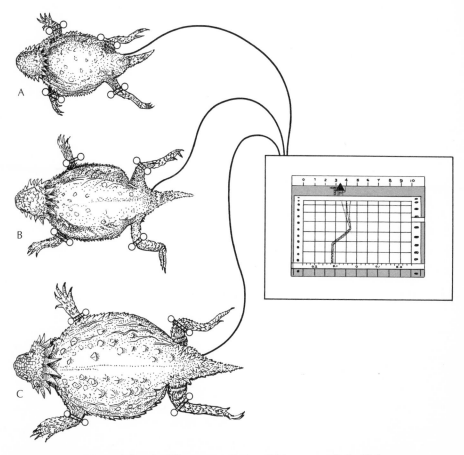

Fig. 6-6. Regal horned lizards (*Phrynosoma solare*) weighing respectively 12.4 grams (*A*), 29.4 grams (*B*), and 85.5 grams (*C*) were exposed to the midday sun while their body temperatures were continuously measured by means of wires from the cloaca of each to a recording potentiometer. The colors of the lizards were nearly the same at start but then changed, the smallest lizard becoming the palest. (From C. M. Bogert, *Scientific American*, 200 (1959), 108.)

widely from the preferred body temperature. There is some evidence that this control is mediated in reptiles by a temperature-sensitive region in the hypothalamus, the region of the brain intimately involved in the regulation of visceral function. The existence of thermal sensitivity in that region is of particular interest in view of evidence, to be discussed below, that the homoiothermy of mammals is regulated by a hypothalamic thermostat. It may well be that some form of behavioral thermoregulation evolved very early in reptiles, perhaps at least as far back as the Permian, and possibly independently in more than one line. Considering that the lines leading respectively to birds and mammals must, on morphological evidence, be regarded as separate from the days of the earliest stem reptiles, it is certainly very probable that the thermoregulatory mechanisms of the two modern groups of homoiotherms were independently evolved.

It is thus at least doubtful whether the extinct reptiles were quite as much at the mercy of the environment as was suggested in the earlier quotation (p. 225). Nevertheless, it must be remembered that this discussion has dealt with small lizards. As Bogert points out, the situation of the large dinosaurs must have been very different, for such enormous bodies require long exposure to a source of heat before they can build up the temperature that modern lizards require for their activity. If, during the night, the body temperature of a ten-ton dinosaur dropped four or five degrees below its threshold for activity, it would, according to Bogert, have to bask for much of the next day in order to regain that threshold level. The assumption is that the larger of these animals must have lived in the relatively constant temperature of a tropical environment. As far as smaller extinct forms are concerned, however, their mode of life may well have resembled that of modern species. Thus it is possible that a hypothalamic sensitivity to temperature, with its potentialities for promoting the integration of the behavioral responses needed to establish the preferred body temperature, could have provided the foundation upon which the small reptilian ancestors of birds and mammals were able to organize their progress toward homoiothermy.

■ THE PRINCIPLES OF HOMOIOTHERMY

Homoiothermy provides both birds and mammals with a body temperature that is in general both high and constant. There is much variation, however, both in the level of body temperature from species to species and in the degree of constancy with which the body temperature is maintained in any one species. Taking rectal temperature as a convenient measure of internal temperature, it is found to be 42.5°C in the fowl, 39°C in the pig, 38°C in the cow, and 37°C in man. In man, however, it shows a diurnal variation, ranging from 36.7°C in the early morning to 37.5°C in the late afternoon. Other mammals show similar fluctuations, the higher level being reached either by day or by night, corresponding to the diurnal or nocturnal habits of the particular species. Thus in dogs and cats the temperature may range from 37.5°C to 39.5°C, in horses and cattle from 37.5°C to 38.5°C. These are the ranges within which normal activity is maintained, and it is known from man's own experience in ill health what devastating consequences result from departure from these ranges.

Unlike poikilotherms, homoiotherms have lost the capacity to withstand large temperature fluctuations in their tissues; but they have gained, in exchange, a large measure of independence from the environment. Reptiles exploit the possibilities of the environment in order to secure a reasonably constant preferred body temperature. Homoiotherms, by contrast, maintain their body temperatures by methods that give them substantial independence of the ambient temperature. Homoiothermy is the end result of a long process of physiological evolution. Not surprisingly, therefore, there are still varying grades of efficiency among mammals; and it is possible to regard some of these animals as being more primitive than others in their homoiothermal organization. Certain species, sometimes referred to as heterotherms, have lower body temperatures than those mentioned above and may also maintain activity over a much wider range of body temperatures. An extreme example is the Madagascar hedgehog, *Centetes ecaudatus*. This is probably one of the most primitive living mammals from any point of view, and it is thus significant that it shows a diurnal temperature cycle of 10°C, and that it can maintain its activity over a body temperature range of 24.1°C to 34.8°C. Another example, although a much less extreme one, is the European hedgehog, *Erinaceus europaeus*. This has a comparatively low body temperature, with an activity range of at least 34.8°C to 36.4°C; according to some accounts, the range is even larger.

A third and striking example is the three-toed sloth, *Bradypus*. This animal shows a temperature range of 27.7°C to 36.8°C at air temperatures ranging from 24.5°C to 32.4°C; it loses heat rapidly in cold air. As a result of this, its body temperature may fall to 20°C after exposure for five hours to an ambient temperature of 10°C. Thus, remarks K. Johansen, it is unable to enter an environment lacking the stability of the moist tropics in which it lives. Such a case gives support to the view that the progressive improvement of homoiothermy may have been associated with the dispersal of homoiotherms from tropical centers into more exacting climatic conditions. However, it would be unwise to suppose that a fluctuating body temperature in mammals is necessarily a sign of primitive organization. Later, in discussing the remarkable case of the camel, it will be seen that fluctuations of body temperature can be an expression of a high level of thermal adaptation.

The fundamental step that made homoiothermy possible in birds and mammals was the achievement of a high basal rate of metabolism, a parameter that is expressed as oxygen consumption per unit weight per unit time. Comparative data to illustrate the difference in this respect between poikilotherms and homoiotherms are best obtained from animals of equivalent size. The reason for this is that although the total oxygen consumption of a large animal is necessarily larger than that of a smaller one of similar physiological organization, the increase is not directly proportional to the increase in size. Oxygen consumption increases at a slower rate, which means that the basal metabolic rate will be relatively higher in the smaller animal. It is, in fact, quite closely correlated with surface area, which is, of course, relatively larger in proportion to size in smaller bodies than in larger ones. As a general illustration of the high metabolic rate of the homoiotherms, therefore, it is helpful to compare a mammal with a reptile of similar size. For example, a python of 32 kg has a total metabolism of 189 kilocalories per 24 hr, as compared with the 997 kilocalories per 24 hr of a human weighing 32.3 kg. Or, to state the comparison in another way, the basal metabolic rates of a rattlesnake and a rabbit, both weighing 2.5 kg, are respectively 7.7 and 44.8 kilocalories per kg per 24 hr. Similar results would be obtained by comparing birds with reptiles.

Birds and mammals, therefore, provide their own source of heat, and it is because of this that they are said, in Bogert's terminology, to be endothermic. It is thus possible for them to maintain a steep gradient between the temperature of the interior of the body (the core temperature) and that of the environment; although this gradient could not in fact be maintained if the metabolic adaptation were not associated with a well-developed surface insulation, provided by feathers in birds, hair in most mammals, and clothing in man. All of these owe their insulating power to their enclosure of a layer of air of low conductivity, which is why two thin layers of clothing conserve the heat of the human body more satisfactorily than a single layer of double the weight.

Given this insulation, it is then necessary for homoiotherms to be able to adjust their internal temperature in accordance with changing ambient temperatures. This is largely provided for by physical thermoregulation — control of the rate at which heat is lost from the body. Indeed, one of the advantages that homoiotherms derive from their high body temperature is precision of control of heat loss; for this is easier to manipulate than is heat production, and it is also easier to regulate when the body is substantially warmer than the environment. Naturally, homoiotherms also gain the advantage of the increased efficiency of biochemical and biophysical processes that are a concomitant of high temperature.

It may seem contradictory to stress the importance of regulation of heat loss when an essential feature of homoiothermy is insulation of the body surface; but, in fact, these two principles are closely interrelated in a very flexible way. For one thing, the insulatory effect of hair and feathers can be increased in cold conditions by erecting the hairs or (which amounts to much the same thing) by fluffing the feathers. This increases the thickness of the layer of air around the body and thus lowers the temperature gradient between the surface of the skin and the mass of air external to the body covering. Further, the insulation of the body is not uniform. Heat can readily be lost through naked or thinly protected regions of the body such as the legs or ventral surface; the animal can regulate this loss by varying its posture, exposing the unprotected regions in warm conditions and concealing them in colder ones. Birds can protect themselves in a similar manner; the dissipation of heat can be encouraged by holding the wings away from the more thinly feathered sides of the body or by exposing the legs. Thus behavioral reactions play a part in homoiothermy as well as in poikilothermy.

Genetic differences in the extent of development of these less protected regions can also be established under the influence of natural selection. Within a given mammalian species, for example, the thinly insulated appendages (ears, limbs, and tail) tend to be shorter in populations inhabiting colder regions, a generalization that is known as Allen's Rule. The effect of this adaptation is to reduce heat loss in colder environments. Of course, the degree of insulation of the body covering is also adapted to the environment. Measurements of insulating capacity, expressed as the reciprocal of the thermal conductivity of the winter fur, show that arctic mammals are much more highly insulated than are tropical ones (*Figs. 6-7; 6-8*). This type of adaptation is further improved by seasonal moulting, which makes it possible for a thick winter covering to be replaced by a thinner summer one. Similar adaptations are found in birds, although in these animals such genetic modifications of insulation are less obvious than in mammals. This is because feathers are used for locomotion as well as for insulation, so that they do not lend themselves quite as well as does hair to these flexible adjustments.

Heat is lost from the body of a homoiotherm along the several paths of exchange that have been considered earlier: conduction, convection, radiation, and evaporation. Conduction will usually be the least important of the four paths, because of the very low conductivity of air and the limited amount of contact between the body and the substratum. Convection is much more important, because of the low specific heat of air. This amounts to 0.24 cal/gm, as compared with a value of 0.83 cal/gm for the body; air in contact with the skin is thus rapidly warmed, with the consequent establishment of convection

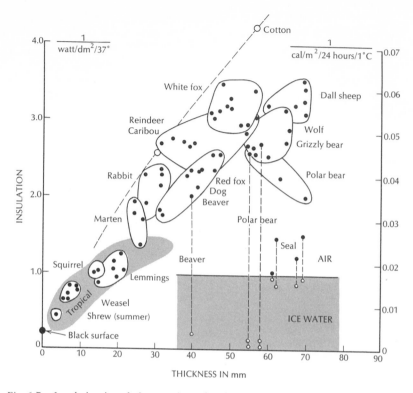

Fig. 6-7. Insulation in relation to winter fur thickness in a series of arctic mammals, expressed as the reciprocal of the thermal conductivity. The insulation in tropical mammals is indicated by the shaded area. In the aquatic mammals (seal, beaver, polar bear) the measurements in 0°C air are connected by vertical lines with the same measurements taken in ice water. The two upper points of the lemmings are from *Dicrostonyx*, the others from *Lemmus*. (From P. F. Scholander, R. Hock, V. Walters, and L. Irving, *Biological Bulletin*, 99 (1950), 230. By permission of the *Biological Bulletin*.)

currents. Radiation can also be an important source of heat loss; for example, the human skin radiates strongly, at a rate proportional to the fourth power of its absolute temperature. As noted previously, the rate of heat transfer along these three paths can be taken as proportional to the temperature gradient, which in this case will be determined by the difference between the temperature of the skin and that of the surroundings. Thus, as the external temperature rises, the possibility of losing heat by convection, conduction, and radiation diminishes, until evaporation alone provides the only path. This means, in practice, that the precise pattern of physical thermoregulation at any moment will depend upon the relation between the body temperature and that of the environment, different responses being brought into play as the need for them develops.

One very important factor in the fine adjustment of heat loss is the control of the flow of blood through the skin. Earlier, it was noted that the action of the circulatory system tends to equalize the distribution of heat through the body. It also provides the path by which heat is most readily transferred from the interior of the body to the surface from which it can be dissipated; increase in cutaneous blood flow will promote heat loss, whereas decrease in flow will conserve heat. Probably, then, an improvement in cardiac output and an increased level of blood pressure were important developments during the evolution of homoiothermy. The contribution of circulation, however, calls for very precise vascular control, particularly of the cutaneous vessels in the thinly insulated or naked parts of the skin. This is especially so in birds, since as already mentioned, the insulation provided by their feathers is not easy to regulate in response to changing needs. The extent to which even the mammalian body makes use of vascular control may be gauged from the fact that in certain areas of the human skin the blood flow may change by a factor

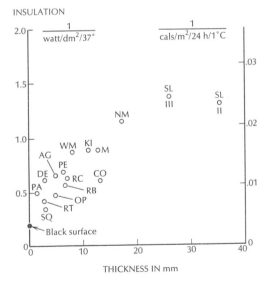

Fig. 6-8. Insulation in relation to fur thickness in tropical mammals. The insulation of the fur in most of these animals is probably close to that of a bare black surface, but is higher in these measurements because of the relative high insulation of the skin in the dead samples.

AG — agouti	M — marmoset	PE — peccary	SL II — 2-toed sloth
CO — coati	NM — night monkey	RB — rabbit	SL III — 3-toed sloth
DE — deer	OP — opossum	RC — raccoon	SQ — squirrel
KI — kinkajou	PA — paca	RT — rat	WM — white-faced monkey

(From P. F. Scholander, R. Hock, V. Walters, and L. Irving, *Biological Bulletin*, 99 (1950), 231. By permission of the *Biological Bulletin*.)

of over a hundred in response to the changing conditions of heat load. Restriction of blood flow is mediated by vasoconstrictor nerve fibers acting under the control of the central nervous system. Vaso-dilation apparently is not under such direct nervous control; it has been suggested that it may be mediated by a vasodilator substance called bradykinin, released in human skin at times when the sweat glands are also active.

At times when the ambient temperature is increasing, the animal reduces its activity and relies at first upon the vasomotor reactions to provide additional cooling; but if they prove inadequate, the body calls upon its power of increasing heat loss by evaporation. Normally, there is always some loss of water by evaporation from the mammalian body, partly through the breath and partly by what is called the insensible perspiration, which is the diffusion of water vapor through the skin. A human being may lose as much as 1200 ml of water per day by these routes, representing, since the loss is of water vapor, a substantial passage of heat. This loss is increased in many mammals by the discharge of sweat from the sweat glands, and this is the reac-tion that is invoked to supplement the vasomotor responses. These glands, which are under the control of the sympathetic nervous sys-tem, are brought into action in man at times of emotional stress as well as for heat regulation.

There is some variation in the mode and efficiency of the action of sweat glands. Their secretion is rich in sodium chloride, but it varies, nevertheless, in its composition as well as in its rate of production. In part, this variation may reflect an acquired adaptation to specific environmental conditions, but individual variations of a nonadaptive character may also be involved. Thus two individuals, working under similar conditions of heat stress, may equilibrate at different tempera-tures: one at 38°C, for example, and another at 39°C.

Sweating begins in man at temperatures of about 29°C; above this level convection can make little contribution to heat loss. Ideally, one should be unaware of sweating, for its efficiency in heat transfer depends upon the secretion of the glands being removed by evapora-tion. The accumulation of sweat on the body is an accumulation of water that is not removing heat; it is associated with increasing dis-comfort. The more humid the atmosphere, the more rapidly will this state of discomfort develop. This explains the difference in the reactions of homoiotherms to hot deserts and wet tropical regions. Deserts have a low relative humidity and intense solar radiation. The dry substratum, with a specific heat perhaps only one fifth that of water, will heat up rapidly during the day and will cool rapidly at night. Animals living there are thus exposed to a large diurnal cycle of temperature, yet they can readily cool themselves by evaporation. Wet tropics are much more unpleasant. The diurnal temperature cycle is small, because of the stabilizing effect of the moisture; but the high relative humidity reduces evaporation and elevates the skin temperature, while a copious flow of blood to the skin reduces the supply of oxygen to other parts of the body.

The utilization of evaporation in physical thermoregulation does not necessarily depend upon the presence of sweat glands. They are absent from birds, so that these animals must rely upon their respiratory system to bring about evaporation cooling through the increase in ventilation called panting. This response develops early in young birds, which has led to the suggestion that it may be a phylogenetically ancient adaptation. Ontogeny is by no means a reliable guide to phylogenetic history; but in this instance the suggestion is plausible, for panting is also well developed as a thermoregulatory device in reptiles. Cooling is aided in birds by the presence of outgrowths of the lungs called air sacs. These, because of their large surface area, are generally thought to aid evaporation, particularly during the rapid respiratory movements of the animal when it is in flight. The air sacs, therefore, provide some compensation for the relatively inflexible level of insulation provided by the feathers.

Panting, associated with salivation, is also familiar in mammals; and it is particularly important in those species (the dog is a well-known example) that do not possess sweat glands. An overheated dog promotes evaporation of abundant saliva by increasing the air movement over the tongue and, in this way, causing fluid evaporation equivalent to the sweat produced by species with glands. An even more instructive demonstration is given by the kangaroo. Although a marsupial, and thus to some extent more primitive in its organization than placental mammals, it maintains its body temperature within the range of 37–38°C and does so at least as successfully as placentals of comparable size. Like placentals, it responds to rising ambient temperature by remaining quiet, increasing its respiratory rate and amplitude, and employing peripheral vasodilatation. At higher temperatures, however, the evaporation of saliva becomes its main thermoregulatory device. A copious flow of saliva sets in, and its evaporation is facilitated by the animal spreading it over its body by licking its legs, feet, tail, and ventral surface.

The remarkable powers of heat loss conferred on mammals and birds by thermoregulation were demonstrated in the eighteenth century by experiments that showed no small degree of adventurousness on the part of those concerned. Reported at that time by C. Blagden to the Royal Society of London, they have often been referred to since because of the vivid contrast that they draw between the thermal behavior of man and of beefsteaks.

The experimenters used a set of rooms which were provided with thermometers and heated by flues in the floor and by boiling water.

On one occasion the temperature was raised to over 260° Fahrenheit, with the further aid of a red-hot stove.

> At this I went into the room, with the addition, to my common clothes, of a pair of thick worsted stockings drawn over my shoes, and reaching some way above my knees; I also put on a pair of gloves, and held a cloth constantly between my face and the cockle stove: all these precautions were necessary to guard against the scorching of the red-hot iron. I remained eight minutes in this situation, frequently walking about to all the different parts of the room, but standing still most of the time in the coolest spot, near the lowest thermometer. The air felt very hot, but still by no means to such a degree as to give pain: on the contrary, I had no doubt of being able to support a much greater heat; and all the gentlemen present, who went into the room, were of the same opinion.
>
> . . . To prove there was no fallacy in the degree of heat shown by the thermometer, but that the air which we breathed was capable of producing all the well-known effects of such an heat on inanimate matter, we put some eggs and a beef-steak upon a tin frame. . . . In about twenty minutes the eggs were taken out, roasted quite hard; and in forty-seven minutes the steak was not only dressed, but almost dry. Another beef-steak was rather overdone in thirty-three minutes.[5]

Blagden and his fellow investigators well appreciated the significance of perspiration, "that cooling evaporation which is a further provision of nature of enabling animals to support great heat." Their observations also brought out the importance of vasomotor control in increasing heat loss from the body surface, although it is only recently that sophisticated analysis by a new technique of measurement called gradient calorimetry has established how constancy of body temperature is maintained under conditions of extreme heat.

> The gradient calorimeter now operated at Bethesda is a chamber large enough to hold a man stretched out at full length. The subject is suspended in an open-weave sling, out of contact with the floor or walls of the chamber, and is free to go through the motions of prescribed exercise when the experiment calls for such exertion.
>
> The new and essential feature of gradient calorimetry is the "gradient layer," a thin foil of material with a uniform resistance to heat flow which lines the entire inner surface of the chamber. Some thousands of thermoelectric junctions interlace the foil in a regular pattern and measure the local difference in temperature (and hence the local heat flow) at as many points across the foil. The junctions are wired in series; their readings are thus recorded in a single potential at the terminals of the circuit. That potential measures the total energetic output from the subject's skin, independent of his position with respect to the surfaces of the gradient layer lining the chamber. The rate of blood flow through the skin can be derived by computing this

measurement against the temperature of the outgoing blood (measured internally) and the temperature of the returning blood (measured on the skin), since the observed transfer of heat per unit time at any given difference between internal and external temperature can be effected by only one calculable rate of blood flow. The energy dissipated by evaporation from the subject's skin is also measured by gradient layers which line heat-exchange meters at the inlet and outlet of the air circuit of the calorimeter. Measurements taken for control make it possible to maintain the same temperature and humidity in the air at these two points, so that the air neither gains nor loses energy as it passes through the system. The unbalanced output from the additional gradient layers thus precisely measures the heat loss by evaporation and hence the sweat-gland activity. Heat loss through the lungs is measured separately and subtracted from the total.[6]

The gulf that separates current sophistication of technique from the pioneer explorations of the eighteenth century could hardly be better illustrated. And the sophistication justifies itself by its results, for it has made possible the resolution of a problem that had been posed, but not solved, by classical physiology. It is now known that scientists are dealing here with a physiological control circuit similar in principle to the feedback models discussed earlier. One must expect, therefore, to be able to identify within the body a sensory organ (to measure variations in temperature), a controller or computer (to compare the observed temperatures with the required set point), and an effector mechanism (to restore normal temperature under instructions from the computer center). It has long been recognized that the effector mechanisms responding to overheating are vasodilation and sweating. Moreover, it has been known since 1884 that the controller is situated in a localized region of the hypothalamus, for the application of temperature stimuli to this region is followed by thermoregulatory responses in the body. But is it the hypothalamus that actually measures the temperature in normal conditions?

The answer to this question is less obvious than might appear, for the situation is complicated by the fact that

. . . the body is also equipped with an elaborate system of millions of tiny sensitive nerve endings, distributed throughout the skin, which produce conscious sensations of warmth. The scientific literature tended to support the view that the skin and not the hypothalamus furnishes the primary temperature measurements to the control center for sweating and the dilation of the arteries. Some investigators held that both systems were involved; a rise in the temperature of the "heat center" in the hypothalamus supposedly made it more responsive to incoming impulses from the temperature-sensing organs of the skin. The question, in this view, was one of determining the relative importance of the two sites. It was also possible, as some believed, that the body possessed a third area sensitive to temperature or heat flow, and that neither the skin nor the brain was involved. . . .

With the help of the gradient calorimeter our group at Bethesda set out to establish the correlations obtaining, on the one hand, between the performance of the effector mechanisms and the temperature of the skin and, on the other hand, between the performance of the effector mechanisms and the internal temperature of the body. In these first experiments it was assumed that rectal temperature provided an adequate index of internal temperature as measured at the temperature-sensing organ, wherever it might be located. But no correlation could be found, in either resting or "working" subjects, between rectal temperature and the observed rates of sweating. Measurements of skin temperature against the same heat-dissipation variable yielded equally meaningless plots. For a time it seemed that all the effort that had gone into the design of the gradient calorimeter had been wasted. The result made sense only in terms of the classical notion that the thermostat in the interior of the body and the temperature-sensing nerve endings in the skin have indissolubly interlaced effects upon the vasodilation and sweating responses.

Then we found a way to measure the internal temperature of the body at a site near the center of temperature regulation in the brain. We introduced a thermocouple through the outer ear canal and held it against the ear drum membrane under slight pressure. The eardrum is near the hypothalamus and shares a common blood supply with it from the internal carotid artery. At the very first attempt we observed temperature changes associated with the eating of ice or the drinking of hot fluids, and we soon found we could detect variations caused by immersion of the limbs in warm water. Parallel rectal measurements did not show these variations at all.

Building on this foundation, it proved possible to establish that thermoregulation in response to overheating was dependent on a temperature-sensing mechanism in the hypothalamus.

. . . the rate of sweating fell off and rose in perfect parallel with the decline and rise in internal head temperature. It was the consequent drying of the skin that caused the skin to be heated by radiation and conduction in the hot environment. But the sensory reception of heat in the skin brought no response from the heat-dissipating mechanism.

These observations accord well with the familiar constancy of the body temperature. It is difficult to see how it could be maintained within the same narrow range, year in and year out, if the heat-controlling responses were not always triggered at the same set point. As these experiments show, moreover, the responses always closely match the magnitude of the stimulus. Such precise regulation of temperature could not be achieved by measurement of skin temperature. As in all feedback systems, the quantity which is controlled must itself be measured. An architect who wants to control the temperature of a house does not distribute thousands of thermometers over the outside walls. One thermostat in the living room suffices. It responds not only to warming and chilling from out-of-doors but to overheating from within. The thermostat in the hypothalamus similarly monitors the internal temperature of the body from the inside and thereby maintains its constancy.

This is not to say that the warm-sensitive nerve endings of the skin have no function in the regulation of body temperature. They are the sensory organs for another system which operates via the centers of consciousness in the cortex, bypassing the unconscious control centers in the hypothalamus. To sensations of heat or cold reported by the skin the body reacts by using the muscles as effector organs. Under the stimulus of discomfort from the extremes of both heat and cold, man seeks a cooler or warmer environment or takes the measures necessary to make his environment comfortably cool or warm. But for all the mastery of external circumstances that follows from this linkage in the body's temperature-sensing equipment, the skin thermoreceptors cannot regulate internal temperature with any degree of precision. They can contribute directly to the regulation of skin temperature alone. The automatic system of hypothalamic temperature regulation takes over from there and achieves the final adjustment with almost unbelievable sensitivity and precision.[7]

The discussion so far has been concerned only with physical thermoregulation. In contrast to this regulation of heat loss, there is also the possibility of dealing with cold conditions by increasing heat production through a rise in metabolic activity; this is termed chemical thermoregulation. Its visible manifestation, both in birds and mammals, is shivering, which is muscular contraction that brings about a rise in heat production in the active muscles. It is likely, however, that this visible shivering is preceded by an invisible increase of muscular tone or by contraction of small groups of fibers that do not give rise to visible movement of the tissue. Possibly, too, metabolism may increase in other tissues as well, although the sheer bulk of the musculature makes it inevitable that the main burden of chemical thermoregulation must fall on that tissue.

The increased output of energy means an increased demand exerted upon the energy store, and here the endocrine system becomes involved. As seen earlier, adrenaline is an important factor in short-term adaptive responses, because it evokes the release of more glucose into the blood; it thus has a part to play in chemical thermoregulation. The thyroid hormones are also involved, because of their influence on metabolic rate. That they are active in thermoregulation is apparent from experiments that show an increased output of thyroid hormones in small mammals when they are removed from a warm room into the cold.

Mention of the thyroid gland and of adrenaline brings one again to the hypothalamus as the integrating center of visceral function. As seen in Chapter 4, secretion of adrenaline is controlled by the sympathetic nervous system, and the thyroid gland is regulated through a feedback relationship with the hypothalamus and the adenohypophysis. It is now apparent, however, that the role of the hypothalamus in thermoregulation goes much further than this, for it contains the thermostat that initiates responses to overheating. The hypothalamus is certainly involved also in the chemical thermoregulatory response to chilling, although here its mode of operation is less well understood. Probably the two control systems operate in different ways.

The use of the term thermostat in this connection is not an over-optimistic use of analogy with engineering practice. It can be amply justified, because, like the thermostat of some heat engine, part of the hypothalamus is a self-actuating mechanism that is set to maintain the temperature of a system (in this case, the living body) at a predetermined level regardless of substantial fluctuations of temperature in the surroundings. Its profound physiological importance is shown by the fact that if the cerebral hemispheres are removed from a rabbit, the animal can still maintain its normal body temperature. If, however, the diencephalon (containing the hypothalamus) is also removed, the animal can no longer maintain normal body temperature. In these circumstances, it becomes essentially poikilothermal.

■ THE PRACTICE OF HOMOIOTHERMY IN THE DESERT HEAT

It is impossible to examine here in adequate detail the precision with which the principles of thermoregulation are applied in birds and mammals in the diverse environments in which these animals can flourish. It must be sufficient to consider them in relation to the survival of certain mammals in extreme conditions, in which the various devices already outlined can be seen in operation.

Under normal circumstances, mammals are unlikely to find themselves exposed to the excessively stringent conditions to which Blagden and his friends subjected themselves. Nevertheless, there are natural habitats that present animals with complex problems of thermoregulation. Of these, the hot desert is of particular interest, because it is characterized by very high maximum temperature and a lack of permanent water. As Schmidt-Nielsen points out, man can sometimes prosper in deserts, but not because of his physiological organization; he depends upon his technological culture and, more especially, upon the water that he brings into the desert with him or that he obtains by drilling. Without this aid, he could not hope to survive for more than a day or two. However, a considerable animal fauna does survive in these conditions; included in this group are two strongly contrasted mammals, the kangaroo rat and the camel. These illustrate how the principles of thermoregulation are deployed to meet the stringent desert conditions.

The kangaroo rat, *Dipodomys merriami,* is one of a number of small rodents that have been able to survive in desert conditions, primarily by virtue of behavioral adaptations rather than by developing special tolerance of high temperature. Indeed, behavioral adaptations often may be as important in homoiotherms as in reptiles, although they are employed in different physiological contexts. Desert rodents avoid the intense daytime heat by remaining in underground burrows until the cool of the evening. The advantage of this behavior is that the very great temperature fluctuations at the surface of the soil are rapidly reduced with increasing depth, so that where, as in Arizona, the surface temperatures may vary over a range of as much as 80°C, this range is reduced to about 12°C at a depth of one meter. At this depth the highest temperature in the desert need not exceed 30°C, so that nocturnal animals living in burrows need not be exposed to any heat stress at all.

Of course, it can be argued that the investigation of burrows disturbs their structure so much that conditions found in them may depart widely from those that the occupants would normally encounter. This argument, however, has been met very ingeniously by capturing animals outside their burrows and tying microclimate recorders to their tails; when the animals retreat, they make a record of their living conditions. Such records have amply confirmed the belief that these animals are free from heat stress when they stay at home during the day. It is well for small rodents that this is so. At ambient temperatures of 43°C, the efforts of the kangaroo rat to thermoregulate would result in its losing water at the rate of about 10 per cent of its body weight per hour. It could not possibly survive such rapid dehydration, particularly when it is remembered that the heat load imposed by this temperature, which is well within the normal temperature of deserts, would be still further increased by the intense solar radiation received directly and by reflection from the substratum.

There is, however, an important physiological adaptation that contributes to the survival of *Dipodomys* in the hot desert. This is its ability to live without access to any drinking water. The demonstration that it can do this comes from the Schmidt-Nielsens' studies of the water balance of the animal when it is maintained in the laboratory on solid food, without any water for drinking. The animal loses water in its urine, in its feces, and by evaporation; while water is gained from the moisture present initially in the food (preformed water) and from the water produced by oxidative metabolism. All of these values can be determined by observation or calculation; illustrations of them are given in *Fig. 6-9,* which shows the total water intake and output during the metabolism of 100 calories of pearl barley.

It will be seen that the total water intake is greater than the minimum water output, provided that the humidity of the environment is above 2.2 mg of water per liter of air (equivalent to a relative humidity of 10 per cent at 25°C). The importance of this relative humidity is that it determines the amount of preformed water present in the pearl barley. This material, although conventionally regarded as "dry" food, is necessarily in equilibrium with the water in the atmosphere, unless, of course, it is artificially dried before being fed to the animal. Direct observations on the burrows of kangaroo rats have shown that the humidity in them is actually considerably higher

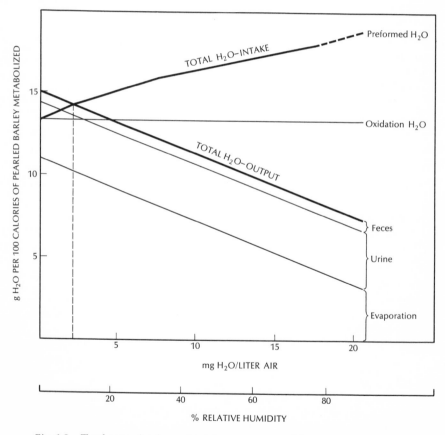

Fig. 6-9. Total water intake and total water output of kangaroo rats at various atmospheric humidities at 25°C. Ordinate: Water intake and output in grams per 100 calories of pearled barley metabolized. Abscissa: Humidity in the environmental air. (From Fig. 1,B, B. Schmidt-Nielsen and K. Schmidt-Nielsen, *Journal of Cellular and Comparative Physiology,* 38 (1951), 172.)

than the limiting value given above. Thus the animal can maintain itself in water balance without access to drinking water and with some margin to allow it to forage outside the burrow at night.

That this capacity of kangaroo rats is a true adaptation and not merely a by-product of the physiological organization of small rodents in general, can be readily judged by comparing the performance of this species with that of the white rat. The essential data are shown in *Fig. 6-10*. It will be seen that the rate of water loss by all three routes (urine, feces, and evaporation) is substantially higher than in the kangaroo rat. Thus, in complete contrast to the latter animal, the white rat, when deprived of drinking water, loses water more rapidly than it can replace it at all humidities below 95-100 per cent relative humidity. One can conclude, therefore, that the kangaroo rat is adapted to desert life not only in its behavior but also in its remarkable reduction of water output. A white rat, living in similar conditions, would be rapidly dehydrated.

An animal that in size and habits presents a complete and engaging contrast to *Dipodomys* is the camel, yet it, too, is no less at home in desert conditions. Physiological investigations of so large and inaccessible an animal present obvious difficulties (Schmidt-Nielsen tells how Homer Smith and an assistant obtained samples of a camel's urine by marching in an evening circus parade with a flashlight and a bucket), but scientists now have a good understanding of how the problems of thermoregulation have been solved. One may review the situation in the succinct and convincing account provided by the Schmidt-Nielsens and their colleagues.

> The camel has a legendary reputation for ability to tolerate water deprivation for prolonged periods of time. It is surprising therefore that scientific literature about its physiology is quite inadequate. The literature on the camel mainly consists of travel reports and veterinary handbooks. . . .
>
> For a large animal like the camel the problems of survival in a desert environment are quite different from those of, for example, a small rodent which has an underground burrow. A large animal cannot escape the heat of the day, and it will consequently have to spend water for evaporative cooling in order to maintain constant body temperature whenever the environment is so warm that the heat transfer between body and environment results in a net heat gain in the body. The small rodents can and must escape the heat because evaporative cooling is too expensive an undertaking for them. Accordingly, small rodents do not spend water for heat regulation, and it is possible for certain of them to maintain water balance even when the water intake is restricted to the preformed water in dry seeds and the water formed by the oxidation of the food in the body. This is accomplished by an extreme degree of water economy [See above].

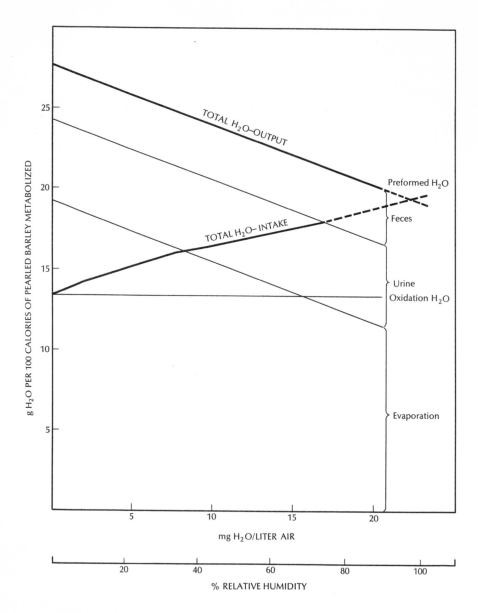

Fig. 6-10. Total water intake and total water output of white rats at various temperatures. *Cf.* Figure 6-9. (From Fig. 2,B, B. Schmidt-Nielsen and K. Schmidt-Nielsen, *Journal of Cellular and Comparative Physiology*, 38 (1951), 174).

However, the large animal that sweats or pants can never become independent of intake of free water, because the amount of water necessary for heat regulation is large compared with the other needs.

The adaptation of the camel to its hot environment does not, therefore, involve independence of drinking water, but it seemed that it might involve an ability to economize with the water available, and an ability to tolerate severe dehydration, possibly coupled with storage of water in the body.

These problems were investigated during an expedition to the Sahara Desert where a research laboratory was set up in the oasis Béni Abbès in southern Algeria (2°W, 30°N). Camels (*Camelus drome-darius*) are used extensively in this area. The majority of the camels are owned by nomads who keep them primarily for meat production and transport. They feed on the sparse vegetation on the hammada (rock desert) and in the erg (sand desert) and along the wadis (dry river beds). The plants in the wadis generally have a considerably higher salt content than the plants in the erg or hammada. In the winter the vegetation contains enough moisture to cover the needs of the camels. According to our own observations as well as from what we were told by the Arabs, the camels do not need drinking water when they are grazing in the winter. . . . In the summer, however, many plants dry up at the same time as the camel's need for water increases. During the summer, grazing camels are watered regularly at intervals of a few days. When grazing in the erg in the summer the camels return to the wells about every three days for water.

As with the kangaroo rat, it is the analysis of water balance that provides the clue to the thermoregulatory mechanism of the camel.

The rate of water expenditure for urine, feces and evaporation in the camel can now be compared with those of some other animals. In *Figure [6-11]* the minimum water expenditure is given for kangaroo rat, white rat, man, donkey and camel. The rate of water expenditure is calculated as liters of water used per liter of water formed in the body by oxidative metabolism; in other words, the comparison is based on metabolic rate.

The figures for kangaroo rats and white rats are taken from previous investigations of these animals [See above]. The rate of evaporation in these two animals is given at 30% relative humidity at 25°C (about 7 mg of water/l. of air). The figures for man are recalculated from Gamble. It was not possible to find data for the minimum rate of water excretion in the cow. The data given in the graph represent the water expenditure of an average grazing cow.

From the graph it is seen that among the animals presented, the kangaroo rat is the only one that is able to keep the expenditure of water within the amount that is gained from oxidation of the food. The water expenditure of the camel is smaller than that of the donkey, mostly because the donkey excretes considerably more water with the

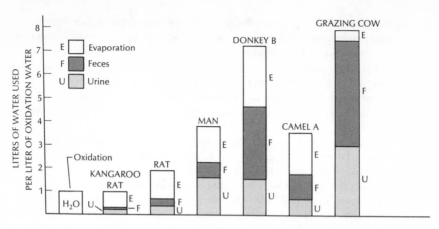

Fig. 6-11. Minimum water expenditure in different mammals presented as liters of water spent per liter of water formed by metabolic oxidation. The evaporation is calculated for a relative humidity of 25% at 25°C. (From B. Schmidt-Nielsen, K. Schmidt-Nielsen, T. R. Houpt, and S. A. Jarnum, *American Journal of Physiology*, 185 (1956), 192.)

feces (larger amount of feces and higher percentage of water in feces).

From the graph it seems as if the camel does not have any particular advantage over man with respect to water expenditure. The rate of urine flow is lower than in man, but at the same time the rate of water loss through feces is higher because of a larger amount of feces excreted. It thus appears as if man should tolerate water deprivation about as well as the camel. This however is a false impression, the camel being far superior to man in this respect for two reasons: *a*) it can tolerate a much higher degree of water depletion and *b*) in the summertime, when deprived of water, it spends only a fraction of the amount of water man spends for evaporative cooling. This is presented in *Figure [6-12]*, which shows the increase in evaporation which is due to the environmental heat load in the summer.[8]

The demonstration that camels expend so little water in evaporative cooling sheds entirely new light on the large variations in body temperature that are shown by these animals. Such variations had led to the belief that camels have only a crude mechanism of temperature control. Although the variations are real enough, the assumption that this reflects crude regulatory mechanisms is now seen to be incorrect and based upon the fallacy that the very constant body temperature of man and other higher mammals is necessarily the ideal situation. It is always dangerous to approach the analysis of adaptations with such a preconception; rather, their value must be judged in the light of the conditions to which a particular species is exposed. The fact is that man is not adapted for desert life, whereas the camel is; and, as Schmidt-Nielsen has convincingly shown, the variable body temperature of the latter animal, related to reduced evaporative loss of water, is highly advantageous in desert conditions.

One of the reasons that the camel has gained a reputation for being a poor temperature regulator is that Sergent found particularly low rectal temperatures, between 34° and 35°C, after rainy nights. It is indeed cold when the desert temperature approaches freezing and winds add to the chilling effect of the rain, but on three occasions when we had such weather, we observed no particular effect on our camels. They maintained their normal temperature for the particular time of the day when it was measured. There is no reason to doubt the observations made by Sergent, an experienced investigator from the Institut Pasteur; one can only note that our camels behaved differently.

In summer the variations in rectal temperature were much greater, with the temperature usually quite low in the morning and high in the afternoon. Morning temperatures were often between 34° and 35°C, and evening temperatures usually near or above 40°C. The greatest change observed in one animal in a day was from 34.5°C at 08.00 hrs. to 40.7°C at 19.00 hrs., that is, a rise of 6.2°C in 11 hours. . . .

Two representative temperature records are given in *Fig. [6-13]*. A most conspicuous feature is that the temperature fluctuations were much greater in the animals when they were deprived of drinking-water. When they were watered every day, the fluctuations decreased to about 2°C per day, which is similar to the daily variations in camels

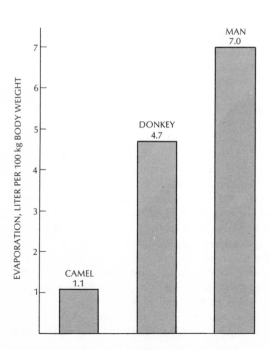

Fig. 6-12. Water used for cooling in the summer, in excess of that used in winter, in animals exposed to direct sunlight in the desert in the month of June, given as liters of water per day per 100 kg of body weight. The figures for the camel and the donkey are figures from periods when the animals were deprived of water. (From K. Schmidt-Nielsen, T. R. Houpt, and S. A. Jarnum, *American Journal of Physiology*, 185 (1956), 193.)

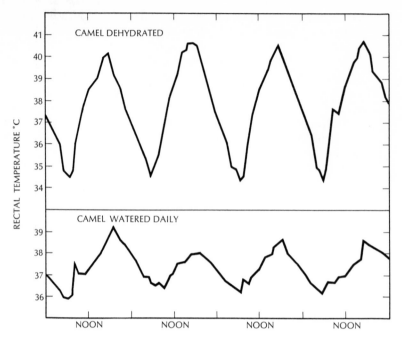

Fig. 6-13.   Diurnal fluctuations in rectal temperature of a camel when dehydrated and when watered daily. (From K. Schmidt-Nielsen, *Desert Animals*, Oxford, The Clarendon Press. 43.)

during the winter. In the periods when they were deprived of water, however, the temperature not only reached a considerably higher daily maximum, but the morning minimum was lowered as well, as can be seen in the upper graph.

The lethal body temperature for a camel is not known, but in no case did we observe a rectal temperature in excess of 40.7°C. This seems to be an approximate limit to which the temperature can rise without harm, but in all probability the camel cannot tolerate any appreciable further increase. In man the upper limit of temperature for survival is about 42°C for the temperature of the brain. The effect of high temperatures depends upon their duration, and it is likely that continued temperatures of 41°C may be dangerous and close to the upper limit of safety for man. The fact that we never observed temperatures in excess of 40.7°C in the camel, in spite of increasing environmental heat stress as the Saharan summer became hotter and hotter, suggests a well-regulated limit, and that any further rise beyond this point is prevented by increased heat dissipation. It would be extremely interesting to know more about the camel's tolerance to high body temperatures, and as opportunities for research improve in countries where camels are common, we can expect that careful and critical studies will give valuable results.

Advantages of a fluctuating body temperature: If the internal temperature is being kept constant as environmental heat impinges upon a body, all the acquired heat must be dissipated at the expense of water. If, instead, the body temperature is permitted to rise, all heat that goes into warming the body can be considered as stored. An example will illustrate the value of such heat storage. If the average body temperature in a 500-kg camel increased by 6°C, the stored heat will be about 2500 kcal (sp. heat $\simeq 0.8$), and the dissipation of all this heat by evaporation would require almost 5 litres of water. Instead, the heat is dissipated in the cool night by conduction and radiation.

Thus, an increase in body temperature during heat stress can be considered as a means to store heat until it can be disposed of without expenditure of water. If the morning temperature is especially low, this increases the amount of heat that can be stored and postpones until later in the day the moment when the tolerable temperature limit has been reached and water *must* be used to prevent further rise.

The high body temperature during the day has another advantage as well. The flow of heat from a hot environment to a cooler body depends on the temperature difference, and if the difference is reduced, the heat flow will be less. Therefore, the rise in the camel's temperature to a level well above 40°C should have a considerable effect in reducing the heat flow from the environment. An exact estimate of the reduction in heat load and the saving in water is virtually impossible to make, because it is so difficult to establish the integrated environmental temperature and the conditions for heat flow to the organism.[9]

■ THE PRACTICE OF HOMOIOTHERMY IN COLD CLIMATES

Thus far thermoregulation has been considered from the standpoint of mammals living in hot climates, faced with the problem of avoiding hyperthermia. The full significance of their adaptations, however, can be judged best by considering the contrasted problems that are encountered by animals living in conditions of extreme cold. The first point to be appreciated here is that the kind of metabolic adaptation found in aquatic poikilotherms does not occur in homoiotherms. In other words, the basal metabolic rate of arctic mammals, for example, is not relatively higher than that of tropical forms. On the contrary, this rate is related in an exponential manner to the size of the body (and, as seen earlier, more probably to its surface area) regardless of the environment that any particular species inhabits. In general, the basal metabolic rate for any mammal from mouse to elephant can be fitted to a straight line when plotted against body size on a double logarithmic grid *(Fig. 6-14)*. Adaptation to cold, like adaptation to heat, must depend, therefore, upon adequate insulation (which is greater in mammals from colder climates), upon the adoption of suitable microclimates, upon vasomotor control at the body surface, and upon a supply to the body of additional heat through thermoregulation.

Mammals can secure insulation additional to that afforded by their hair by depositing a layer of subcutaneous fat. This is never seen in reptiles, for in these ectothermal animals it would reduce the uptake of the radiant heat upon which they are so dependent. In the endothermal homoiotherms, however, it aids in the retention of heat, particularly so in seals and whales, which are amply protected by their thick layer of subcutaneous blubber. The polar bear presents an interesting contrast in this respect; for it lacks blubber and is undoubtedly prone to considerable heat loss while it is in the water, particularly because the water penetrates the loose hair and makes contact with the skin surface *(Fig. 6-7)*. Heat loss in this animal is probably compensated by vasoconstriction and by the high rate of heat production during swimming. On emerging from the water, however, it is in the position of a human being exposed to the air in clothing

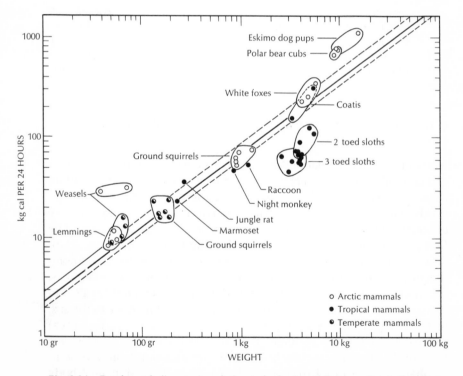

Fig. 6-14. Basal metabolic rate in relation to body size. Full drawn line is the mouse to elephant curve drawn according to the equation Kg Cal/day = $70 \times kg^{3/4}$, which takes account of the fact that metabolic rate is related more closely to surface area than to weight (see p. 00). Dotted parallel lines are 20% deviations. (From P. F. Scholander, R. Hock, V. Walters, and L. Irving, *Biological Bulletin,* 99 (1950), 263. By permission of the *Biological Bulletin.*)

that is soaked with water. This is a dangerous state for man; it is virtually equivalent to being naked and is a common cause of death by exposure in damp climates. The reason for this is that wet clothing facilitates chilling by evaporation, the heat loss being further enhanced by the greater thermal conductivity of water as compared with air. The polar bear reacts to this situation with a characteristic behavioral response; it vigorously shakes itself dry when it leaves the water.

For smaller mammals, however, physical thermoregulation has its severe limitations in a cold climate; since, because of their relatively large surface area in proportion to volume, they are more prone to lose heat than larger animals. Some of the factors that influence size in animals have already been reviewed. It can now be seen that thermodynamic principles must also play a part, as Haldane made clear in his discussion quoted earlier. He points out that 5000 mice weigh as much as one man but have seventeen times his surface area. And it is this area, and not their weight, that determines the amount of food that they require to maintain their body temperature, for it is surface area that influences heat loss. So a mouse must eat about one quarter of its weight per day, largely in order to keep warm. It is thus thermodynamically advantageous for a homoiotherm to be large, and the advantage increases in colder climates. There is, in consequence, a tendency for the members of a particular species to be larger in the colder areas of its range, a tendency referred to as Bergmann's Rule.

A further difficulty for smaller mammals in cold climates is that the size of the body limits the length of the hair that they can carry; insulation of the body, therefore, is restricted. In such animals the selection of climate or microclimate becomes of crucial importance. Thus small mammals burrow beneath snow or into the substratum, where the temperature is much higher. A few birds, for example the ptarmigan (*Lagopus*), also do this. It seems, however, that the organization of birds is not as well suited for fossorial habits, and so the primary behavioral response of these animals is migratory flight. Of course, small homoiotherms can always, in theory, resort to chemical thermoregulation; but this makes extravagant use of food reserves, and in practice it is of more value as an emergency response than a permanent or seasonal adaptation. Its limitations are apparent in the results reported by Selye (p. 152).

The varying extent to which mammals call upon chemical thermoregulation is, in fact, a major element in their ability to survive cold conditions. In considering this matter, one can recognize a zone of ambient temperature over which any one species is able to maintain its metabolism at its lowest level. This zone, called the thermoneutral zone, is the range over which the species concerned maintains its

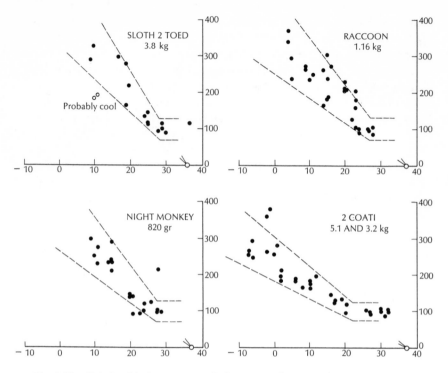

Fig. 6-15. Relationship between metabolic rate (ordinate) and ambient temperature (abcissa) in some tropical mammals. Basal metabolic rate = 100. The thermoneutral zones are narrow. (From P. F. Scholander, R. Hock, V. Walters, and L. Irving, *Biological Bulletin*, 99 (1950), 244. By permission of the *Biological Bulletin*.)

normal body temperature by physical thermoregulation alone. If the ambient temperature rises above this zone, and the animal is unable to evade it by some behavioral response, hyperthermia sets in and must eventually lead to heat death. If, on the other hand, the ambient temperature falls below the thermoneutral zone, the animal can resort to chemical thermoregulation; the temperature at which the transition to increased metabolism takes place is then called the critical temperature for that species. As previously stated, chemical thermoregulation is metabolically expensive. It calls for reserves of energy that an animal may be unable to replace, so that eventually exhaustion may supervene; the animal will pass into a state of hypothermia and will die of cold.

Critical temperatures and zones of thermoneutrality vary greatly from species to species, an indication of the adaptive qualities involved. A naked man has a critical temperature of about 27°C, which means that he is rather sensitive to temperature change. This makes him an essentially tropical form, for several tropical mammals are known to be equally sensitive and to manifest comparable critical temperatures and narrow thermoneutral zones *(Fig. 6-15)*. Man, it has been said, is a tropical animal who, by virtue of his clothing and his technology, carries his tropical environment with him.

The arctic fox and the eskimo dog stand in sharp contrast to man and the tropical mammals, for they are both extremely hardy *(Fig. 6-16)*. Their critical temperatures lie between −45°C and −50°C, and because of this they can tolerate the coldest temperatures on earth without the aid of technological resources. All that they have to do, even at this ultimate extreme, is to increase their metabolism by some 30–40 per cent, a level of increase that would raise the temperature tolerance of a tropical mammal by only a few degrees *(Fig. 6-17)*. Thus an arctic dog can sleep on the open snow at −40°, while an arctic fox has been known to endure a temperature of −80°C for one hour without showing any fall in its body temperature. All of this (together with the similar situation in birds, *Fig. 6-18*) is made pos-

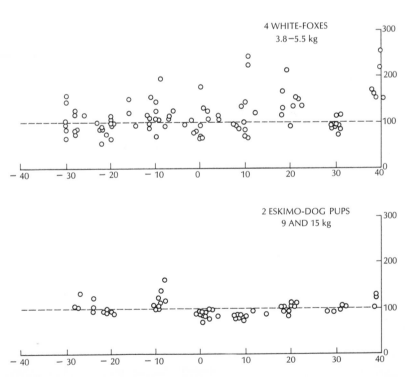

Fig. 6-16. Relationship between metabolic rate and ambient temperature in the white fox and the eskimo dog. The thermoneutral zones are very broad. (From P. F. Scholander, R. Hock, V. Walters, F. Johnson, and L. Irving, *Biological Bulletin*, 99 (1950), 242. By permission of the *Biological Bulletin*.)

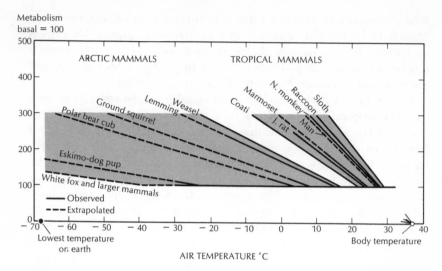

Fig. 6-17. Heat regulation and temperature sensitivity in arctic and tropical mammals. The fox needs only a slight increase in metabolic rate to withstand the coldest temperature on earth. (From P. F. Scholander, R. Hock, V. Walters, F. Johnson, and L. Irving, *Biological Bulletin,* 99 (1950), 254. By permission of the *Biological Bulletin.*)

sible by adaptations that have been outlined in principle: highly efficient vasomotor control, adequate insulation, and the adoption of a suitable posture. Indeed, the perplexing problem in such animals is not so much how they are able to endure cold, but rather how they are able to dissipate heat in a warm environment. It has been recorded that an Eskimo dog, brought into the summer heat of the United States, got rid of its surplus heat by stretching itself out on its back, exposing its thinly haired abdomen, and panting vigorously. One can feel sure that it would have welcomed the further aid of air-conditioning.

■ **HYPOTHERMIA IN MAMMALS**

Although the dog can deal successfully with a cold climate, one must not forget that small mammals cannot possibly solve their problems in this way. Repeated emphasis has been given to the significance of the small animal's high ratio of surface area to volume. The arctic fox and the Eskimo dog can accept extreme cold; small mammals can only survive by avoiding it. It is particularly important for the latter to economize as much as possible in their use of food; therefore, any adaptation serving to reduce the need for food will be of great selective value. This is the principle that underlies the evolution of hibernation, a habit exemplified in the dormouse, the hamster, the hedgehog, and the marmot. It is known to occur also in certain birds, for example, in Nuttall's poorwill *(Phalaeonptilus nuttalli)*, which has been observed hibernating in the Chuckawalla Mountains of the Colorado Desert.

One way of economizing in the output of energy, and accordingly the need for food, is to sleep. Thus the so-called heterotherms may pass readily into a deep cold narcosis at low air temperatures. The lowest values for the body temperature of *Centetes,* for example, are found when it is recovering from a long period of such dormancy. More familiar illustrations are the deep sleep of the brown bear, or the retirement of human beings to their beds at times of famine. Heavy sleep requires no elaborate physiological adaptation; the brown bear remains fully homoiothermal and shows no decline in body temperature. Heterotherms, like *Centetes,* however, often show a tendency to hypothermia, dropping their temperature a few degrees below their normal activity range; it is possible that the ability to tolerate such a fall may have been the foundation for the evolution of hibernation. Nevertheless, it must be emphasized that this habit is not a primitive one, reflecting some imperfection of thermoregulatory equipment. On the contrary, it is dependent upon physiological specialization that deserves attention not only for its intrinsic interest but also for its bearing on some recent advances in human surgery (see p. 263).

When hibernators are awake, they are perfectly well able to thermoregulate; in this state they resemble the typical homoiotherms,

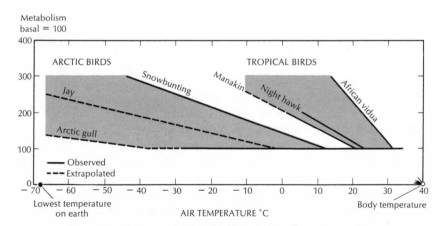

Fig. 6-18. Heat regulation and temperature sensitivity in arctic and tropical birds. (From P. F. Scholander, R. Hock, V. Walters, F. Johnson, and L. Irving, *Biological Bulletin,* 99 (1950), 255. By permission of the *Biological Bulletin.*)

although their body temperatures may vary more widely. The characteristic feature of their hibernation is a profound drop in temperature, with concurrent decreases in metabolic rate and the frequency of heart beat, while they coil into a tight ball, with erect hair, to minimize heat loss. In this condition the body temperature follows closely that of the environment, tending to lie a degree or so above it; to this extent the animals are now poikilothermous, although, as will be seen, they have not entirely abandoned their link with homoiothermy. Their sleep, however, is at a much deeper level of insensibility than ordinary winter sleep, and their metabolic rate is lowered to as little as one thirtieth to one hundredth of normal.

Hibernation thus overcomes the problem of providing food for winter, for such energy as is required can be obtained, at least in part, from fat reserves. The other source of food is material stored in the nest, for example, by marmots or dormice. It is possible for these animals to utilize such stores, because hibernation is not continuous throughout the winter. The animals wake periodically, and periods of activity may alternate with periods of sleep. In itself this behavior, together with the physiological specialization just outlined, shows that the hibernant is more than a dormant poikilotherm; and the same conclusion is equally apparent when such an animal is compared with an overwintering reptile. For one thing, the metabolic rate of the mammal remains much higher than that of the reptile. A snake with a rectal temperature of 9°C has a heat production of eight kilocalories per sq meter of surface area, but the corresponding figure for a marmot is 25–30 kilocalories. In addition, there are two specializations that are particularly characteristic of the hibernant. First, when the ambient temperature falls to the freezing point, the animal responds by increasing its metabolism, so that it will usually be able to preserve itself from freezing. Thus if the environmental temperature of the hamster is lowered from 5°C to 3°C, the body temperature is maintained at 3°C by a tripling or even quadrupling of the metabolic rate. Therefore, while it is sometimes said that during hibernation the hypothalamic thermostat is put out of circuit, this is an oversimplification. Clearly, it remains capable of evoking protective responses at these low temperatures, something that is beyond the capacity of the overwintering reptile, which can only survive frost by selecting a retreat where it will be protected.

The other characteristic specialization of hibernants is their method of wakening. The course of events during this process is critical; in particular, it is distinguishable from the wakening of lower vertebrates from their winter sleep by the rapid rise in metabolic rate. In fact, the metabolic rise is so rapid, the body temperature of an awakening hibernant may rise in a few hours to 37°C. Note that the process does not depend upon a rise in the temperature of the environment;

the stimulus of handling, for example, may awaken the animal even at low ambient temperatures.

The muscles are of primary importance in bringing about the rapid rise in body temperature. At first, there are ill-defined contractions, but these soon pass into violent shivering. Meanwhile, the heart rate increases in frequency, and the heart itself begins to warm. The heat generated by these activities is distributed around the body in a pattern that is regulated by vascular specialization. Studies of the hamster have shown that the flow of blood in the posterior region of the body is reduced by vasoconstriction. This ensures rapid circulation to the lungs and the head, with the result that the respiratory system is soon fully activated, while the tissue of the brain, which is always a highly thermosensitive organ, is rapidly warmed. Eventually, the circulation becomes normal, and the body is fully and uniformly warmed. It can be well understood, in light of these events, that a hibernant whose muscles have been paralyzed with curare can warm itself only very slowly; indeed, it can never reach a normal temperature.

These facts, derived particularly from studies of hamsters, are probably true of other hibernating species as well. However, special mention must be made of bats, for these remarkable mammals are essentially poikilothermal at all ambient temperatures throughout the year. Moreover, their metabolic rate and body temperature both fall precipitously whenever they are inactive; and they pass into a state essentially similar to hibernation, except that it is not restricted to any particular season. In these respects bats are unique among mammals, although hummingbirds behave in something of the same way. These birds pass readily into a state of torpor in which, according to one observer, they can be laid on a table like so many dried skins. Like bats, they have a daily cycle of torpor, not merely a seasonal one like typical hibernants. As in the latter, however, this cycle is a device for economizing in the output of energy, and it is significant that both hummingbirds and bats have a small body size and a high rate of metabolism when they are fully active.

In the common brown bat of North America, which one may take as an illustration, the body temperature of the resting animal approximates the ambient level over a wide range of temperature (from 0.5°C to 44°C). This is seen in Table 6-3, which shows how rapidly the animal equilibrates after exposure to a given temperature. As the ambient temperature rises, the metabolism increases, apparently because of increased activity in the tissues and organs. During the early stages of the rise, the animal is incapable of locomotion, for its flying temperature is at 41.5°C. During the winter the brown bat hibernates in caves and at this time behaves physiologically like other hibernants.

TABLE 6-3

Body Temperature of the Little Brown Bat (Myotis
lucifugus lucifugus) *in Relation to Ambient Temperature.
Temperature Measured After a Steady Resting State Had
Been Attained in a Vial Placed in a Water Bath.*[a]

Experimental temperature (°C.)		Bat temperature (°C.)		Length of experiment (min)
Water bath	Air in vial	At start	At end	
1.3	1.3	19.1	1.35	45
23.0	23.1	24.7	23.2	30
30.2	30.2	36.3	31.2	90
37.0	35.5	35.7	37.5	15

[a] From R. J. Hock, *Biological Bulletin,* 101 (1951), 290.

That hibernants can survive temperatures down to freezing levels
has long been recognized; but it was formerly thought that such low
temperatures must necessarily be fatal to nonhibernants, for in normal circumstances most nonhibernating mammals are unable to
tolerate rectal temperatures below 15°C. It is now known, however,
that their capacity for survival is not as restricted as this temperature
limit suggests. In fact, they are inherently as resistant to deep hypothermia as are hibernants; the cause of their failure to survive is
simply that they lack the specialized adaptations for warming and
recovery.

That such survival is possible has been demonstrated by using
adult rats. These animals can survive cooling to 1°C, despite the fact
that their respiration ceases at about 9°C and their heart beat at about
6°C. Survival cannot be guaranteed at such a low temperature (it is
easier to ensure if the ambient temperature goes no lower than 9°C),
but, nevertheless, it can be secured in some instances if the warming
process is carefully controlled. The principle employed is to ensure,
as in the normal awakening of the hamster, that the muscles warm
first, and that the brain is kept cool until it can be provided with an
adequate oxygen supply. In practice, the heart is warmed by local
application of heat, and breathing is aided by the application of artificial respiration.

The elucidation of these principles has provided a foundation for
remarkable advances in cardiac surgery, in cases where it is desirable
to arrest the circulation for a substantial time. These advances depend
upon subjecting the patient to acute hypothermia under carefully
controlled conditions, so that the tissues can survive at low temperatures in the absence of the normal circulatory flow and can then be
brought back into full activity with restored circulation. Cooling of

the anaesthetized patient to 15°C by immersion, for example, in a cold bath, makes it possible to operate upon the open heart with a success thought impossible as recently as 1955. A difficulty with this type of procedure, however, is the possibility of cardiac failure, and this has led to the development of another technique. In this the blood stream is shunted into an external pump and heat exchanger, and the body of the patient cooled to a nasopharyngeal temperature of 13–15°C. At this temperature, which corresponds closely to the temperature of the brain, it is possible to interrupt in safety both circulation and respiration, so that the surgeon can operate upon a dry heart. C. E. Drew describes the procedure as follows.

The method is demonstrated in *Fig. [6-19]*. Inguinal incisions are made to mobilize the femoral arteries. The left artery is cannulated and the right artery will receive a catheter to record central aortic pressure. This is done after the heart has been exposed and the patient given 1.5 mg. of heparin/kg. body-wt. The surgical approach is usually made through a median sternotomy. A cannula is placed in the left atrium, usually through the appendage, and held in position by a purse-string suture, the ends of which are threaded through a soft rubber tube and used as a snare. All cannulations in the chest are made secure in this way. Blood is then allowed to drain into the left atrial reservoir. The amount is controlled by an adjustable stop on the venous line and varies from 150 ml./min. in an infant to about 1,000 ml./min. in an adult. The same volume is pumped from the reservoir through the heat exchanger into the femoral artery. As cooling progresses, the circulation will begin to fail, because of either poor ventricular contraction or the onset of ventricular fibrillation. A cannula previously placed in the right atrium is then allowed to drain blood into the right venous reservoir. From here blood is pumped into the pulmonary artery through a cannula inserted into the infundibulum of the right ventricle. The flow through the pumps is then increased and the stops on the venous lines are gradually removed. The systemic flow is regulated to give a mean blood pressure of about 70–80 mm. Hg. This determines the amount of blood returning to the right atrial reservoir, and the right ventricular pump is adjusted to keep the reservoir levels constant. Stabilization is rapidly achieved and little readjustment is required. With the establishment of artificial pulmonary and systemic circulations, cooling proceeds until a level of 13–15°C. is recorded in the nasopharynx. The pumps are then stopped and artificial respiration ceases. Clamps are placed on the venae cavae and the heart is drained of blood through the venous lines. An aortic clamp is applied to prevent air embolism once the heart is opened. The appropriate surgery on the heart and neighbouring great vessels may now be undertaken, any cannulae which obstruct the approach being temporarily removed. When the intracardiac surgery is completed, air is displaced from the heart in the following way. After right atriotomy or ventriculotomy, near the

Cannula into
pulmonary artery

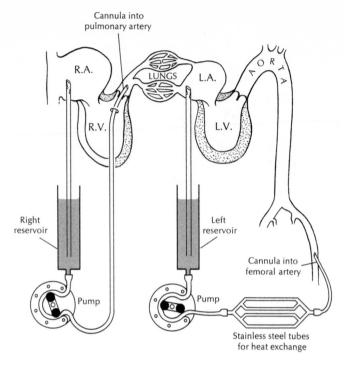

R.A. : right auricle   L.A. : left auricle
R.V. : right ventricle   L.V. : left ventricle

Fig. 6-19. Diagram showing method of cooling and re-warming the human body to provide for profound hypothermia during cardiac surgery. (From C. E. Drew, *British Medical Bulletin*, 17 (1961), 38.)

completion of septal and wall repair, a few turns are made manually on the left ventricular pump after the caval clamps are removed. Air is displaced by blood returning to the right side of the heart. After left atriotomy or aortotomy, the right ventricular pump is used in a similar way to drive blood through the lungs to the left side of the heart to eliminate entrained air. When the heart has been repaired, the cannulae replaced, and all vascular and line clamps have been removed, the pumps are restarted and the patient is rewarmed.

The heart is usually in asystole or beating very slowly during circulatory arrest. It may resume normal rhythm or its ventricles may fibrillate with spontaneous recovery later on. Sometimes it is necessary to defibrillate the heart electrically when the nasopharyngeal temperature has risen to 30–33°C.

Re-warming is continued until a nasopharyngeal temperature of at least 33°C. has been reached and the muscle temperature is about 30°C. The pumps are gradually slowed when the heart beat is satisfactory. Partial right ventricular by-pass is stopped and the cannulae removed from the right side of the heart. Finally, left ventricular by-pass is suspended and the cannulae removed from the left atrium and femoral artery. As the cardiac cannulae are removed, the ligatures are left untied until the heart action is satisfactory, to allow recannulation if necessary. The recording arterial catheter is also withdrawn and the vessels repaired. Protamine or Polybrene is given to neutralize the effect of heparin.[10]

Such are the achievements of contemporary biological technology. The study of hibernation and hypothermia has contributed to the prolongation of human life, just as the study of respiratory adaptations and of the regulation of water balance has contributed to an extending range of environmental conditions in which human beings can live and work. Here, as in all aspects of physiological adaptation, the growth of man's understanding reflects the questing spirit of a unique tropical species. Capable of transmitting instructions orally as well as by the genetic mechanisms on which all other species must depend, man seeks to use new knowledge to extend his fields of activity far beyond their present limits. Thus he demonstrates with unquenchable enthusiasm his conviction that "it is better to be a crystal and be broken than to remain perfect like a tile upon the house-top."

1. J. A. Moore, "Geographic Variation of Adaptive Characters in *Rana pipiens* Schreber," *Evolution*, 3 (1949), 2, 8–10.
2. *Ibid.*, p. 23.
3. A. C. Burton and O. G. Edholm, *Man in a Cold Environment* (London: Edward Arnold, Ltd., 1955), p. 5.
4. C. M. Bogert, "How Reptiles Regulate Their Body Temperature," *Scientific American*, 200 (April 1959), 120, 112–118. Copyright © 1959 by Scientific American, Inc. All rights reserved.
5. C. Blagden, "Experiments and Observations in an Heated Room," *Philosophical Transactions of the Royal Society of London*, 65 (1775), 485–491.
6. T. H. Benzinger, "The Human Thermostat," *Scientific American*, 240 (January 1961), 138–139. Copyright © 1961 by Scientific American, Inc. All rights reserved.
7. *Ibid.*, pp. 137, 139–140, 144.
8. K. Schmidt-Nielsen *et al.*, "Water Balance of the Camel," *American Journal of Physiology*, 185 (1956), 185–186, 191–192.
9. K. Schmidt-Nielsen, *Desert Animals* (Oxford: The Clarendon Press, 1964), pp. 42. 43–44. By permission of The Clarendon Press, Oxford.
10. C. E. Drew, "Profound Hypothermia in Cardiac Surgery," *British Medical Bulletin*, 17 (1961), 38–39.

SELECTED READINGS

CHAPTER 1

Fox, H. M., and Vevers, H. G. *The Nature of Animal Colours.* London: Sidgwick and Jackson Ltd., 1960.

Goodfield, G. J. *The Growth of Scientific Philosophy.* London: Hutchinson and Company Ltd., 1960.

Haldane, J. B. S., and Priestley, J. G. *Respiration.* London: Oxford University Press, 1935.

Hughes, G. M. *Comparative Physiology of Vertebrate Respiration.* London: William Heineman Medical Books Ltd., 1963.

Krogh, A. *The Comparative Physiology of Respiratory Mechanisms.* Philadelphia: University of Pennsylvania Press, 1941.

CHAPTER 2

Babkin, B. P. *Pavlov: A Biography.* Chicago: University of Chicago Press, 1949.

Barrington, E. J. W. *An Introduction to General and Comparative Endocrinology.* Oxford: The Clarendon Press, 1962.

Beaumont, P. B. *Experiments and Observations on the Gastric Juice and the Physiology of Digestion.* New York: Dover Publications, Inc., 1959.

Gabriel, M. L., and Fogel, S. *Great Experiments in Biology.* Englewood Cliffs, New Jersey: Prentice-Hall, Inc., 1955.

Holter, H. "How Things Get into Cells," *Scientific American*, 205 (March 1961), 167-180.

Medawar, P. B. *The Art of the Soluble.* London: Methuen & Company Ltd., 1967.

Solomon, A. K. "Pumps in the Living Cell," *Scientific American*, 207 (February 1962), 100-108.

CHAPTER 3

Bernard, C. *An Introduction to the Study of Experimental Medicine.* trans. H. C. Greene. New York: Dover Publications, Inc., 1957.

Best, C. H. "A Canadian Trail of Medical Research," *Journal of Endocrinology*, 19 (1959), i-xvii.

Cannon, W. B. *The Wisdom of the Body.* New York: W. W. Norton & Co., Inc., 1939.

Young, F. G., ed. "Insulin," *British Medical Bulletin*, 16 (1960), 175-261.

CHAPTER 4

Barrington, E. J. W. *Hormones and Evolution*. London: English Universities Press, 1964.
Harris, G. W. *Neural Control of the Pituitary Gland*. London: E. J. Arnold & Son Ltd., 1955.
Heller, H. H., ed. *Comparative Aspects of Neurohypophyseal Physiology. Symposia of the Zoological Society, London*, No. 9.
Krogh, A. *Osmotic Regulation in Aquatic Animals*. London: Cambridge University Press, 1939.
Potts, W. T. W., and Parry, G. *Osmotic and Ionic Regulation in Animals*. London: Pergamon Press Ltd., 1964.
Selye, H. *The Stress of Life*. London: Longmans, Green & Co., Ltd., 1957.

CHAPTER 5

Brett, J. P. "Some Principles in the Thermal Requirements of Fishes," *Quarterly Review of Biology*, 31 (1956), 75-87.
Fisher, K. C. "An Approach to the Organ and Cellular Physiology of Adaptation of Temperature in Fish and Small Mammals," *Physiological Adaptation*, ed. C. L. Prosser. Washington, D.C.: American Physiological Society, 1958.
Gunn, D. L. "Body Temperatures in Poikilothermal Animals," *Biological Reviews*, 17 (1942), 293-314.
Salt, R. W. "Resistance of Poikilothermic Animals to Cold," *British Medical Bulletin*, 17 (1961), 5-8.

CHAPTER 6

Bishop, B. C. "Wintering on the Roof of the World," *National Geographic*, 122 (1962), 503-547.
Burton, A. C., and Edholm, O. G. *Man in A Cold Environment*. London: E. J. Arnold & Son Ltd., 1955.
Dill, D. B. *Life, Heat, and Altitude*. Cambridge: Harvard University Press, 1938.
Harrison, L. H. "Hibernation in Birds and Mammals," *British Medical Bulletin*, 17 (1961), 9-13.
Johansen, K. "Evolution of Temperature Regulation in Mammals," *Comparative Physiology of Temperature Regulation*, ed. J. P. Hannon and E. Viereck. Fort Wainwright, Alaska: Arctic Aeromedical Laboratory, 1962.
Kayser, C., ed. *The Physiology of Natural Hibernation*. London: Pergamon Press Ltd., 1961.
Schmidt-Nielson, K. *Desert Animals*. Oxford: The Clarendon Press, 1964.

INDEX

H

I

J